PRENTICE-HALL ELECTRICAL ENGINEERING SERIES

W. L. EVERITT, Ph.D., *Editor*

Electric Network Synthesis

IMAGE PARAMETER METHOD

BY

MYRIL B. REED

Professor of Electrical Engineering
Michigan State University

Prentice-Hall, Inc.

ENGLEWOOD CLIFFS, N.J., 1955

PRINTED IN THE UNITED STATES OF AMERICA
24695

Preface

THE ORIGINAL technique of filter design in terms of the constant-k and m-derived concepts has been refined and amplified by years of experience into what now may be characterized as the image parameter method. This image parameter method, presented here in terms of image impedance function and image transfer function, has proved the most widely useful of the synthesis methods. Since analysis must precede synthesis for the latter to be most effective, the image parameter method is presented here first on an analysis basis. The results of this analysis are then utilized as the foundation for establishing charts, tabulations, and other useful design auxiliaries. An elaborate detailed design is given to epitomize the whole presentation.

The core as well as much of the detail of the image parameter method presented here stems from the design techniques used at Bell Telephone Laboratories. Mr. A. R. D'heedene of Bell Telephone Laboratories is largely responsible for this book coming into existence. It was while the author was working under Mr. D'heedene's direction at Bell Telephone Laboratories that the idea for such a book was conceived, and it has been through Mr. D'heedene's continued efforts in terms of much work and interest that the book has finally been completed. The basic structure, the know-how of experience, the charts, and the main filter design of the book have all been supplied, as a point of departure, through Mr. D'heedene and the courtesy of the Bell Telephone Laboratories. It must be emphasized, however, that the statements, conclusions, charts, and finally even the basic ideas have all been subjected to the author's interpretation. Consequently, the author is fully responsible for the statements and interpretations given in this book.

M. B. R.

Contents

CHAPTER ONE

Two-Terminal Networks Containing
Inductance and Capacitance Only

The electric networks considered in this book, both in terms of analysis and synthesis, are only such as can be exhibited as combinations of two-terminal networks (2TN). These 2TN are combinations of the well-known resistance, inductance, and capacitance elements. The general pattern of approach to the synthesis (design) problem, which is the main thesis of this book, is to consider purely reactive networks as the first approximation. Following the establishment of the reactive network pattern, corrections are made for the irremovable resistance effects of the physical counterpart of the purely reactive network. The latter network is, of course, only a mathematical one.

This chapter consists of a discussion of the properties of 2TN which are pertinent to the design problem of filters and equalizers.

1.1 One- and two-element reactive two-terminal networks

As a preliminary, consider the frequency characteristics of some simple reactive 2TN—the combinations shown in Fig. 1.1.1.

Two important aspects of the design of two-terminal electric networks are the pattern of possible frequency characteristics of the driving-point impedance $Z_d(\omega)$, or reactance $X_d(\omega)$, or perhaps of the admittance $Y_d(\omega)$, or susceptance $B_d(\omega)$, and the number of parameters which must be assigned values to fix a specific frequency characteristic. For a pure inductor, for example Fig. 1.1.1a,

$$Z_d(\omega) = j\omega L, \quad X_d(\omega) = \omega L, \quad B_d(\omega) = \frac{-1}{\omega L} \qquad (1.1.1)$$

and for a pure capacitor, Fig. 1.1.1b,

$$Z_d(\omega) = \frac{1}{j\omega C}, \quad X_d(\omega) = \frac{-1}{\omega C}, \quad B_d(\omega) - \omega C \qquad (1.1.2)$$

The frequency characteristic of either of these 2TN is therefore fixed by assignment of value to one parameter. A useful method of making such an assignment is to specify a value of, say, reactance or susceptance at any specified value of ω, i.e., at any specific frequency.

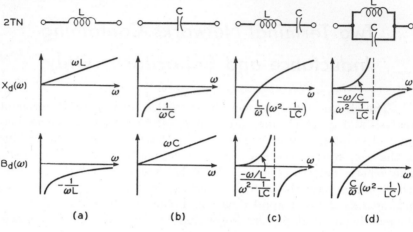

Fig. 1.1.1

When the network contains two elements, there are two parameters in the impedance expressions. For the series resonant circuit, the reactance is

$$X_d(\omega) = \frac{L}{\omega}\left(\omega^2 - \frac{1}{LC}\right) \qquad (1.1.3)$$

and the susceptance is

$$B_d(\omega) = \frac{-\omega/L}{\omega^2 - 1/LC} \qquad (1.1.4)$$

For the parallel resonant circuit, the reactance is

$$X_d(\omega) = \frac{-\omega/C}{\omega^2 - 1/LC} \qquad (1.1.5)$$

and the susceptance is

$$B_d(\omega) = \frac{C}{\omega}\left(\omega^2 - \frac{1}{LC}\right) \qquad (1.1.6)$$

In each case there is one parameter present as a multiplying constant. The other parameter may be taken as the product LC which establishes the resonant frequency through the relation

$$\omega_R = 1/\sqrt{LC} \qquad (1.1.7)$$

The element values may be established by fixing this resonant frequency and the reactance at any other one frequency, $\omega \neq 0$, $\omega \neq \infty$. The element values may also be established by fixing the reactance at any two nonresonant frequencies, $\omega \neq 0$, $\omega \neq \infty$.

Of particular interest in all the foregoing equations is the fact that the reactances and susceptances are the ratios of simple polynomials in ω. More elaborate reactive 2TN also have driving-point impedances which are ratios of polynomials. The remainder of this chapter is largely devoted to this aspect of reactive 2TN.

1.2 General properties of the driving-point impedance of a purely reactive two-terminal network

The equations for a general two-terminal network (Fig. 1.2.1) can be expressed as (sinusoidal steady state)

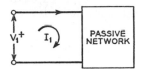

Fig. 1.2.1

$$
\begin{bmatrix} V_1 \\ 0 \\ \cdot \\ \cdot \\ \cdot \\ 0 \end{bmatrix} = \begin{bmatrix} Z_{11} & Z_{12} & Z_{13} & \cdots & Z_{1n} \\ Z_{21} & Z_{22} & Z_{23} & \cdots & Z_{2n} \\ \cdot & \cdot & \cdot & & \cdot \\ \cdot & \cdot & \cdot & & \cdot \\ \cdot & \cdot & \cdot & & \cdot \\ Z_{n1} & Z_{n2} & Z_{n3} & & Z_{nn} \end{bmatrix} \begin{bmatrix} I_1 \\ I_2 \\ \cdot \\ \cdot \\ \cdot \\ I_n \end{bmatrix} \tag{1.2.1}
$$

If this matrix equation is solved for the currents, the result is

$$
\begin{bmatrix} I_1 \\ I_2 \\ \cdot \\ \cdot \\ \cdot \\ I_n \end{bmatrix} = \begin{bmatrix} Y_{11} & Y_{12} & Y_{13} & \cdots & Y_{1n} \\ Y_{21} & Y_{22} & Y_{23} & \cdots & Y_{2n} \\ \cdot & \cdot & \cdot & & \cdot \\ \cdot & \cdot & \cdot & & \cdot \\ \cdot & \cdot & \cdot & & \cdot \\ Y_{n1} & Y_{n2} & Y_{n3} & \cdots & Y_{nn} \end{bmatrix} \begin{bmatrix} V_1 \\ 0 \\ \cdot \\ \cdot \\ \cdot \\ 0 \end{bmatrix}
$$

$$
= \frac{1}{\Delta} \begin{bmatrix} \Delta_{11} & \Delta_{12} & \Delta_{13} & \cdots & \Delta_{1n} \\ \Delta_{21} & \Delta_{22} & \Delta_{23} & \cdots & \Delta_{2n} \\ \cdot & \cdot & \cdot & & \cdot \\ \cdot & \cdot & \cdot & & \cdot \\ \cdot & \cdot & \cdot & & \cdot \\ \Delta_{n1} & \Delta_{n2} & \Delta_{n3} & \cdots & \Delta_{nn} \end{bmatrix} \begin{bmatrix} V_1 \\ 0 \\ \cdot \\ \cdot \\ \cdot \\ 0 \end{bmatrix} \tag{1.2.2}
$$

where Δ_{ij} = cofactor of Z_{ji} in the determinant of the impedance matrix, Δ = the determinant of the impedance matrix, $Y_{ij} = \Delta_{ij}/\Delta$. From this matrix Eq. (1.2.2), the driving-point current I_1 of the network is

$$I_1 = \frac{\Delta_{11}}{\Delta} V_1 \qquad (1.2.3)$$

Hence the driving-point impedance $Z_d(\omega) = V_1/I_1$ is

$$Z_d(\omega) = \frac{\Delta(\omega)}{\Delta_{11}(\omega)} \qquad (1.2.4)$$

The expansion of a determinant consists of a sum of terms each of which is a product of various elements in the determinant. For purely reactive networks each element of Δ or Δ_{11} represents the impedance of an inductor alone, a capacitor alone, or of both in series, expressed mathematically by

$$Z_{ij}(\omega) = (j\omega)L_{ij}, \quad (j\omega)^{-1}\frac{1}{C_{ij}}, \quad \text{or} \quad (j\omega)^{-1}\frac{1 - \omega^2 LC}{C} \qquad (1.2.5)$$

Consequently, the driving-point impedance is a ratio of two polynomials in ω of the general form (m and n both even integers):

$$Z_d(\omega) = (j\omega)^{\pm 1}\frac{A_m\omega^m + A_{m-2}\omega^{m-2} + \ldots + A_2\omega^2 + A_0}{B_n\omega^n + B_{n-2}\omega^{n-2} + \ldots + B_2\omega^2 + B_0} \qquad (1.2.6)$$

An alternative form of this expression for $Z_d(\omega)$ may be obtained by determining the zeros and writing the equation in terms of these zeros. Thus

$$Z_d(\omega) = (j\omega)^{\pm 1}k\left[\frac{(\omega^2 - \omega_2^2)(\omega^2 - \omega_4^2)\ldots(\omega^2 - \omega_m^2)}{(\omega^2 - \omega_1^2)(\omega^2 - \omega_3^2)\ldots(\omega - \omega_n^2)}\right] \qquad (1.2.7)$$

The zeros of the numerator specify the frequencies of zero impedance (zeros or short circuits) of the driving-point impedance, and the zeros of the denominator specify the frequencies of infinite impedance (poles or open circuits).

Example 1.2.1

Determine the ratio of polynomials for the driving-point impedance of the network of Fig. 1.2.2. The element values of the network are: $L_a = 100 \ \mu h$, $L_b = 200 \ \mu h$, $L_c = 300 \ \mu h$, $C_b = 30,000 \ \mu\mu f$, $C_c = 10,000 \ \mu\mu f$.

Solution

The determinant for the network is, if p is used to replace $j\omega$,

$$\Delta = \begin{vmatrix} 3p \times 10^{-4} + \dfrac{10^8}{3p} & -2p \times 10^{-4} - \dfrac{10^8}{3p} \\[2ex] -2p \times 10^{-4} - \dfrac{10^8}{3p} & 5p \times 10^{-4} + \dfrac{4 \times 10^8}{3p} \end{vmatrix}$$

$$= \frac{33p^4 \times 10^{-8} + 13p^2 \times 10^4 + 10^{16}}{3p^2}$$

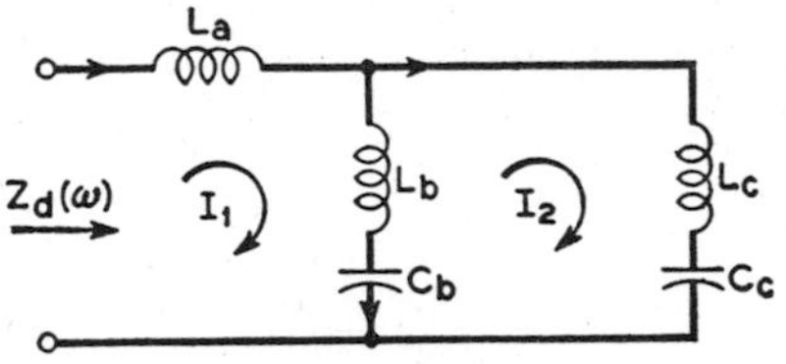

Fig. 1.2.2

Dividing this expression by

$$\Delta_{11} = 5p \times 10^{-4} + \frac{4 \times 10^8}{3p}$$

gives

$$Z_d(p) = \frac{33p^4 \times 10^{-8} + 13p^2 \times 10^4 + 10^{16}}{p(15p^2 \times 10^{-4} + 4 \times 10^8)}$$

Replacing p by $j\omega$ and multiplying numerator and denominator by 10^8,

$$Z_d(\omega) = \frac{1}{j\omega} \frac{33\omega^4 - 13\omega^2 \times 10^{12} + 10^{24}}{-15\omega^2 \times 10^4 + 4 \times 10^{16}}$$

Note that this last equation is in the form of the ratio of polynomials of Eq. (1.2.6). The alternative form corresponding to Eq. (1.2.7) is

$$Z_d(\omega) = j\omega 2.2 \times 10^{-4} \frac{(\omega^2 - 10.48 \times 10^{10})(\omega^2 - 28.9 \times 10^{10})}{\omega^2(\omega^2 - 26.67 \times 10^{10})}$$

The study of the mathematical properties of the driving-point impedance of a purely reactive two-terminal network, instigated by Campbell,[1] has been treated extensively elsewhere.[2] Because of the ready accessibility of these studies, only the results are given here.

[1] Campbell, G. A., *Collected Papers*, American Telephone & Telegraph Co., 1937.

[2] Foster, R. M., "A Reactance Theorem," *Bell System Tech. J.*, April 1924, pp. 259–267; Bode, H. W., *Network Analysis and Feedback Amplifier Design*, D. Van Nostrand Company, Inc., New York, 1945; Reed, Myril B., *Alternating Current Circuit Theory*, Harper & Brothers, New York, 1948.

These results, in terms of the mathematical expression for the driving-point impedance $Z_d(\omega)$ of the 2TN are:

1. The derivatives of $X_d(\omega)$ and $B_d(\omega)$ have the property

$$\frac{dX_d(\omega)}{d\omega} > 0, \qquad \frac{dB_d(\omega)}{d\omega} > 0$$

See Fig. 1.2.3.

2. The impedance $Z_d(\omega)$ is purely reactive.

3. Either a pole or a zero exists at $\omega = 0$ and $\omega = \infty$. Such poles and zeros are called *external* in contrast to all others, which are designated *internal*. The four possible arrangements of external poles and zeros provide a convenient means for classifying networks, as described

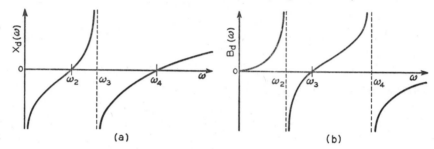

Fig. 1.2.3

in more detail in Sec. 1.5. A network with the frequency response shown in Fig. 1.2.3 is designated a CL network because at $\omega = 0$ it has a pole of impedance as does a capacitor, and at $\omega = \infty$ it has a pole of impedance as does an inductor.

4. The internal zeros and poles of $X_d(\omega)$ are all real and are all simple. The external poles and zeros are also simple. These restrictions on the zeros are intrinsic properties of a stable network, which can be demonstrated by study of the transient response of the network.

5. The poles and zeros of $X_d(\omega)$ and $B_d(\omega)$ alternate and are separate. The alternation is required by the positive slope, and means that the poles and zeros occur on the ω axis in the order pole-zero-pole-zero-..., or zero-pole-zero-pole-..., etc. The final equation of Ex. 1.2.1 corresponds to pole-zero-pole-zero-pole if both external and internal poles and zeros are considered.

The poles and zeros are separate, since mathematically a coincident pole and zero means an identical factor in numerator and denominator. Such a factor pair cannot affect the frequency behavior of $X_d(\omega)$ or $B_d(\omega)$. Such equal numerator and denominator factors would appear, for example, in $Z_d(\omega)$ for Fig. 1.2.2 if $L_b = L_c$ and $C_b = C_c$.

6. For a reactive network, the degree of numerator and denominator of $X_d(\omega)$ or $B_d(\omega)$ can and must differ only by unity. It is always possible to factor an ω from either the numerator or denominator but not both.

7. After the ω has been factored, as in Eq. (1.2.6), the degree of the polynomials can differ by at most 2. These polynomials contain only even powers of ω.

8. The total number of poles and zeros (internal and external) are equal or differ by unity.

9. The driving-point impedance is completely determined once the internal poles and zeros and the value of the impedance at any other frequency are specified; see Eq. (1.2.7) where the poles and zeros determine the polynomials of the ratio as functions of ω^2, and the specified impedance at a particular ω determines the multiplying constant. An important characteristic of the factored form of $Z_d(\omega)$, as given by Eq. (1.2.7), is that the curve of $Z_d(\omega)$ versus ω can be sketched directly from the equation. Thus at ω_3, $Z_d(\omega)$ is infinite (has a pole) and at ω_2 and ω_4, impedance $Z_d(\omega)$ is zero (has a zero). The positive slope of $X_d(\omega)$ and the alternating property of the poles and zeros require that this curve have the general shape shown in Fig. 1.2.3 ($\omega_2 < \omega_3 < \omega_4$).

1.3 *Equivalent two-terminal networks—same $Z_d(\omega)$*

The expressions representing the driving-point impedance of 2TN can be used to establish equivalent alternative networks which have the same driving-point impedance frequency-response.

Consider the partial fraction expansion of the driving-point impedance function

$$Z_d(\omega) = j\omega k \frac{(\omega^2 - \omega_2{}^2)(\omega^2 - \omega_4{}^2)(\omega^2 - \omega_6{}^2)}{\omega^2(\omega^2 - \omega_3{}^2)(\omega^2 - \omega_5{}^2)} \tag{1.3.1}$$

$$= j\omega k \left(1 + \frac{a_0}{\omega^2} + \frac{a_3}{\omega^2 - \omega_3{}^2} + \frac{a_5}{\omega^2 - \omega_5{}^2} \right) \tag{1.3.2}$$

Each term on the right of this expression may be recognized as being of the form taken by reactances of one- or two-element networks as given in Sec. 1.1. Consequently, a network which has the impedance represented by Eqs. (1.3.1) and (1.3.2) is of the form shown in Fig. 1.3.1a. The element values are obtained from a comparison of the terms of Eq. (1.3.2) and the reactance equations of Sec. 1.1.

The reactance curve corresponding to the network of Fig. 1.3.1a may be sketched from the fact that the two parallel resonant components constitute two internal poles, and the series inductor and capacitor constitute poles at $\omega = \infty$ and $\omega = 0$, respectively. Then, because of the positive slope and separation of poles and zeros, Fig. 1.3.1b shows the form the reactance curve must take. Note the correspondence of the internal poles and zeros as indicated in Eq. (1.3.1) and on this curve of Fig. 1.3.1b.

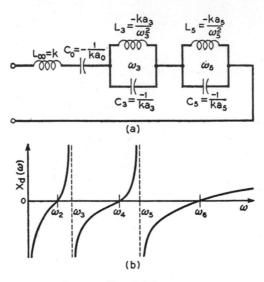

(a)

(b)

Fig. 1.3.1

The subscript designations on L_∞, C_∞, L_0, and C_0 are used for single elements when those elements determine the network behavior at $\omega = \infty$ and $\omega = 0$. Thus in Fig. 1.3.1a, the capacitor C_0 opens the network at $\omega = 0$ and so determines the network behavior at $\omega = 0$. On the other hand, the inductor L_∞ opens the network at $\omega = \infty$ and so determines the network behavior at $\omega = \infty$ independently of all other elements of the network.

A second all-frequency driving-point equivalent can be established by treating the driving-point admittance as a partial fraction expansion. Thus the admittance corresponding to Eq. (1.3.1) is

$$Y_d(\omega) = \frac{1}{Z_d(\omega)}$$

$$= -j\omega K \frac{(\omega^2 - \omega_3{}^2)(\omega^2 - \omega_5{}^2)}{(\omega^2 - \omega_2{}^2)(\omega^2 - \omega_4{}^2)(\omega^2 - \omega_6{}^2)} \quad (1.3.3)$$

$$= j\omega K \left(\frac{A_2}{\omega^2 - \omega_2{}^2} + \frac{A_4}{\omega^2 - \omega_4{}^2} + \frac{A_6}{\omega^2 - \omega_6{}^2} \right) \quad (1.3.4)$$

where $K = 1/k$. Each term on the right can be recognized as the admittance of a series resonator from the expression presented in Eq. (1.1.4). Consequently, the 2TN of Fig. 1.3.2a is the desired equivalent. The element values are obtained by comparing the terms of Eq. (1.3.4) with the admittance expression given in Eq. (1.1.4). Element value determination is treated in greater detail in Sec. 1.5.

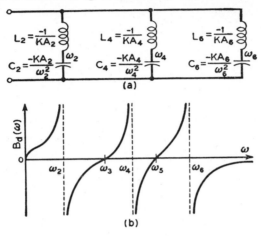

(a)

(b)

Fig. 1.3.2

The susceptance versus ω curve for the network of Fig. 1.3.2a can be established by plotting the negative reciprocal of Fig. 1.3.1b. The appearance of the negative sign arises from the fact that

$$Y_d(\omega) = jB_d(\omega) = \frac{1}{Z_d(\omega)} = \frac{1}{jX_d(\omega)} = -j\frac{1}{X_d(\omega)} \qquad (1.3.5)$$

from which

$$B_d(\omega) = \frac{-1}{X_d(\omega)} \qquad (1.3.6)$$

Hence the curve of $B_d(\omega)$ is readily drawn as shown in Fig. 1.3.2b. Note that this curve has the required positive slope.

The curve of Fig. 1.3.2b can also be sketched from the network and positive slope property. The three resonant components of Eq. (1.3.4) mean three internal poles of susceptance. At $\omega = \infty$ and $\omega = 0$ the inductors and capacitors, respectively, produce zero susceptance, hence the susceptance curve is as shown.

Example 1.3.1

Determine the series resonant and parallel resonant types of equivalent networks corresponding to the driving-point impedance of Ex. 1.2.1.

$$Z_d(\omega) = j\omega 2.2 \times 10^{-4}\frac{(\omega^2 - 10.48 \times 10^{10})(\omega^2 - 28.9 \times 10^{10})}{\omega^2(\omega^2 - 26.67 \times 10^{10})}$$

Solution

The partial fraction expansion of the driving-point impedance takes the form

$$\frac{(\omega^2 - 10.48 \times 10^{10})(\omega^2 - 28.9 \times 10^{10})}{\omega^2(\omega^2 - 26.67 \times 10^{10})} = 1 + \frac{a_0}{\omega^2} + \frac{a_3}{\omega^2 - 26.67 \times 10^{10}}$$

The numerator constants are[3]

$$a_0 = \left. \frac{(\omega^2 - 10.48 \times 10^{10})(\omega^2 - 28.9 \times 10^{10})}{\omega^2 - 26.67 \times 10^{10}} \right|_{\omega=0} = -11.36 \times 10^{10}$$

$$a_3 = \left. \frac{(\omega^2 - 10.48 \times 10^{10})(\omega^2 - 28.9 \times 10^{10})}{\omega^2} \right|_{\omega^2=26.67\times10^{10}} = -1.35 \times 10^{10}$$

The parallel-resonant type of network, therefore, from the formulas on Fig. 1.3.1a and these numerical results, is as shown on Fig. 1.3.3a.

The series-resonant type network equivalent is determined by the admittance

$$Y_d(\omega) = -j\omega 4550 \frac{\omega^2 - 26.67 \times 10^{10}}{(\omega^2 - 10.48 \times 10^{10})(\omega^2 - 28.9 \times 10^{10})}$$

$$= j\omega 4550 \left(\frac{A_2}{\omega^2 - 10.48 \times 10^{10}} + \frac{A_4}{\omega^2 - 28.9 \times 10^{10}} \right)$$

The constants A_2 and A_4 are

$$A_2 = \left. \frac{-(\omega^2 - 26.67 \times 10^{10})}{\omega^2 - 28.9 \times 10^{10}} \right|_{\omega^2=10.48\times10^{10}} = -0.879$$

$$A_4 = \left. \frac{-(\omega^2 - 26.67 \times 10^{10})}{\omega^2 - 10.48 \times 10^{10}} \right|_{\omega^2=28.9\times10^{10}} = -0.121$$

The equivalent network shown in Fig. 1.3.3b is obtained from the formulas of Fig. 1.3.2a and these constants.

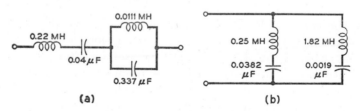

0.0111 MH

0.22 MH

0.04 μF

0.337 μF

0.25 MH   1.82 MH

0.0382 μF   0.0019 μF

(a)   **(b)**

Fig. 1.3.3

In addition to the series and parallel resonant forms of 2TN equivalents, two other types are readily available by the method of

[3] Reed, Myril B., and Georgia B., *Mathematical Methods in Electrical Engineering*, Harper & Brothers, New York, 1951, Chap. 5.

continued fractions.[4] The networks of Fig. 1.3.4 are equivalents, by the continued fraction method, of the 2TN of the preceding example.

Evidently any two-terminal portion of a network can be replaced by any of its equivalents, thus leading to a great variety of possible equivalents for any complicated 2TN.

These various equivalents afford a useful flexibility in the final shape that a network design may take. While the number of inductors and capacitors does not change through any of these transformations, the numerical values of the elements do change along with the position of the element in the network. When the elements of a particular configuration are either too large or too small for convenient physical realization, it often is possible to select another equivalent configuration having preferred element values. Furthermore, because of the

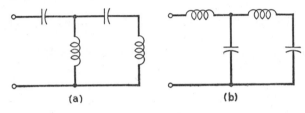

(a)   (b)

Fig. 1.3.4

change in position in the network, it is sometimes possible to relocate elements so as to permit absorption of parasitic inductances and capacitances into the design.

The selection of a network configuration is frequently governed by consideration of the need of and the means for precise adjustments. Greater precision in the measurement of frequency is possible than in the measurement of inductance or capacitance. Consequently the most accurate adjustment of a network is based on precisely controlled resonant frequencies. If frequency is used as the standard, the resonant types of networks, rather than those of Fig. 1.3.4, must be used so that the series and parallel resonators can be adjusted to the precise frequency specified. Hence only the series and parallel resonant types of networks are considered here.

1.4 Determination of network from specified poles, zeros, and impedances

Examination of Eq. (1.3.1) shows that the driving-point impedance is completely determined if the locations of the poles and zeros

[4] *Ibid.*, Chap. 5.

are specified and if the constant k is determined from a specified value
of reactance at some other than a zero or pole frequency. Viewed from
a design standpoint this property of reactive 2TN is an outstanding
advantage. It defines completely a network which will produce a particular required frequency response, which is the essence of the design
problem.

Example 1.4.1

Determine the driving-point impedance function, sketch the curve of
$X_d(\omega)$ vs ω, and sketch the series resonant and parallel resonant type networks
having poles at $\omega_1 = 100$, $\omega_3 = 1000$; zeros at $\omega_2 = 500$, $\omega_4 = 3000$, and
$Z_d(2000) = -j100$. Note that these networks are of the LL class.

Solution

The driving-point impedance function can be written immediately as

$$Z_d(\omega) = j\omega k \frac{(\omega^2 - 25 \times 10^4)(\omega^2 - 9 \times 10^6)}{(\omega^2 - 10^4)(\omega^2 - 10^6)}$$

The constant k can be determined from

$$Z_d(2000) = -j100$$
$$= j2000k \frac{(4 \times 10^6 - 25 \times 10^4)(4 \times 10^6 - 9 \times 10^6)}{(4 \times 10^6 - 10^4)(4 \times 10^6 - 10^6)}$$

whereby $\qquad\qquad k = 0.0319$

The curve of reactance vs ω is shown in Fig. 1.4.1a. The internal poles and
zeros and the positive slope requirement makes this curve shape the only one
which is possible. Note that the poles and zeros alternate and that the specified impedance at $\omega = 2000$ must be negative. If a positive impedance were
required at $\omega = 2000$ a passive network could not be obtained.

The parallel resonant network of Fig. 1.4.1b opens at ω_1, ω_3, and $\omega = \infty$
(by L_∞) as the reactance curve requires. This network also short-circuits at
$\omega = 0$, ω_2, and ω_4, but only the zero at $\omega = 0$ (all the coils in series) is evident
from inspection of the network. However, parallel resonant branches act as
inductors below and as capacitors above resonance (see Fig. 1.1.1). Consequently for $100 \le \omega \le 1000$, the L_1C_1 combination of Fig. 1.4.1b acts as a
capacitor. This effective capacitor resonates with L_∞ and the inductive equivalent of the L_3C_3 combination at $\omega = 500$. Above $\omega = 1000$ both parallel
resonant components act as capacitors which resonate with L_∞ at $\omega = 3000$.

The resonant type of network of Fig. 1.4.1c places the zeros in evidence
at 0, ω_2, and ω_4. The poles at ω_1 and ω_3 are produced by the network, but
evidence of their existence must be sought in terms of the inductive and
capacitive equivalents of the resonant components. The pole at $\omega = \infty$ is

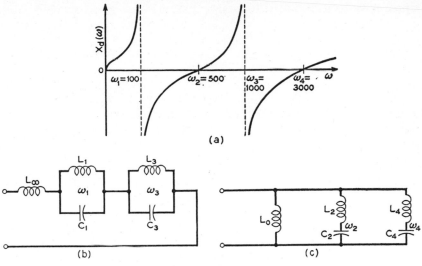

Fig. 1.4.1

produced by all the coils opening, and the zero at $\omega = 0$ is produced by a short circuit through L_0.

The element values of both of the networks of Fig. 1.4.1 can be obtained, of course, by the method of partial fractions given in Sec. 1.3.

1.5 Element value and critical frequency relations

The two preceding sections describe a method for obtaining the element values of a series or parallel resonant type network from specified poles and zeros and the impedance at one other frequency. Explicit formulas for these element values in terms of critical (internal pole and zero) frequencies were not given, however. Because of the importance of such formulas for design work, they are developed and summarized in this and the next section.

Element-value formulas are given in Figs. 1.3.1a and 1.3.2a, but some of these formulas are expressed only indirectly in terms of the critical frequencies. In order to make the expressions explicit functions of the critical frequencies, consider again the CL network of Fig. 1.3.1 and its driving-point impedance given by

$$Z_d(\omega) = j\omega k \frac{(\omega^2 - \omega_2{}^2)(\omega^2 - \omega_4{}^2)(\omega^2 - \omega_6{}^2)}{\omega^2(\omega^2 - \omega_3{}^2)(\omega^2 - \omega_5{}^2)} \qquad (1.5.1)$$

$$= j\omega k \left(1 + \frac{a_0}{\omega^2} + \frac{a_3}{\omega^2 - \omega_3{}^2} + \frac{a_5}{\omega^2 - \omega_5{}^2} \right) \qquad (1.5.2)$$

The a may be determined from the relation

$$\frac{(\omega^2 - \omega_2{}^2)(\omega^2 - \omega_4{}^2)(\omega^2 - \omega_6{}^2)}{\omega^2(\omega^2 - \omega_3{}^2)(\omega^2 - \omega_5{}^2)} = 1 + \frac{a_0}{\omega^2} + \frac{a_3}{\omega^2 - \omega_3{}^2}$$

$$+ \frac{a_5}{\omega^2 - \omega_5{}^2} \quad (1.5.3)$$

For example, on multiplying both sides of this expression by $(\omega^2 - \omega_3{}^2)$, canceling this term from the denominator where possible, and taking the limit as ω approaches ω_3,

$$a_3 = \frac{(\omega_3{}^2 - \omega_2{}^2)(\omega_3{}^2 - \omega_4{}^2)(\omega_3{}^2 - \omega_6{}^2)}{\omega_3{}^2(\omega_3{}^2 - \omega_5{}^2)} \quad (1.5.4)$$

From Fig. 1.3.1a, this last relation, and others of similar form, the element values are as follows: from Fig. 1.3.1a directly,

$$L_\infty = k \quad (1.5.5)$$

$$C_3 = -1/ka_3 \quad (1.5.6)$$

Further, since $\quad L_3 = 1/C_3\omega_3{}^2$

from the last four equations,

$$C_3 = \frac{1}{\omega_3{}^2 L_3} = -\frac{\omega_3{}^2(\omega_3{}^2 - \omega_5{}^2)}{L_\infty(\omega_3{}^2 - \omega_2{}^2)(\omega_3{}^2 - \omega_4{}^2)(\omega_3{}^2 - \omega_6{}^2)} \quad (1.5.7)$$

Thus the element values C_3 and L_3 are specified in terms of the poles and zeros and L_∞.

If Eqs. (1.5.4) and (1.5.7) are written in a more general form

$$a_j = (\omega^2 - \omega_j{}^2) \frac{(\omega^2 - \omega_2{}^2)(\omega^2 - \omega_4{}^2)(\omega^2 - \omega_6{}^2)}{\omega^2(\omega^2 - \omega_3{}^2)(\omega^2 - \omega_5{}^2)} \Bigg|_{\omega = \omega_j; \, j = 3,5} \quad (1.5.8)$$

$$C_j = \frac{1}{\omega_j{}^2 L_j} = -\frac{1}{ka_j}$$

$$= \frac{1}{\omega^2 - \omega_j{}^2} \frac{-\omega^2(\omega^2 - \omega_3{}^2)(\omega^2 - \omega_5{}^2)}{L_\infty(\omega^2 - \omega_2{}^2)(\omega^2 - \omega_4{}^2)(\omega^2 - \omega_6{}^2)} \Bigg|_{\omega = \omega_j; \, j = 3,5} \quad (1.5.9)$$

The element values C_3 and L_3 are determined by setting $j = 3$ in Eqs. (1.5.8) and (1.5.9), with the result shown in Eq. (1.5.7.). Similarly, values of C_5 and L_5 are determined by setting $j = 5$ in Eqs. (1.5.8) and (1.5.9).

Following this same process, a_0 of Eq. (1.5.3) can be derived by multiplying both sides of the equation by ω^2 and taking the limit as ω approaches zero. Again, referring to Fig. 1.3.1a,

$$C_0 = \frac{-1}{ka_0} = \frac{-(-\omega_3{}^2)(-\omega_5{}^2)}{L_\infty(-\omega_2{}^2)(-\omega_4{}^2)(-\omega_6{}^2)} \qquad (1.5.10)$$

Note that this expression also may be derived from Eqs. (1.5.8) and (1.5.9) by setting $j = 0$, $\omega_j = 0$, and evaluating the resulting expression for $\omega = 0$.

Note also that these last two formulas, (1.5.9) and (1.5.10), can be extended to fit networks of this same class (CL) containing any number of parallel resonant components. For example, to obtain the element values for a network with one parallel resonant component (Fig. 1.3.3a) it is necessary merely to remove the terms containing ω_5 and ω_6 in Eq. (1.5.9), and to remove ω_5 and ω_6 from Eq. (1.5.10). In order to obtain the element values for CL networks with more than two parallel resonant components, Eq. (1.5.9) should be multiplied on the right by the ratio $(\omega^2 - \omega_7{}^2)/(\omega^2 - \omega_8{}^2)$ for three parallel resonant components, etc. Also Eq. (1.5.10) should be multiplied (on the right) by the ratio $(-\omega_7{}^2)/(-\omega_8{}^2)$ for three parallel resonant components, etc.

The element values of the series resonant type CL network of Fig. 1.3.2a can also be expressed in terms of the poles and zeros and an arbitrary constant. Thus from Eqs. (1.3.3) and (1.3.4), the equation

$$\frac{-(\omega^2 - \omega_3{}^2)(\omega^2 - \omega_5{}^2)}{(\omega^2 - \omega_2{}^2)(\omega^2 - \omega_4{}^2)(\omega^2 - \omega_6{}^2)} = \frac{A_2}{\omega^2 - \omega_2{}^2} + \frac{A_4}{\omega^2 - \omega_4{}^2}$$

$$+ \frac{A_6}{\omega^2 - \omega_6{}^2} \qquad (1.5.11)$$

leads to a formula which specifies any one of the A_j. This formula is

$$A_j = (\omega^2 - \omega_j{}^2) \left[\frac{-(\omega^2 - \omega_3{}^2)(\omega^2 - \omega_5{}^2)}{(\omega^2 - \omega_2{}^2)(\omega^2 - \omega_4{}^2)(\omega^2 - \omega_6{}^2)} \right]_{\omega=\omega_j; j = 2,4,6}$$

$$(1.5.12)$$

The numerator term $(\omega^2 - \omega_j{}^2)$ must cancel the corresponding denominator term before this last expression can be evaluated. Next referring to the formulas of Fig. 1.3.2a, and using this last equation and Eq. (1.5.5), the element-value formulas are

$$L_j = \frac{1}{\omega_j{}^2 C_j} = \frac{-1}{KA_j} = \frac{-k}{A_j} = \frac{-L_\infty}{A_j}$$

$$= \frac{1}{\omega^2 - \omega_j{}^2} \frac{L_\infty(\omega^2 - \omega_2{}^2)(\omega^2 - \omega_4{}^2)(\omega^2 - \omega_6{}^2)}{(\omega^2 - \omega_3{}^2)(\omega^2 - \omega_5{}^2)} \bigg|_{\omega=\omega_j; \; j = 2,4,6}$$

$$(1.5.13)$$

This last formula can be extended or reduced to specify the element values of CL networks of more or less than three resonant components by inserting or removing the proper ratio of the type $(\omega^2 - \omega_6^2)/(\omega^2 - \omega_5^2)$.

Example 1.5.1

Determine the element values of the parallel resonant and series resonant type networks which have zeros at $\omega_2 = 2.5 \times 10^6$, $\omega_4 = 4 \times 10^6$, and a pole at $\omega_3 = 3 \times 10^6$.

Solution

Since the lowest and highest critical frequencies are specified as zeros, the networks required are of the CL class; both external critical frequencies are poles.

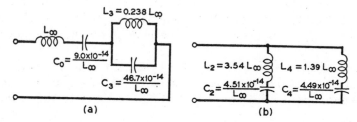

Fig. 1.5.1

The parallel resonant type of network must have the configuration shown in Fig. 1.5.1a. The element values are obtained from Eqs. (1.5.9) and (1.5.10) as follows.

$$C_0 = \frac{-(-\omega_3^2)}{L_\infty(-\omega_2^2)(-\omega_4^2)} = \frac{9 \times 10^{12}}{L_\infty 6.25 \times 10^{12} \times 16 \times 10^{12}} = \frac{9 \times 10^{-14}}{L_\infty} \quad \text{farad}$$

$$C_3 = \frac{-\omega^2}{L_\infty(\omega^2 - \omega_2^2)(\omega^2 - \omega_4^2)}\bigg|_{\omega=3\times10^6}$$

$$= \frac{-9 \times 10^{12}}{L_\infty(9 \times 10^{12} - 6.25 \times 10^{12})(9 \times 10^{12} - 16 \times 10^{12})}$$

$$= \frac{46.7 \times 10^{-14}}{L_\infty} \quad \text{farad}$$

$$L_3 = \frac{1}{\omega_3^2 C_3} = \frac{L_\infty}{9 \times 10^{12} \times 46.7 \times 10^{-14}} = 0.238 L_\infty \quad \text{henry}$$

Under the conditions stated in the problem $L_\infty = k$ cannot be evaluated. The value of the network reactance at other than a pole or zero is required (see Ex. 1.4.1) to determine this still arbitrary element value.

The element values of the series resonant type network are specified by Eq. (1.5.13) if the last terms in both numerator and denominator are removed. Then

$$L_2 = \frac{L_\infty(\omega^2 - \omega_4{}^2)}{\omega^2 - \omega_3{}^2}\bigg|_{\omega = 2.5 \times 10^6} = L_\infty \frac{6.25 \times 10^{12} - 16 \times 10^{12}}{6.25 \times 10^{12} - 9 \times 10^{12}}$$

$$= 3.54 L_\infty \quad \text{henry}$$

$$C_2 = \frac{1}{\omega_2{}^2 L_2} = \frac{1}{6.25 \times 10^{12} \times 3.54 L_\infty} = \frac{4.52 \times 10^{-14}}{L_\infty} \quad \text{farad}$$

$$L_4 = \frac{L_\infty(\omega^2 - \omega_2{}^2)}{\omega^2 - \omega_3{}^2}\bigg|_{\omega = 4 \times 10^6} = L_\infty \frac{16 \times 10^{12} - 6.25 \times 10^{12}}{16 \times 10^{12} - 9 \times 10^{12}} = 1.39 L_\infty \quad \text{henry}$$

$$C_4 = \frac{1}{\omega_4{}^2 L_4} = \frac{1}{16 \times 10^{12} \times 1.39 L_\infty} = \frac{4.49 \times 10^{-14}}{L_\infty} \quad \text{farad}$$

These element values are shown in Fig. 1.5.1b.

The two networks of Fig. 1.5.1, of course, have identical driving-point impedances. Note that the element values are different, which is often an advantage in building the physical counterpart.

As already indicated, the two networks considered thus far in this section are classed as CL networks. There are three other classes corresponding to the existence of a pole or zero at zero and infinity. These three other classes are CC, LL, and LC. The networks, of both the series and the parallel resonant type, the reactance and susceptance curves, and the element value formulas are different for each of these classes of networks. However, the method of establishing the appropriate curve, diagrams, or formulas is covered in the foregoing and so is not considered further. Tabulations 1.5.1, 1.5.2, 1.5.3, 1.5.4 give, for ready reference, the useful information concerning each of the four classes of 2TN. The preceding material of this section should be referred to for the meaning of the various symbols and equations and for the method of extending the formula and networks of these tabulations to more or fewer elements.

CL Network

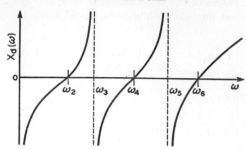

Fig. 1.5.2

Parallel Resonant Type:

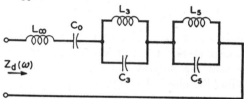

Fig. 1.5.3

$$Z_d(\omega) = j\omega L_\infty \frac{(\omega^2 - \omega_2{}^2)(\omega^2 - \omega_4{}^2)(\omega^2 - \omega_6{}^2)}{\omega^2(\omega^2 - \omega_3{}^2)(\omega^2 - \omega_5{}^2)} \qquad (1.5.14)$$

$$C_i = \frac{1}{\omega_j{}^2 L_j} = \frac{1}{\omega^2 - \omega_j{}^2} \left. \frac{-\omega^2(\omega^2 - \omega_3{}^2)(\omega^2 - \omega_5{}^2)}{L_\infty(\omega^2 - \omega_2{}^2)(\omega^2 - \omega_4{}^2)(\omega^2 - \omega_6{}^2)} \right|_{\omega = \omega_j; j = 3,5}$$

$$(1.5.15)$$

$$C_0 = \frac{-(-\omega_3{}^2)(-\omega_5{}^2)}{L_\infty(-\omega_2{}^2)(-\omega_4{}^2)(-\omega_6{}^2)} \qquad (1.5.16)$$

Series Resonant Type:

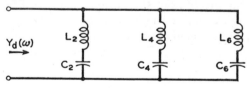

Fig. 1.5.4

$$Y_d(\omega) = -j \frac{\omega}{L_\infty} \frac{(\omega^2 - \omega_3{}^2)(\omega^2 - \omega_5{}^2)}{(\omega^2 - \omega_2{}^2)(\omega^2 - \omega_4{}^2)(\omega^2 - \omega_6{}^2)} \qquad (1.5.17)$$

$$L_i = \frac{1}{\omega_j{}^2 C_j} = \frac{1}{\omega^2 - \omega_j{}^2} \left. \frac{L_\infty(\omega^2 - \omega_2{}^2)(\omega^2 - \omega_4{}^2)(\omega^2 - \omega_6{}^2)}{(\omega^2 - \omega_3{}^2)(\omega^2 - \omega_5{}^2)} \right|_{\omega = \omega_j; j = 2,4,6}$$

$$(1.5.18)$$

CC NETWORK

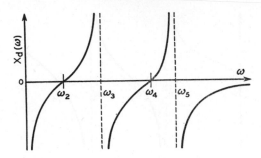

Fig. 1.5.5

Parallel Resonant Type:

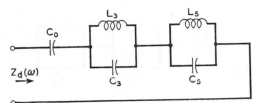

Fig. 1.5.6

$$Z_d(\omega) = -j\,\frac{\omega}{C_\infty}\,\frac{(\omega^2 - \omega_2{}^2)(\omega^2 - \omega_4{}^2)}{\omega^2(\omega^2 - \omega_3{}^2)(\omega^2 - \omega_5{}^2)} \tag{1.5.19}$$

$$C_i = \frac{1}{\omega_j{}^2 L_j} = \frac{1}{\omega^2 - \omega_j{}^2}\,\frac{C_\infty \omega^2(\omega^2 - \omega_3{}^2)(\omega^2 - \omega_5{}^2)}{(\omega^2 - \omega_2{}^2)(\omega^2 - \omega_4{}^2)}\bigg|_{\omega = \omega_j; j = 3,5} \tag{1.5.20}$$

$$C_0 = C_\infty\,\frac{(-\omega_3{}^2)(-\omega_5{}^2)}{(-\omega_2{}^2)(-\omega_4{}^2)} \tag{1.5.21}$$

Series Resonant Type:

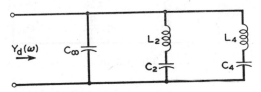

Fig. 1.5.7

$$Y_d(\omega) = j\omega C_\infty\,\frac{(\omega^2 - \omega_3{}^2)(\omega^2 - \omega_5{}^2)}{(\omega^2 - \omega_2{}^2)(\omega^2 - \omega_4{}^2)} \tag{1.5.22}$$

$$L_i = \frac{1}{\omega_j{}^2 C_j} = \frac{1}{\omega^2 - \omega_j{}^2}\,\frac{-(\omega^2 - \omega_2{}^2)(\omega^2 - \omega_4{}^2)}{C_\infty(\omega^2 - \omega_3{}^2)(\omega^2 - \omega_5{}^2)}\bigg|_{\omega = \omega_j; j = 2,4} \tag{1.5.23}$$

TABULATION 1.5.3

LL NETWORK

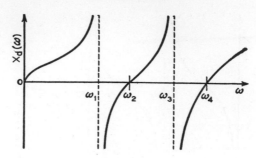

Fig. 1.5.8

Parallel Resonant Type:

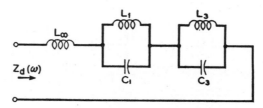

Fig. 1.5.9

$$Z_d(\omega) = j\omega L_\infty \frac{(\omega^2 - \omega_2^2)(\omega^2 - \omega_4^2)}{(\omega^2 - \omega_1^2)(\omega^2 - \omega_3^2)} \tag{1.5.24}$$

$$C_i = \frac{1}{\omega_j^2 L_j} = \frac{1}{\omega^2 - \omega_j^2} \frac{-(\omega^2 - \omega_1^2)(\omega^2 - \omega_3^2)}{L_\infty(\omega^2 - \omega_2^2)(\omega^2 - \omega_4^2)} \Bigg|_{\omega = \omega_i;\, j = 1,3} \tag{1.5.25}$$

Series Resonant Type:

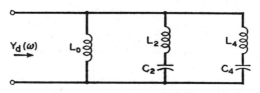

Fig. 1.5.10

$$Y_d(\omega) = -j\frac{\omega}{L_\infty} \frac{(\omega^2 - \omega_1^2)(\omega^2 - \omega_3^2)}{\omega^2(\omega^2 - \omega_2^2)(\omega^2 - \omega_4^2)} \tag{1.5.26}$$

$$L_i = \frac{1}{\omega_j^2 C_j} = \frac{1}{\omega^2 - \omega_j^2} \frac{L_\infty \omega^2(\omega^2 - \omega_2^2)(\omega^2 - \omega_4^2)}{(\omega^2 - \omega_1^2)(\omega^2 - \omega_3^2)} \Bigg|_{\omega = \omega_i;\, j = 2,4} \tag{1.5.27}$$

$$L_0 = L_\infty \frac{(-\omega_2^2)(-\omega_4^2)}{(-\omega_1^2)(-\omega_3^2)} \tag{1.5.28}$$

20

LC NETWORK

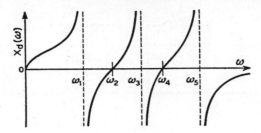

Fig. 1.5.11

Parallel Resonant Type:

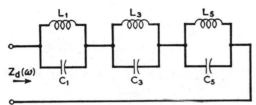

Fig. 1.5.12

$$Z_d(\omega) = -j\,\frac{\omega}{C_\infty}\,\frac{(\omega^2 - \omega_2^2)(\omega^2 - \omega_4^2)}{(\omega^2 - \omega_1^2)(\omega^2 - \omega_3^2)(\omega^2 - \omega_5^2)} \qquad (1.5.29)$$

$$C_i = \frac{1}{\omega_i^2 L_i} = \frac{1}{\omega^2 - \omega_i^2}\,\frac{C_\infty(\omega^2 - \omega_1^2)(\omega^2 - \omega_3^2)(\omega^2 - \omega_5^2)}{(\omega^2 - \omega_2^2)(\omega^2 - \omega_4^2)}\Bigg|_{\omega = \omega_i;\, j = 1,3,5}$$
$$(1.5.30)$$

Series Resonant Type:

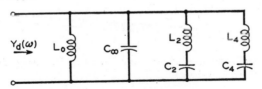

Fig. 1.5.13

$$Y_d(\omega) = j\omega C_\infty\,\frac{(\omega^2 - \omega_1^2)(\omega^2 - \omega_3^2)(\omega^2 - \omega_5^2)}{\omega^2(\omega^2 - \omega_2^2)(\omega^2 - \omega_4^2)} \qquad (1.5.31)$$

$$L_i = \frac{1}{\omega_i^2 C_i} = \frac{1}{\omega^2 - \omega_i^2}\,\frac{-\omega(\omega^2 - \omega_2^2)(\omega^2 - \omega_4^2)}{C_\infty(\omega^2 - \omega_1^2)(\omega^2 - \omega_3^2)(\omega^2 - \omega_5^2)}\Bigg|_{\omega = \omega_i;\, j = 2,4}$$
$$(1.5.32)$$

$$L_0 = \frac{-(-\omega_2^2)(-\omega_4^2)}{C_\infty(-\omega_1^2)(-\omega_3^2)(-\omega_5^2)} \qquad (1.5.33)$$

THREE-ELEMENT-NETWORK EQUIVALENT

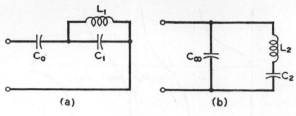

(a)   (b)

Fig. 1.6.1

Two-terminal networks which have the same frequency response for element values related as follows:

$$C_0 = C_\infty + C_2 \qquad\qquad C_\infty = \frac{C_0 C_1}{C_0 + C_1}$$

$$C_1 = \frac{C_\infty}{C_2}(C_\infty + C_2) \qquad\qquad L_2 = L_1(1 + C_1/C_0)^2$$

$$L_1 = \frac{L_2}{(1 + C_\infty/C_2)^2} \qquad\qquad C_2 = \frac{C_0{}^2}{C_0 + C_1}$$

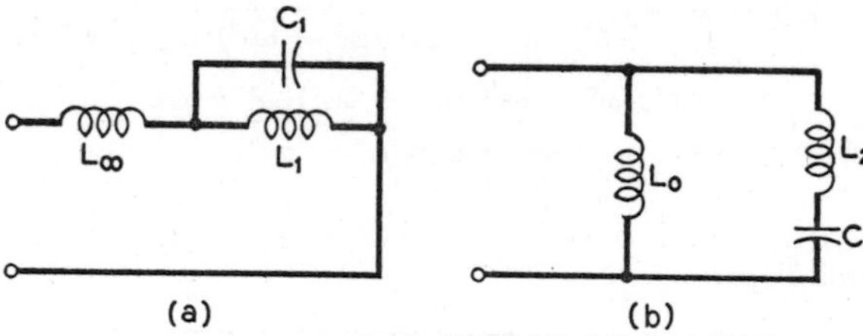

(a)   (b)

Fig. 1.6.2

Two-terminal networks which have the same frequency response for element values related as follows:

$$L_\infty = \frac{L_0 L_2}{L_0 + L_2} \qquad\qquad L_0 = L_\infty + L_1$$

$$L_1 = \frac{L_0{}^2}{L_0 + L_2} \qquad\qquad L_2 = \frac{L_\infty(L_\infty + L_1)}{L_1}$$

$$C_1 = C_2(1 + L_2/L_1)^2 \qquad\qquad C_2 = \frac{C_1}{(1 + L_\infty/L_1)^2}$$

1.6 Transformation from a series resonant to a parallel resonant network and vice versa

Because the element values of the series resonant and parallel resonant type networks, for a particular frequency response, are usually different, it is helpful to be able to use either type of network at will. As indicated in the foregoing, the design problem is formulated in terms of the poles and zeros (critical frequencies) and the value of reactance at some frequency other than a pole or zero. All the constants required to establish both the series resonant and parallel resonant type networks according to Tabulations 1.5.1 through 1.5.4, therefore, are available in any design. The results given in these tabulations, as a consequence, are sufficient for obtaining both the series resonant and parallel resonant networks.

Direct transformation from the element values of the parallel resonant type network to the element values of the equivalent series resonant type and vice versa is too complicated for practical usage except in the simplest cases. These transformations for three-element networks are the most widely used. The following example indicates one method of deriving the transformation formulas for three-element reactive networks, and Tabulation 1.6.1 gives the element value interrelations.

Example 1.6.1

Show that the element value formulas associated with Fig. 1.6.1b specify this network as having the same frequency response as the network of Fig. 1.6.1a.

Solution

Since the equivalence sought is to be for all frequencies, the driving-point impedances (or admittances) of the two networks must be identical at all frequencies. Such an identity can be assured by equating the driving-point impedance (or admittance) functions obtained from the two networks.

The driving-point admittance of the network of Fig. 1.6.1a is

$$Y_d(\omega) = j\omega \, \frac{C_0 C_1}{C_0 + C_1} \, \frac{\omega^2 - 1/L_1 C_1}{\omega^2 - 1/L_1(C_0 + C_1)}$$

and that of the network of Fig. 1.6.1b is

$$Y_d(\omega) = j\omega C_\infty \frac{\omega^2 - (1/L_2 C_2 + 1/L_2 C_\infty)}{\omega^2 - 1/L_2 C_2}$$

In order that these two admittance functions be equal at all frequencies, corresponding coefficients must be equal, i.e.,

$$C_\infty = \frac{C_0 C_1}{C_0 + C_1}, \quad \frac{1}{L_1 C_1} = \frac{1}{L_2 C_2} + \frac{1}{L_2 C_\infty}, \quad \frac{1}{L_1(C_0 + C_1)} = \frac{1}{L_2 C_2}$$

The solution of these last equations for the elements C_∞, C_2, L_2, or for C_0, C_1, L_1 gives the results associated with Fig. 1.6.1 of Tabulation 1.6.1.

It should be noted in connection with the idea of transforming from the series to the parallel resonant type networks that it is never possible in such a transformation to eliminate an inductor or capacitor. The equivalent networks of Tabulations 1.5.1 through 1.5.4 demonstrate that the number of inductors and capacitors does not change from one network to its equivalent in this transformation.

1.7 Inverse networks

In the process of designing filters and equalizers, it is important to be able to determine a two-terminal network driving-point impedance $Z_i(\omega)$ which is related to $Z_d(\omega)$ by

$$Z_i(\omega) Z_d(\omega) = R_0^2 \tag{1.7.1}$$

where R_0 is a positive constant. Thus

$$Z_i(\omega) = \frac{R_0^2}{Z_d(\omega)} = R_0^2 Y_d(\omega) \tag{1.7.2}$$

The driving-point impedance $Z_i(\omega)$ is known as the inverse with respect to R_0 of $Z_d(\omega)$.

One immediately evident way of getting an inverse network of driving-point impedance $Z_i(\omega)$ is to multiply $Y_d(\omega)$ by R_0^2 (see Eq. 1.7.2) and then to determine the network from the resulting polynomial ratio as in the preceding parts of this chapter. A simpler approach which requires little computation can be formulated in terms of node equations.[5] Knowledge of the node method is assumed here.

Briefly, the inverse with respect to R_0 may be obtained by writing the impedance matrix on the mesh basis, dividing each element of this matrix by R_0^2, considering the result as the admittance matrix on the node basis, and then drawing the inverse network directly from this

[5] Reed, Myril B., *Alternating Current Circuit Theory*, Harper & Brothers, New York, 1948, Chap. 9.

node matrix. To demonstrate the validity of this technique consider the expression

$$Y_i(\omega) = \frac{Z_d(\omega)}{R_0^2} \tag{1.7.3}$$

Substituting from Eq. (1.2.4) this expression becomes

$$Y_i(\omega) = \frac{\Delta}{R_0^2 \Delta_{11}} = \frac{\Delta/R_0^2}{\Delta_{11}} \tag{1.7.4}$$

If the determinant Δ is of nth order, division of numerator and denominator by R_0^{2n-2} leads to

$$Y_i(\omega) = \frac{\Delta/R_0^{2n}}{\Delta_{11}/R_0^{2(n-1)}} = \frac{\Delta'}{\Delta'_{11}} \tag{1.7.5}$$

where Δ' and Δ'_{11} are exactly the same as Δ and Δ_{11} except that each element of Δ' and Δ'_{11} is divided by R_0^2.

The driving-point admittance of a 2TN, computed from the node equations, has exactly the form given on the right of Eq. (1.7.5).[6] The determinant Δ', however, under such circumstances is that of the node admittance matrix. Since the nth order determinant $\Delta' = \Delta/R_0^{2n}$ may be considered the determinant of the node equations of an $n - 1$ node network, the desired inverse network can be sketched immediately from this determinant. The element values of the inverse network are also very easily determined from known values of the original network. The following example should help to clarify the computation of an inverse network.

Example 1.7.1

Determine the inverse with respect to R_0 of the CL network of the parallel resonant type of Fig. 1.5.3.

Solution

The determinant Δ of the mesh equations is, for three clockwise mesh currents: first through L_∞, C_0, C_3, and C_5, second through L_3 and C_3, and third through L_5 and C_5, ($p = j\omega$)

$$\Delta = \begin{vmatrix} pL_\infty + \dfrac{1}{pC_0} + \dfrac{1}{pC_3} + \dfrac{1}{pC_5} & -\dfrac{1}{pC_3} & -\dfrac{1}{pC_5} \\[2mm] -\dfrac{1}{pC_3} & pL_3 + \dfrac{1}{pC_3} & 0 \\[2mm] -\dfrac{1}{pC_5} & 0 & pL_5 + \dfrac{1}{pC_5} \end{vmatrix}$$

[6] Bode, H. W., *op. cit.*, Chap. 1.

At once the determinant of the node equations is obtained by dividing this determinant by R_0^2, i.e.,

$$\Delta' = \begin{vmatrix} p\dfrac{L_\infty}{R_0^2} + \dfrac{1}{pC_0R_0^2} + \dfrac{1}{pC_3R_0^2} + \dfrac{1}{pC_5R_0^2} & -\dfrac{1}{pC_3R_0^2} & -\dfrac{1}{pC_5R_0^2} \\[2mm] -\dfrac{1}{pC_3R_0^2} & p\dfrac{L_3}{R_0^2} + \dfrac{1}{pC_3R_0^2} & 0 \\[2mm] -\dfrac{1}{pC_5R_0^2} & 0 & p\dfrac{L_5}{R_0^2} + \dfrac{1}{pC_5R_0^2} \end{vmatrix}$$

Viewing this determinant as that of the node equations of a four-node network, the inverse network is as given by Fig. 1.7.1 with nodes 1, 2, 3 and reference as shown. Incidentally, this inverse network derived from a CL class network is itself an LC network.

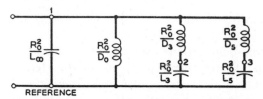

Fig. 1.7.1

Notice that each capacitor and inductor of the inverse network is determined by an inductor or capacitor of the original network. Each pair is related by the condition $L/C = R_0^2$. That is, $L_i = C_iR_0^2$ and $C_i = L_i/R_0^2$. Also note that series and parallel combinations of the original network become, respectively, parallel and series combinations in the inverse network. Results which are particularly easy to remember are shown in Fig. 1.7.1, where $D = 1/C$ is used rather than C.

The process given in the foregoing for determining an inverse network is not restricted to purely reactive networks. The following example demonstrates this fact.

Example 1.7.2

Determine the 2TN which has a driving-point impedance inverse to that of the network of Fig. 1.7.2a.

Solution

The determinant of the mesh equations of Fig. 1.7.2a is

$$\Delta = \begin{vmatrix} R_1+R_2+pL_1+pL_2+\dfrac{D_2}{p} & -R_2-pL_2-\dfrac{D_2}{p} & 0 \\[2mm] -R_2-pL_2-\dfrac{D_2}{p} & R_2+R_4+R_5+pL_2+pL_4+\dfrac{D_2}{p}+\dfrac{D_5}{p} & -R_4-pL_4 \\[2mm] 0 & -R_4-pL_4 & R_3+R_4+pL_3+pL_4 \end{vmatrix}$$

Dividing this determinant by $R_0{}^2$ and viewing the result as the node-equation determinant in terms of R, L, and D, the inverse network is as given by Fig. 1.7.2b.

Note should be taken of the fact that it is not possible to obtain an inverse to every network where both the original and inverse networks contain only combinations of R, L, and D. In particular, the inverse of networks

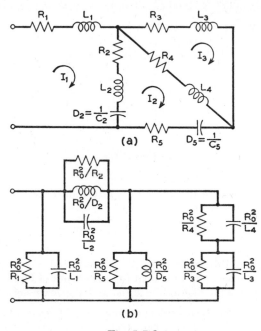

Fig. 1.7.2

with irremovable crossovers (nonplanar) cannot be obtained without use of ideal transformers.

Problems

1.1 Prove that if $dX_d(\omega)/d\omega > 0$, then $dB_d(\omega)/d\omega > 0$.

1.2 Prove that: (a) $Z_d(\omega)$ for a reactive network is a pure imaginary function, i.e., j may be factored from the generalized expression; (b) numerator and denominator of $Z_d(\omega)$ contain only even degree terms after ω or $1/\omega$ is factored from the ratio. Prove this relation from a consideration of the typical elements of $\Delta(\omega)$ and $\Delta_{11}(\omega)$.

1.3 Prove that the squared roots of $\Delta(\omega)$ and $\Delta_{11}(\omega)$ are real. Prove this property by consideration of the transient response of a purely reactive network.

1.4 Prove that the roots of $\Delta(\omega)$ and $\Delta_{11}(\omega)$ must be simple. Also that the factor ω must appear in either numerator or denominator but not both, of $X_d(\omega)$. Prove these results from the fact that the derivatives of Problem 1.1 are positive.

1.5 Determine the driving-point impedance of the network of Fig. P.1.5, for the element values: $L_1 = 1$ μh, $L_2 = 10$ μh, $L_3 = 50$ μh, $C_1 = 10,000$ $\mu\mu$f, $C_2 = 20,000$ $\mu\mu$f, and $C_3 = 1000$ $\mu\mu$f. Use Eq. (1.2.4) and express the result as

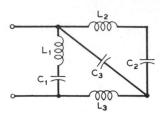

Fig. P.1.5

a function of ω in both of the alternative forms illustrated in Example 1.2.1. Sketch the curve of reactance versus ω.

1.6 Repeat the preceding problem if C_3 is replaced by a coil of inductance $L_4 = 5$ μh.

1.7 Determine the series parallel-resonant and shunt series-resonant types of networks which are equivalent to the network of Fig. P.1.5 (like those of Figs. 1.3.1 and 1.3.2). Sketch the $Z_d(\omega)$ and $Y_d(\omega)$ versus ω curves.

1.8 Determine the series resonant and parallel resonant type networks which have poles at $\omega = 1000, 2000, 5000$; zeros at $\omega = 1500, 3000$; and an impedance of $j100$ ohms at $\omega = 100$. Sketch the reactance and susceptance curves.

1.9 Determine the series resonant and parallel resonant type networks for poles at $\omega = 3 \times 10^6$, 3.05×10^6, 3.2×10^6, and zeros at $\omega = 2.4 \times 10^6$, 3.025×10^6, 3.1×10^6. Sketch the reactance and susceptance curves with $Z_d(2 \times 10^6) = -j100$.

1.10 Use the formulas of Sec. 1.5 properly modified to determine the CL, parallel resonant and series resonant networks which have zeros at $\omega = 2 \times 10^5$, 2.2×10^5, 4×10^5, 5.5×10^5, poles at $\omega = 2.1 \times 10^5$, 3×10^5, 5×10^5. At $\omega = 1.8 \times 10^5$ the driving point impedance is $-j1000$.

1.11 Derive the formulas of Tabulations 1.5.2, 1.5.3, and 1.5.4.

1.12 Investigate the possibility of expressing the element values of a CL network of the parallel resonant type in terms of the element values of the series resonant type, for structures of greater complexity than those shown in Tabulation 1.6.1.

1.13 Establish the determinant Δ' (as defined in Sec. 1.7) and from it the inverse network for all the networks (except the CL parallel resonant type network) of Tabulation 1.5.1.

1.14 Determine the networks which are inverse with respect to $R_0{}^2$ of those of Fig. 1.3.4.

1.15 Determine the inverse of Fig. P.1.5 with respect to $R_0 = 100$ ohms.

1.16 Show that the series connection of n identical 2TN is equivalent to a 2TN having the same configuration as one of the original 2TN, but for which the impedance of each branch is multiplied by n.

1.17 Show that the parallel connection of n identical 2TN is equivalent to a 2TN having the same configuration as one of the original 2TN, but for which the impedance of each branch is divided by n.

1.18 Consider two 2TN, the reactance of each being expressed by Eq. (1.1.3), but with different values for L and ω_R. Develop the driving-point impedance for these two networks connected in series.

CHAPTER TWO

General Properties of Passive
Four-Terminal Networks

The discussions of this book center about the electrical properties of a particular group of electric networks known as four-terminal networks (4TN). Broadly, 4TN are the building blocks of communication systems and include such units as transmission lines, amplifiers, filters, modulators, equalizers, transistors, and oscillators. These networks are called four-terminal because they are characterized by having a pair of input terminals and a pair of output terminals.

Four-terminal networks are classified either as active or passive. Active 4TN contain a source of energy, as in the case of an amplifier. Passive 4TN do not contain such a source of energy, as typified by filters and equalizers. Since this book is concerned specifically with filters and equalizers, attention is restricted to passive 4TN. Also, the assumption here is that the 4TN are reciprocal; that is, if the 4TN is energized by a source and terminated by a load, the ratio between the source voltage and the load current is independent of the direction of transmission. In this chapter the properties of reciprocal passive 4TN are derived.

2.1 T equivalent of any passive four-terminal network[1]

In this section it is shown that the transmission properties of the general, passive, reciprocal network can be characterized by the specification of three independent parametric functions. In particular these three parameters may take the form of the three impedance functions which may be associated with a T network of two series branches and one shunt branch. The T network is of particular interest because it is one of the simplest 4TN which, at any particular frequency, completely specifies the performance of any passive reciprocal 4TN.

[1] Campbell, G. A., "Cissoidal Oscillations," *Trans. AIEE*, **30**, 873–909 (1911); Reed, Myril B., *Alternating Current Circuit Theory*, Harper & Brothers, New York, 1948.

Since the element values of the networks under consideration here are constant and since the elements conduct identically in either direction, the equations for the networks may always be so written that the impedance matrix is symmetric. Use is made of this symmetry relation without specific mention of it in the following.

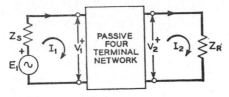

Fig. 2.1.1

Consider the general symbolization of a 4TN as shown in Fig. 2.1.1. If this network is passive and reciprocal the equations for its electrical behavior, when driven under sinusoidal steady state, are

$$
\begin{bmatrix} V_1 \\ -V_2 \\ 0 \\ \cdot \\ \cdot \\ \cdot \\ 0 \end{bmatrix}
=
\begin{bmatrix}
Z_{11} & Z_{12} & Z_{13} & \cdots & Z_{1n} \\
Z_{12} & Z_{22} & Z_{23} & \cdots & Z_{2n} \\
Z_{13} & Z_{23} & Z_{33} & \cdots & Z_{3n} \\
\cdot & \cdot & \cdot & & \cdot \\
\cdot & \cdot & \cdot & & \cdot \\
\cdot & \cdot & \cdot & & \cdot \\
Z_{1n} & Z_{2n} & Z_{3n} & \cdots & Z_{nn}
\end{bmatrix}
\begin{bmatrix} I_1 \\ I_2 \\ I_3 \\ \cdot \\ \cdot \\ \cdot \\ I_n \end{bmatrix}
\qquad (2.1.1)
$$

The symbolic solution of a similar set of equations is given by Eq. (1.2.2). Using the symbol Y_{ij} for the elements of the inverse of the impedance matrix of Eq. (2.1.1), the solution is

$$
\begin{bmatrix} I_1 \\ I_2 \\ I_3 \\ \cdot \\ \cdot \\ \cdot \\ I_n \end{bmatrix}
=
\begin{bmatrix}
Y_{11} & Y_{12} & Y_{13} & \cdots & Y_{1n} \\
Y_{12} & Y_{22} & Y_{23} & \cdots & Y_{2n} \\
Y_{13} & Y_{23} & Y_{33} & \cdots & Y_{3n} \\
\cdot & \cdot & \cdot & & \cdot \\
\cdot & \cdot & \cdot & & \cdot \\
\cdot & \cdot & \cdot & & \cdot \\
Y_{1n} & Y_{2n} & Y_{3n} & \cdots & Y_{nn}
\end{bmatrix}
\begin{bmatrix} V_1 \\ -V_2 \\ 0 \\ \cdot \\ \cdot \\ \cdot \\ 0 \end{bmatrix}
\qquad (2.1.2)
$$

Since all the elements of the voltage matrix but the first two are zero, this last equation may be written

$$
\begin{bmatrix} I_1 \\ I_2 \\ I_3 \\ \cdot \\ \cdot \\ \cdot \\ I_n \end{bmatrix}
=
\begin{bmatrix}
Y_{11} & Y_{12} \\
Y_{12} & Y_{22} \\
Y_{13} & Y_{23} \\
\cdot & \cdot \\
\cdot & \cdot \\
\cdot & \cdot \\
Y_{1n} & Y_{2n}
\end{bmatrix}
\begin{bmatrix} V_1 \\ -V_2 \end{bmatrix}
\qquad (2.1.3)
$$

The input and output currents I_1 and I_2, and the input and output terminal voltages V_1 and V_2 specify completely the external behavior of a 4TN. Consequently, since the external behavior only is of interest in this discussion, the first two of Eqs. (2.1.3) in the form

$$\begin{bmatrix} I_1 \\ I_2 \end{bmatrix} = \begin{bmatrix} Y_{11} & Y_{12} \\ Y_{12} & Y_{22} \end{bmatrix} \begin{bmatrix} V_1 \\ -V_2 \end{bmatrix} \tag{2.1.4}$$

specify the 4TN behavior pertinent to the problem under consideration. It should be observed that the network is completely specified in terms of three parameters. From this fact it follows that any network, such as a T network, which provides three independent parameters, is sufficient to represent the general 4TN. Indeed, parametric functions, three in number, may be invented, as the image parameters have been, for describing the transmission properties of 4TN with no concern whether these parameters arise directly as impedances from any network.

From the original set of Eqs. (2.1.1) and the definitions following Eq. (1.2.2), this last equation is

$$\begin{bmatrix} I_1 \\ I_2 \end{bmatrix} = \begin{bmatrix} \dfrac{\Delta_{11}}{\Delta} & \dfrac{\Delta_{12}}{\Delta} \\ \dfrac{\Delta_{12}}{\Delta} & \dfrac{\Delta_{22}}{\Delta} \end{bmatrix} \begin{bmatrix} V_1 \\ -V_2 \end{bmatrix} \tag{2.1.5}$$

If these equations are solved for the voltages, the result is

$$\begin{bmatrix} V_1 \\ -V_2 \end{bmatrix} = \frac{\Delta^2}{\Delta_{11}\Delta_{22} - \Delta_{12}{}^2} \begin{bmatrix} \dfrac{\Delta_{22}}{\Delta} & \dfrac{-\Delta_{12}}{\Delta} \\ \dfrac{-\Delta_{12}}{\Delta} & \dfrac{\Delta_{11}}{\Delta} \end{bmatrix} \begin{bmatrix} I_1 \\ I_2 \end{bmatrix} \tag{2.1.6}$$

But

$$\Delta_{11}\Delta_{22} - \Delta_{12}{}^2 = \begin{vmatrix} \Delta_{11} & \Delta_{12} \\ \Delta_{12} & \Delta_{22} \end{vmatrix} = \Delta\Delta_{1122} \tag{2.1.7}$$

where Δ_{1122} is the remainder after removing the first two rows and columns of Δ.[2] Therefore Eq. (2.1.6) can be expressed as

$$\begin{bmatrix} V_1 \\ -V_2 \end{bmatrix} = \begin{bmatrix} \dfrac{\Delta_{22}}{\Delta_{1122}} & \dfrac{-\Delta_{12}}{\Delta_{1122}} \\ \dfrac{-\Delta_{12}}{\Delta_{1122}} & \dfrac{\Delta_{11}}{\Delta_{1122}} \end{bmatrix} \begin{bmatrix} I_1 \\ I_2 \end{bmatrix} \tag{2.1.8}$$

[2] Bocher, M., *Introduction to Higher Algebra*, The MacMillan Company, New York, 1938, p. 33.

Consider next the matrix equation for a T network (Fig. 2.1.2) in the form

$$\begin{bmatrix} V_1 \\ -V_2 \end{bmatrix} = \begin{bmatrix} Z_a + Z_b & -Z_b \\ -Z_b & Z_b + Z_c \end{bmatrix} \begin{bmatrix} I_1 \\ I_2 \end{bmatrix} \qquad (2.1.9)$$

The T network equivalent, in so far as external behavior is concerned, to the general 4TN can be obtained by making corresponding elements

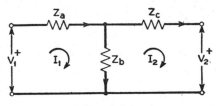

Fig. 2.1.2

of the impedance matrices of these last two equations equal. Thus, if corresponding elements are equated,

$$Z_a + Z_b = \frac{\Delta_{22}}{\Delta_{1122}}, \quad Z_b = \frac{\Delta_{12}}{\Delta_{1122}}, \quad Z_b + Z_c = \frac{\Delta_{11}}{\Delta_{1122}} \qquad (2.1.10)$$

If Eqs. (2.1.10) are solved for Z_a, Z_b, and Z_c,

$$Z_a = \frac{\Delta_{22} - \Delta_{12}}{\Delta_{1122}}, \quad Z_b = \frac{\Delta_{12}}{\Delta_{1122}}, \quad Z_c = \frac{\Delta_{11} - \Delta_{12}}{\Delta_{1122}} \qquad (2.1.11)$$

Three impedances Z_a, Z_b, and Z_c, computed from any passive reciprocal 4TN in accordance with these last formulas, and placed in a T as shown by Fig. 2.1.2, determine a T network equivalent to the original 4TN. If only a mathematical equivalence is desired the resulting T network can be taken as an all-frequency equivalent at the input and output terminals. Note particularly, however, that the equivalence formed by evaluating Z_a, Z_b, and Z_c at a particular frequency produces a T network which is equivalent to the original network only at that one frequency.

The mathematical all-frequency T equivalent which has been established in the foregoing serves as a convenient starting point from which to develop the electrical properties of passive 4TN in general. The remainder of this chapter is devoted to formulation of such electrical properties.

2.2 Symmetrical 4TN

The relations developed in Sec. 2.1 may be further simplified if they refer to a symmetrical 4TN. A symmetrical network is one which may have its input and output ends interchanged without affecting the external behavior of the network. For illustration, consider the general T equivalent of Fig. 2.1.2 connected between terminations as in Fig. 2.2.1. The network can be symmetrical only if $Z_a = Z_c$. Hence, from Eqs. (2.1.11) under the requirement that the 4TN be symmetrical,

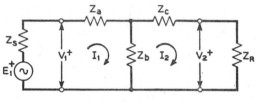

Fig. 2.2.1

$\Delta_{11} = \Delta_{22}$, so that two independent parameters suffice to describe any symmetrical 4TN.

2.3 Open-circuit and short-circuit parameters

The discussion of the next two sections is somewhat historical in character, aimed at tracing the pattern by which the image parameters arose. Since the image parameters are actually rather artificial, such a brief discussion seems in order to clear these parameters of certain obscuring encumbrances. Actually, the only requirement of three independent parameters for describing the electrical behavior of a 4TN is that they do the job. Whether these parameters can be obtained from direct observation of the network, from mathematical abstractions, or pure invention is immaterial if they are ultimately useful. The image parameters are in this latter class as the following discussion indicates.

Consider first the general T equivalent of Fig. 2.1.2. The open-circuit impedance looking in from the left (right side open) is

$$Z_{o1} = Z_a + Z_b \tag{2.3.1}$$

The short-circuit impedance from the same terminals is

$$Z_{s1} = Z_a + \frac{Z_b Z_c}{Z_b + Z_c} \tag{2.3.2}$$

Substituting into these last two equations from Eqs. (2.1.11) leads to

$$Z_{o1} = \frac{\Delta_{22}}{\Delta_{1122}} \tag{2.3.3}$$

$$Z_{s1} = \frac{\Delta}{\Delta_{11}} \tag{2.3.4}$$

Similarly, measurements from the right end lead to the results

$$Z_{o2} = \frac{\Delta_{11}}{\Delta_{1122}} \tag{2.3.5}$$

$$Z_{s2} = \frac{\Delta}{\Delta_{22}} \tag{2.3.6}$$

Note, though, that

$$\frac{Z_{s1}}{Z_{o1}} = \frac{\Delta\Delta_{1122}}{\Delta_{11}\Delta_{22}} = \frac{Z_{s2}}{Z_{o2}} \tag{2.3.7}$$

Hence the open- and short-circuit impedances (four total) are not independent. However, any set of three of the open- and short-circuit impedances constitute an independent set of parameters which describe the performance of a 4TN except for a sign ambiguity. These open- and short-circuit impedances do not detect a reversal of input or output terminals (see Problem 2.2).

However, a set of three independent circuit parameters which may be used to specify *without ambiguity* the behavior of a 4TN may be derived from *open* circuit measurements only. In addition to the two open-circuit measurements defined in the preceding, an open-circuit transfer impedance may be used. This transfer impedance Z_{ot} (the same from either side of the network; see Problem 2.3) is specified unambiguously by the ratio of the open-circuit voltage of the output, $V_{2,o2}$, and the input current, $I_{1,o2}$, of the network open at the output, i.e., from Eq. (2.1.8) with $I_2 = 0$,

$$-V_{2,o2} = \frac{-\Delta_{12}}{\Delta_{1122}} I_{1,o2} \tag{2.3.8}$$

and
$$Z_{ot} = \frac{V_{2,o2}}{I_{1,o2}} = \frac{\Delta_{12}}{\Delta_{1122}} \tag{2.3.9}$$

On the basis of this last relation and Eqs. (2.3.3) and (2.3.5), Eq. (2.1.8) may be expressed as

$$\begin{bmatrix} V_1 \\ -V_2 \end{bmatrix} = \begin{bmatrix} Z_{o1} & -Z_{ot} \\ -Z_{ot} & Z_{o2} \end{bmatrix} \begin{bmatrix} I_1 \\ I_2 \end{bmatrix} \tag{2.3.10}$$

This last relation establishes uniquely the T and CT equivalents of Fig. 2.3.1. Many situations arise in which a CT physical equivalent exists if the T does not and vice versa.

Three short-circuit measurements or computations may also be used to determine unambiguously the behavior of a 4TN, thus bringing to four (determinants and combinations of open- and short-circuit

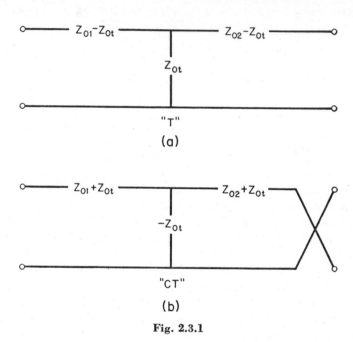

Fig. 2.3.1

parameters) the sets of parameters already established in this chapter for determination of the behavior of a 4TN. Still other sets of parameters are in use.

2.4 Iterative parameters[3]

Another set of 4TN parameters, established as part of the theory of long lines, are the iterative parameters. These iterative parameters are not in common use in present-day network theory, but they are of interest in connection with networks because they, in their turn, led to the formulation of the image parameters which are now in general use.

[3] Johnson, K. S., *Transmission Circuits for Telephone Communication*, D. Van Nostrand Company, Inc., New York, 1925, p. 121.

In the analysis of long lines, it can be assumed that the lines consist of a tandem connection of identical component sections (4TN). Each of these sections consists of a portion of the total R, L, and C combination comprising the line, and is a symmetrical 4TN. If the line length is assumed to increase indefinitely in either direction, its input impedance does not increase indefinitely but approaches a certain limit. This limiting impedance value is called the iterative impedance (sometimes characteristic impedance), designated Z_k, and is one of the iterative parameters. In view of the condition of symmetry, the iterative impedances are the same in either direction and so specify only one parameter. One other parameter, in addition to the iterative impedance, is required to specify the line behavior (symmetric 4TN).

The second iterative parameter is obtained from the ratio of the input and output currents of each component section of the infinitely long line. Considering any particular section, the input and output are unchanged if the sections (or lines) extending indefinitely from the output end are replaced by a termination consisting of the iterative impedance. Hence the ratio of input to output current is invariant from section to section of an infinite set of these sections in tandem (the infinite line). The parameter derived from this current ratio is known as the propagation constant P_k, and is defined in terms of this current ratio by

$$\epsilon^{P_k} = \frac{I_1}{I_2} \tag{2.4.1}$$

The iterative parameters Z_k and P_k may be expressed in terms of pairs of independent open- and short-circuit functions as follows (see Problem 2.7 for suggestions for showing these relations are valid):

$$Z_k = \pm \sqrt{Z_s Z_o} = \pm \sqrt{Z_o^2 - Z_{ot}^2} \tag{2.4.2}$$

$$\epsilon^{P_k} = \pm \sqrt{\frac{1 \pm \sqrt{Z_s/Z_o}}{1 \mp \sqrt{Z_s/Z_o}}} = \pm \sqrt{\frac{1 \pm \sqrt{1 - (Z_{ot}/Z_o)^2}}{1 \mp \sqrt{1 - (Z_{ot}/Z_o)^2}}} \tag{2.4.3}$$

Since, because of the square roots, these last equations define the iterative parameters with an unavoidable sign ambiguity, there is no virtue in straining to avoid the additional sign ambiguity arising from not using the transfer impedance (Sec. 2.3). Consequently, it is general practice to use the simplest mathematical formulation and to use physical realizability to determine the proper sign. According to Eqs. (2.4.2) and (2.4.3) the formulation in terms of open- and short-circuit impedances only is certainly simplest. The formulas involving the transfer impedance are rarely if ever used therefore, since they are the more complicated and are equally ambiguous in so far as sign is concerned.

One of the most important contributions of the theory of long lines to that of the theory of lumped 4TN is the suggestion that perhaps parameters similar to the iterative parameters might be useful in lumped network theory. The image parameters which are of such outstanding importance in lumped network theory were originally defined precisely in this manner—by direct analogy from long-line theory. Image parameters form the basis of the treatment of filters as presented in this book.

2.5 Image parameters: impedances

As pointed out in Sec. 2.1, three independent parameters are required to specify the general 4TN completely. Three independent image parameters are required, consequently. Two of these parameters, in the form of impedance functions (one for each end of the 4TN), are called image impedances and are defined by direct analogy from the definition of iterative impedances as

$$Z_{I1} = \pm \sqrt{Z_{s}Z_{o1}} \qquad (2.5.1)$$

$$Z_{I2} = \pm \sqrt{Z_{s2}Z_{o2}} \qquad (2.5.2)$$

Note that if the network is symmetric, these two impedance functions reduce to the same impedance function, which is in fact the iterative impedance.

In terms of the open-circuit transfer impedance it can be shown that the image impedance parameters are specified by

$$Z_{I1} = \pm \sqrt{\frac{Z_{o1}}{Z_{o2}}(Z_{o1}Z_{o2} - Z_{ot}^2)}$$

$$Z_{I2} = \pm \sqrt{\frac{Z_{o2}}{Z_{o1}}(Z_{o1}Z_{o2} - Z_{ot}^2)}$$

However, as is evident from these formulas, the sign ambiguity is not removed by using the transfer impedance in the more complicated formulas. Therefore the simpler formulas of Eqs. (2.5.1) and (2.5.2) are taken as the definitions of the image impedances. The sign to be used is determined to fit the particular situation as is pointed out in various places in the remainder of this book. In much of the symbolic manipulation which follows, as is customary, the $\pm$ symbols are not appended to the radicals. However, both signs are always there potentially.

The image impedances may be expressed in terms of the determinants of a 4TN as follows: From the relations of Eqs. (2.3.3), (2.3.4), and (2.5.1),

$$Z_{I1} = \sqrt{\frac{\Delta_{22}\Delta}{\Delta_{11}\Delta_{1122}}} \tag{2.5.3}$$

and from Eqs. (2.3.5), (2.3.6), and (2.5.2)

$$Z_{I2} = \sqrt{\frac{\Delta_{11}\Delta}{\Delta_{22}\Delta_{1122}}} \tag{2.5.4}$$

If the 4TN is symmetric, as indicated in Sec. 2.2, $\Delta_{11} = \Delta_{22}$, and the two image impedances become

$$Z_I = \sqrt{\frac{\Delta}{\Delta_{1122}}} \tag{2.5.5}$$

The image impedances, so defined purely by analogy from the iterative impedance, have useful properties. Perhaps their most important characteristic is the way they ensure an impedance match at each

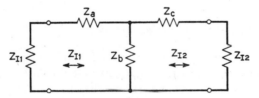

Fig. 2.5.1

end of an image impedance terminated 4TN. This important matching is indicated on Fig. 2.5.1. In words: the image impedances of any 4TN are those impedances which terminate the network in such a way that at both ends the impedance in either direction is the same. The following derivation demonstrates the validity of this statement concerning the matching effect of the image impedances.

The impedance expressions at the two ends of the network of Fig. 2.5.1 are

$$Z_{I1} = Z_a + \frac{Z_b(Z_c + Z_{I2})}{Z_b + Z_c + Z_{I2}} \tag{2.5.6}$$

$$Z_{I2} = Z_c + \frac{Z_b(Z_a + Z_{I1})}{Z_a + Z_b + Z_{I1}} \tag{2.5.7}$$

Solving these equations for Z_{I1} and Z_{I2},

$$Z_{I1} = \sqrt{\frac{Z_a + Z_b}{Z_b + Z_c} (Z_a Z_b + Z_a Z_c + Z_b Z_c)} \qquad (2.5.8)$$

and

$$Z_{I2} = \sqrt{\frac{Z_c + Z_b}{Z_b + Z_a} (Z_a Z_b + Z_a Z_c + Z_b Z_c)} \qquad (2.5.9)$$

However, substituting the relations of Eqs. (2.3.1) and (2.3.2) into Eq. (2.5.1),

$$Z_{I1} = \sqrt{\frac{Z_a + Z_b}{Z_b + Z_c} (Z_a Z_b + Z_a Z_c + Z_b Z_c)} \qquad (2.5.10)$$

which is identical with Eq. (2.5.8). Similarly, by substituting equations similar to Eqs. (2.3.1) and (2.3.2) into Eq. (2.5.2),

$$Z_{I2} = \sqrt{\frac{Z_c + Z_b}{Z_b + Z_a} (Z_a Z_b + Z_a Z_c + Z_b Z_c)} \qquad (2.5.11)$$

which is identical with Eq. (2.5.9). The image impedances therefore effect the impedance match at each end of a nonsymmetrical 4TN as indicated by Fig. 2.5.1.

2.6 Image parameters: transfer function

The third image parameter, called the transfer function and symbolized by $P_I(\omega) = A_I(\omega) + jB_I(\omega)$, is defined directly by analogy from the propagation constant formula (Eq. 2.4.3). Therefore because of the equality of Eq. (2.3.7) the transfer function is by definition either of

$$\epsilon^{P_I} = \pm \sqrt{\frac{1 + \sqrt{Z_{s1}/Z_{o1}}}{1 - \sqrt{Z_{s1}/Z_{o1}}}} = \pm \sqrt{\frac{1 + \sqrt{Z_{s2}/Z_{o2}}}{1 - \sqrt{Z_{s2}/Z_{o2}}}} \qquad (2.6.1)$$

Expressed in terms of the determinants of the general 4TN by using this last equation and Eq. (2.3.7), the transfer function is defined by

$$\epsilon^{P_I} = \pm \sqrt{\frac{1 + \sqrt{\Delta\Delta_{1122}/\Delta_{11}\Delta_{22}}}{1 - \sqrt{\Delta\Delta_{1122}/\Delta_{11}\Delta_{22}}}} \qquad (2.6.2)$$

As indicated by Eq. (2.4.1) the propagation constant is defined in terms of the ratio of the input to output current, when the network is terminated in its iterative impedances. In the case of the transfer

function, there is a somewhat similar relationship for an image impedance terminated network, but this relation is more complicated and
indeed not very meaningful. It is shown in the following that

$$\epsilon^{P_I} = \epsilon^{A_I + jB_I} = \sqrt{\frac{I_1 V_1}{I_2 V_2}} \qquad (2.6.3)$$

Since the products $I_1 V_1$ and $I_2 V_2$ have been assigned no particular
meaning, this particular definition of P_I is not a fruitful one, but is of
historical interest.

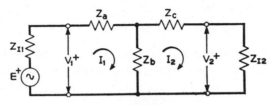

Fig. 2.6.1

Referring to Fig. 2.6.1, $V_1 = I_1 Z_{I1}$ and $V_2 = I_2 Z_{I2}$. Hence

$$\sqrt{\frac{I_1 V_1}{I_2 V_2}} = \frac{I_1}{I_2} \sqrt{\frac{Z_{I1}}{Z_{I2}}} \qquad (2.6.4)$$

Also, from Fig. 2.6.1, it can be seen that

$$I_1 = I_2 + \frac{Z_c + Z_{I2}}{Z_b} I_2$$

from which
$$\frac{I_1}{I_2} = 1 + \frac{Z_c}{Z_b} + \frac{Z_{I2}}{Z_b} \qquad (2.6.5)$$

Substituting the values for Z_b, Z_c, and Z_{I2} from Eqs. (2.1.11) and
(2.5.4) into this last equation,

$$\frac{I_1}{I_2} = 1 + \frac{\Delta_{11} - \Delta_{12}}{\Delta_{12}} + \frac{\Delta_{1122}}{\Delta_{12}} \sqrt{\frac{\Delta_{11}\Delta}{\Delta_{22}\Delta_{1122}}}$$

$$= \frac{\Delta_{11}}{\Delta_{12}} + \frac{1}{\Delta_{12}} \sqrt{\frac{\Delta_{11}\Delta\Delta_{1122}}{\Delta_{22}}} \qquad (2.6.6)$$

From Eqs. (2.5.3) and (2.5.4)

$$\sqrt{\frac{Z_{I1}}{Z_{I2}}} = \sqrt{\frac{\Delta_{22}}{\Delta_{11}}} \qquad (2.6.7)$$

Substituting Eqs. (2.6.6) and (2.6.7) into Eq. (2.6.4),

$$\sqrt{\frac{I_1 V_1}{I_2 V_2}} = \frac{\sqrt{\Delta_{11}\Delta_{22}} + \sqrt{\Delta\Delta_{1122}}}{\Delta_{12}} \qquad (2.6.8)$$

Consider next the following alteration of Eq. (2.6.2), squaring and changing algebraically

$$\epsilon^{2PI} = \frac{1 + \sqrt{\Delta\Delta_{1122}/\Delta_{11}\Delta_{22}}}{1 - \sqrt{\Delta\Delta_{1122}/\Delta_{11}\Delta_{22}}} = \frac{\sqrt{\Delta_{11}\Delta_{22}} + \sqrt{\Delta\Delta_{1122}}}{\sqrt{\Delta_{11}\Delta_{22}} - \sqrt{\Delta\Delta_{1122}}}$$

$$= \frac{(\sqrt{\Delta_{11}\Delta_{22}} + \sqrt{\Delta\Delta_{1122}})^2}{\Delta_{11}\Delta_{22} - \Delta\Delta_{1122}} \qquad (2.6.9)$$

If the denominator of this last expression is replaced by its equivalent from Eq. (2.1.7) and the square root of both sides of the equation is taken,

$$\epsilon^{PI} = \pm \frac{\sqrt{\Delta_{11}\Delta_{22}} + \sqrt{\Delta\Delta_{1122}}}{\Delta_{12}} \qquad (2.6.10)$$

Hence from Eq. (2.6.8),

$$\epsilon^{PI} = \sqrt{\frac{I_1 V_1}{I_2 V_2}} \qquad (2.6.11)$$

This last relation is the basis for a commonly used definition of the transfer function (transfer constant),[4] hence is of historical interest but not a logical starting point from which to define the image parameters.

2.7 T equivalent in terms of image parameters

Since the treatment of this book is based on image parameters, certain network formulas in terms of these parameters are useful. The remainder of this chapter is devoted to establishing such formulas.

For example, it is useful to express the impedances of the T equivalent in terms of the image parameters. The formulas for the image parameters, image impedances from Eqs. (2.5.3) and (2.5.4), and image transfer function from an alteration of Eq. (2.6.2), are repeated here for convenience:

[4] Johnson, K. S., *op. cit.*, p. 76; Shea, T. E., *Transmission Networks and Wave Filters*, D. Van Nostrand Company, Inc., New York, 1929, pp. 82–83; Mason, W. P., *Electromechanical Transducers and Wave Filters*, D. Van Nostrand Company, Inc., New York, 1942, p. 21.

$$Z_{I1} = \sqrt{\Delta_{22}\Delta/\Delta_{11}\Delta_{1122}} \qquad (2.7.1)$$

$$Z_{I2} = \sqrt{\Delta_{11}\Delta/\Delta_{22}\Delta_{1122}} \qquad (2.7.2)$$

$$\frac{\epsilon^{P_I} - \epsilon^{-P_I}}{\epsilon^{P_I} + \epsilon^{-P_I}} = \sqrt{\frac{\Delta\Delta_{1122}}{\Delta_{11}\Delta_{22}}} \qquad (2.7.3)$$

Three other useful formulas can be obtained, namely, from Eqs. (2.7.1) and (2.7.2),

$$\sqrt{Z_{I1}Z_{I2}} = \sqrt{\Delta/\Delta_{1122}} \qquad (2.7.4)$$

and from Eq. (2.6.10) or Eq. (2.6.2),

$$\epsilon^{P_I} + \epsilon^{-P_I} = 2\sqrt{\Delta_{11}\Delta_{22}}/\Delta_{12} \qquad (2.7.5)$$

$$\epsilon^{P_I} - \epsilon^{-P_I} = 2\sqrt{\Delta\Delta_{1122}}/\Delta_{12} \qquad (2.7.6)$$

These last three expressions can now be used to evaluate the impedances of the T equivalent as defined by Eq. (2.1.11) in terms of the image parameters as

$$Z_b = \frac{\Delta_{12}}{\Delta_{1122}} = \frac{2\sqrt{Z_{I1}Z_{I2}}}{\epsilon^{P_I} - \epsilon^{-P_I}} \qquad (2.7.7)$$

$$Z_a = \frac{\Delta_{22}}{\Delta_{1122}} - \frac{\Delta_{12}}{\Delta_{1122}}$$

$$= \frac{Z_{I1}(\epsilon^{P_I} + \epsilon^{-P_I}) - 2\sqrt{Z_{I1}Z_{I2}}}{\epsilon^{P_I} - \epsilon^{-P_I}} \qquad (2.7.8)$$

$$Z_c = \frac{\Delta_{11}}{\Delta_{1122}} - \frac{\Delta_{12}}{\Delta_{1122}} = \frac{Z_{I2}(\epsilon^{P_I} + \epsilon^{-P_I}) - 2\sqrt{Z_{I1}Z_{I2}}}{\epsilon^{P_I} - \epsilon^{-P_I}} \qquad (2.7.9)$$

2.8 Current and voltage relations of a passive 4TN as functions of the image parameters

Consider the network of Fig. 2.2.1. The mesh equations which determine the electrical behavior of this network are, in terms of the last three equations of the preceding section,

$$\begin{bmatrix} E_1 \\ 0 \end{bmatrix} = \begin{bmatrix} Z_S + \dfrac{Z_{I1}(\epsilon^{P_I} + \epsilon^{-P_I})}{\epsilon^{P_I} - \epsilon^{-P_I}} & \dfrac{-2\sqrt{Z_{I1}Z_{I2}}}{\epsilon^{P_I} - \epsilon^{-P_I}} \\ \dfrac{-2\sqrt{Z_{I1}Z_{I2}}}{\epsilon^{P_I} - \epsilon^{-P_I}} & Z_R + \dfrac{Z_{I2}(\epsilon^{P_I} + \epsilon^{-P_I})}{\epsilon^{P_I} - \epsilon^{-P_I}} \end{bmatrix} \begin{bmatrix} I_1 \\ I_2 \end{bmatrix} \qquad (2.8.1)$$

The solution of this matrix equation leads to expressions for the input and output currents of a passive 4TN as

$$I_1 = \frac{E_1[Z_R(\epsilon^{P_I} - \epsilon^{-P_I}) + Z_{I2}(\epsilon^{P_I} + \epsilon^{-P_I})]}{(Z_SZ_R + Z_{I1}Z_{I2})(\epsilon^{P_I} - \epsilon^{-P_I}) + (Z_SZ_{I2} + Z_RZ_{I1})(\epsilon^{P_I} + \epsilon^{-P_I})}$$

(2.8.2)

and

$$I_2 = \frac{E_1 2\sqrt{Z_{I1}Z_{I2}}}{(Z_SZ_R + Z_{I1}Z_{I2})(\epsilon^{P_I} - \epsilon^{-P_I}) + (Z_SZ_{I2} + Z_RZ_{I1})(\epsilon^{P_I} + \epsilon^{-P_I})}$$

(2.8.3)

These last two equations may be rearranged into a more convenient form in terms of the factors

$$K_S = \frac{Z_S - Z_{I1}}{Z_S + Z_{I1}}$$

(2.8.4)

$$K_R = \frac{Z_R - Z_{I2}}{Z_R + Z_{I2}}$$

(2.8.5)

The resulting expressions for the currents are

$$I_1 = E_1 \frac{1 - K_R\epsilon^{-2P_I}}{(Z_S + Z_{I1})(1 - K_SK_R\epsilon^{-2P_I})}$$

(2.8.6)

$$I_2 = E_1 \frac{2\left(\frac{\sqrt{Z_{I1}}}{Z_S + Z_{I1}}\right)\left(\frac{\sqrt{Z_{I2}}}{Z_R + Z_{I2}}\right)\epsilon^{-P_I}}{1 - K_SK_R\epsilon^{-2P_I}}$$

(2.8.7)

Consider next the establishment of expressions, corresponding to these last two, for the voltages. From Fig. 2.2.1,

$$\begin{bmatrix} V_1 \\ V_2 \end{bmatrix} = \begin{bmatrix} E_1 - Z_SI_1 \\ 0 + Z_RI_2 \end{bmatrix}$$

(2.8.8)

Hence from the last three equations,

$$V_1 = E_1 \left[1 - \frac{Z_S(1 - K_R\epsilon^{-2P_I})}{(Z_S + Z_{I1})(1 - K_SK_R\epsilon^{-2P_I})} \right]$$

(2.8.9)

$$V_2 = E_1 \left[\frac{2Z_R\left(\frac{\sqrt{Z_{I1}}}{Z_S + Z_{I1}}\right)\left(\frac{\sqrt{Z_{I2}}}{Z_R + Z_{I2}}\right)\epsilon^{-P_I}}{1 - K_SK_R\epsilon^{-2P_I}} \right]$$

(2.8.10)

The special forms which these current and voltage equations take if the 4TN is image impedance terminated are important. In fact such special equations indicate the first approximation to the network behavior which is the basis of the design technique presented in this book. Thus for image impedance termination ($Z_S = Z_{I1}$ and $Z_R = Z_{I2}$) the terms K_S and K_R vanish, so that

$$I_1 = \frac{E_1}{2Z_{I1}} \tag{2.8.11}$$

$$I_2 = \frac{E_1 \epsilon^{-P_I}}{2\sqrt{Z_{I1}Z_{I2}}} \tag{2.8.12}$$

$$V_1 = \frac{E_1}{2} \tag{2.8.13}$$

$$V_2 = \frac{E_1}{2}\sqrt{\frac{Z_{I2}}{Z_{I1}}}\,\epsilon^{-P_I} \tag{2.8.14}$$

As is discussed in detail in Chapter 9, the various factors which appear in Eqs. (2.8.6), (2.8.7), (2.8.9), and (2.8.10) are interpreted as corrections on what may be considered as the basic behavior given by the last four equations.

Note that the ratios of currents and voltages are, for an image impedance terminated unsymmetric network (Eqs. 2.8.11 through 2.8.14),

$$\frac{I_1}{I_2} = \sqrt{\frac{Z_{I2}}{Z_{I1}}}\,\epsilon^{P_I} \tag{2.8.15}$$

and

$$\frac{V_1}{V_2} = \sqrt{\frac{Z_{I1}}{Z_{I2}}}\,\epsilon^{P_I} \tag{2.8.16}$$

whereas

$$\frac{I_1}{I_2} = \frac{V_1}{V_2} = \epsilon^{P_I} = \epsilon^{(A_I + jB_I)} \tag{2.8.17}$$

for a symmetric network ($Z_{I1} = Z_{I2}$). These ratios serve to show the importance of the transfer function. The closer the terminations approximate the image impedances the closer the network behavior is specified by ϵ^{P_I}.

2.9 Cascaded four-terminal networks

Consider a cascaded arrangement of image impedance matched networks as in Fig. 2.9.1. This image impedance matching has a marked effect on the behavior of the total network, the exact nature of which is shown in the following discussion.

First consider a single 4TN. Rearrangement of Eq. (2.1.8), coupled with use of Eq. (2.1.7) leads to

$$\begin{bmatrix} V_1 \\ I_1 \end{bmatrix} = \begin{bmatrix} \dfrac{\Delta_{22}}{\Delta_{12}} & \dfrac{\Delta}{\Delta_{12}} \\ \dfrac{\Delta_{1122}}{\Delta_{12}} & \dfrac{\Delta_{11}}{\Delta_{12}} \end{bmatrix} \begin{bmatrix} V_2 \\ I_2 \end{bmatrix} = \begin{bmatrix} A & B \\ C & D \end{bmatrix} \begin{bmatrix} V_2 \\ I_2 \end{bmatrix} \tag{2.9.1}$$

where the A, B, C, D parameters are defined by this last relation. Use of some of the various formulas given in the foregoing, which relate

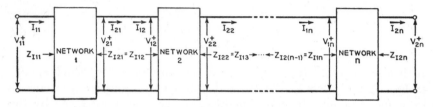

Fig. 2.9.1

the image parameters and the Δ's, indicates that an alternate form of Eq. (2.9.1) is

$$\begin{bmatrix} V_1 \\ I_1 \end{bmatrix} = \begin{bmatrix} \dfrac{\epsilon^{P_I} + \epsilon^{-P_I}}{2}\sqrt{\dfrac{Z_{I1}}{Z_{I2}}} & \dfrac{\epsilon^{P_I} - \epsilon^{-P_I}}{2}\sqrt{Z_{I1}Z_{I2}} \\ \dfrac{\epsilon^{P_I} - \epsilon^{-P_I}}{2\sqrt{Z_{I1}Z_{I2}}} & \dfrac{\epsilon^{P_I} + \epsilon^{-P_I}}{2}\sqrt{\dfrac{Z_{I2}}{Z_{I1}}} \end{bmatrix} \begin{bmatrix} V_2 \\ I_2 \end{bmatrix} \tag{2.9.2}$$

Next note that for the cascaded arrangement of Fig. 2.9.1

$$\begin{bmatrix} V_{21} \\ I_{21} \end{bmatrix} = \begin{bmatrix} V_{12} \\ I_{12} \end{bmatrix}, \begin{bmatrix} V_{22} \\ I_{22} \end{bmatrix} = \begin{bmatrix} V_{13} \\ I_{13} \end{bmatrix}, \cdots, \begin{bmatrix} V_{2(n-1)} \\ I_{2(n-1)} \end{bmatrix} = \begin{bmatrix} V_{1n} \\ I_{1n} \end{bmatrix} \tag{2.9.3}$$

which specifies that

$$\begin{bmatrix} V_{11} \\ I_{11} \end{bmatrix} = \begin{bmatrix} A_1 & B_1 \\ C_1 & D_1 \end{bmatrix} \begin{bmatrix} A_2 & B_2 \\ C_2 & D_2 \end{bmatrix} \cdots \begin{bmatrix} A_n & B_n \\ C_n & D_n \end{bmatrix} \begin{bmatrix} V_{2n} \\ I_{2n} \end{bmatrix} \tag{2.9.4}$$

If the indicated product of matrices of this last expression is carried out in terms of the definitions of Eq. (2.9.2) and the proper combinations of terms are made, it may be deduced that

$$\begin{bmatrix} V_{11} \\ I_{11} \end{bmatrix} = \begin{bmatrix} \dfrac{\epsilon^{P_{I0}} + \epsilon^{-P_{I0}}}{2}\sqrt{\dfrac{Z_{I11}}{Z_{I2n}}} & \dfrac{\epsilon^{P_{I0}} - \epsilon^{-P_{I0}}}{2}\sqrt{Z_{I11}Z_{I2n}} \\ \dfrac{\epsilon^{P_{I0}} - \epsilon^{-P_{I0}}}{2\sqrt{Z_{I11}Z_{I2n}}} & \dfrac{\epsilon^{P_{I0}} + \epsilon^{-P_{I0}}}{2}\sqrt{\dfrac{Z_{I2n}}{Z_{I11}}} \end{bmatrix}\begin{bmatrix} V_{2n} \\ I_{2n} \end{bmatrix} \qquad (2.9.5)$$

where
$$P_{I0} = P_{I1} + P_{I2} + \ldots + P_{In} \qquad (2.9.6)$$

Note that Eq. (2.9.5) specifies the behavior of the cascaded set of 4TN in a form which differs from that of a single 4TN (Eq. 2.9.2) only in the definition of transfer function (Eq. 2.9.6). Furthermore, the only image impedance of this more general expression are those at the input and output.

The alteration of Eqs. (2.8.4) through (2.8.7), and (2.8.9) through (2.8.14) to correspond to the cascading of 4TN is accomplished easily on the basis of the foregoing discussion, namely, replace Z_{I1} by Z_{I11}, Z_{I2} by Z_{I2n}, and P_I by P_{I0}. In terms of these more general expressions, if the cascaded 4TN are also image impedance terminated (as well as image impedance matched),

$$\frac{I_{11}}{I_{2n}} = \epsilon^{P_{I0}}\sqrt{\frac{Z_{I2n}}{Z_{I11}}} \qquad (2.9.7)$$

from which

$$\epsilon^{P_{I0}} = \frac{I_{11}}{I_{2n}}\sqrt{\frac{Z_{I11}}{Z_{I2n}}} = \sqrt{\frac{V_{11}I_{11}}{V_{2n}I_{2n}}} \qquad (2.9.8)$$

Note from this last expression that, even though image impedance matched, a 4TN, or a cascaded set of 4TN, does not have its transfer function defining the input and output current ratio in the simple manner of Eq. (2.4.1) for the iterative propagation constant. The one exception would be, of course, for a symmetric combination.

Problems

2.1 Work out in detail the transformations from Eqs. (2.1.2) and (2.1.3) to (2.1.4) and (2.1.5).

2.2 (a) On the basis of Eqs. (2.1.11) and of Eqs. (2.3.3) through (2.3.7), determine the form a T equivalent to a 4TN takes in terms of open- and short-circuit measurements or computations. Show that a sign ambiguity exists in this equivalent.

(b) To point up this sign ambiguity consider two symmetric lattices, Fig. P.2.2. For network A: $Z_x = 20 + j0$, $Z_y = 10 + j0$; for network B: $Z_x = 10 + j0$, $Z_y = 20 + j0$. Find the T equivalent by the formulas of part (a). Show that the negative square root must be used for one equivalent and the positive square root for the other for physical realizability and equivalence. Verifying the equivalence requirement by computing the in and out currents of each lattice and its equivalent.

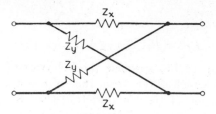

Fig. P.2.2

2.3 Prove that the same transfer impedance is obtained from the ratio of the open-circuit voltage at one end of the 4TN and the input current at the other end measured at the same time the open-circuit voltage is measured. Obtain the formula for this Z_{ot} by terminating the 4TN in Z and then determining the open-circuit voltage by computing the limit of $I_2 Z$ as Z increases indefinitely.

2.4 Establish a formula in terms of determinants for the short-circuit transfer impedance Z_{st}. Prove that there is only one such impedance. Establish the equivalent T and CT networks as in Fig. 2.3.1.

2.5 Determine the T equivalent of the symmetric lattice shown in Fig. P.2.5, at $\omega = 10^6$. Calculate the output current in a load of 1 ohm resistance

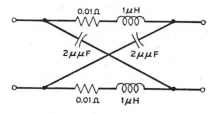

Fig. P.2.5

for an input terminal voltage of 1 volt at $\omega = 2 \times 10^6$ for both the lattice and the equivalent T. Are the networks equivalent at $\omega = 10^6$?

2.6 For the lattice of Fig. P.2.5, determine Z_{oc} and Z_{sc} at $\omega = 10^6$ and $\omega = 2 \times 10^6$.

2.7 Suppose that a section of a two-wire transmission line is represented by its symmetric equivalent T, i.e., the parameters have the proper frequency variation and $Z_a = Z_c$ in Fig. 2.1.2.

(a) The iterative impedance Z_k is such that Z_k is the input impedance at one two-terminal pair (input or output) if Z_k is connected across the other two-terminal pair. Show that Eq. (2.4.2) is correct by using the equivalent T.

(b) If $Z_S = Z_R = Z_k$ of Fig. 2.1.1 and the network of this figure is a symmetric T, show that Eq. (2.4.3) is correct on the basis of the definition of P_k as given by Eq. (2.4.1).

2.8 Verify the formulas in terms of Z_o and Z_{ot} as given by Eqs. (2.4.2) and (2.4.3).

2.9 Establish formulas for Z_{k1} and Z_{k2} (iterative impedances) on the basis that: $Z_{\text{input end}} = Z_{k1}$ if Z_{k1} is across the output end, and $Z_{\text{output end}} = Z_{k2}$ if Z_{k2} is across the input end.

2.10 (a) Verify the formulas in terms of open-circuit parameters as given by the two equations following Eq. (2.5.2).

(b) Determine Z_{I1} and Z_{I2} in terms of three independent short-circuit parameters.

2.11 (a) For the symmetrical lattice of Fig. P.2.5, solve for Z_k and P_k in terms of Z_x and Z_y, using Eqs. (2.4.2) and (2.4.3).

(b) Determine the values of Z_x and Z_y as functions of Z_k and $P_k/2$.

(c) If the lattice is terminated in Z_k, what is the impedance looking into the other end?

(d) Show that if the lattice is terminated in Z_k the ratio of input to output current is expressed by Eq. (2.4.1).

2.12 Solve Eqs. (2.5.6) and (2.5.7) to obtain the explicit expressions of Eqs. (2.5.8) and (2.5.9).

2.13 Determine Z_{I1} and Z_{I2} for the lattice of Fig. P.2.5, at $\omega = 10^6$ and $\omega = 2 \times 10^6$. If Z_S and Z_R are both built as an $R + jX$ series combination so as to match the image impedances at $\omega = 10^6$, will image impedance match still occur at $\omega = 2 \times 10^6$? Explain.

2.14 (a) For the network of Fig. P.2.14 solve for Z_{oc} and Z_{sc} at both ends of the network at the following frequencies: $\omega = 0.4 \times 10^6$, 0.8×10^6, 1.2×10^6, and 2.0×10^6.

(b) At these same frequencies, solve for Z_{I1}, Z_{I2}, and P_I.

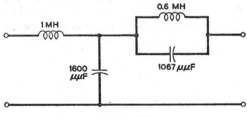

Fig. P.2.14

2.15 Plot the transfer function components $A_I(\omega)$ and $B_I(\omega)$ against ω for the network of Fig. P.2.5. Cover a wide enough frequency range to show the salient features of the transfer function.

2.16 Repeat the preceding problem with the resistances omitted.

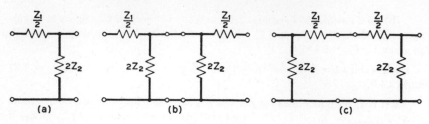

Fig. P.2.17

2.17 The network represented by Fig. P.2.17(a) is known as a half section. Two such sections can be used to form a T or a π section as indicated by Figs. P. 2.17(b) and (c).

(a) Derive the image impedance and transfer function formulas for the half section in terms of Z_1 and Z_2.

(b) Repeat part (a) for the T network.

(c) Repeat part (a) for the π network.

(d) The image impedances of these three networks bear an important relation to each other. What is this relation?

(e) Show the relation between P_I for the half section and for the other two sections.

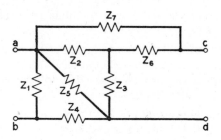

Fig. P.2.18

2.18 Write out the determinants Δ_{11}, Δ_{22}, Δ, and Δ_{1122} for the network of Fig. P.2.18, oriented as shown and the a–b and c–d ends interchanged. Show from the results that the transfer function P_I does not depend on the network orientation.

CHAPTER THREE

Image Parameters for Reactive Symmetric Lattice Sections

An effective starting point for understanding filter design is analysis of the lattice or bridge type section (4TN). This approach is a powerful one, and filter design is frequently based on the lattice section, even when ultimately the structure is to be realized in other forms. The technique described in this book is wholly that of obtaining design parameters on the basis of the symmetric lattice and using these parameters to realize the desired network form.

3.1 *Symmetric lattice equivalent of a general symmetric 4TN*

In Sec. 2.1, mesh equations are given for the general 4TN, and relations are established between the voltages and currents of two pairs of terminals. Subsequently, two equations are given for the T network, which has only two meshes, and comparison is made with these two equations and the two equations for the general network. The conclusion is reached thereby that if the T network is to provide the same transmission between the two pairs of terminals as the general 4TN, Eqs. (2.1.11) must be satisfied. It is to be noted that the term "general 4TN" as used in this book refers only to 4TN for which one pair of terminals is specified as input terminals and the other pair as output terminals.

Like the T section, the lattice is a specific 4TN, the symmetric form of which is illustrated in two ways by Fig. 3.1.1. As established in the preceding chapter, two independent parameters completely specify the electrical behavior of a symmetric 4TN. Such a pair of parameters for the symmetric lattice is the impedance $Z_x(\omega)$ of the series branch and $Z_y(\omega)$ of the diagonal branch of Fig. 3.1.1a.

Consider the mesh equations as written from Fig. 3.1.1b, namely,

$$\begin{bmatrix} V_1 \\ -V_2 \\ 0 \end{bmatrix} = \begin{bmatrix} Z_x + Z_y & -Z_y & -Z_x - Z_y \\ -Z_y & Z_x + Z_y & Z_x + Z_y \\ -Z_x - Z_y & Z_x + Z_y & 2Z_x + 2Z_y \end{bmatrix} \begin{bmatrix} I_1 \\ I_2 \\ I_3 \end{bmatrix} \quad (3.1.1)$$

51

The elimination of I_3 from this equation leads to

$$\begin{bmatrix} V_1 \\ -V_2 \end{bmatrix} = \begin{bmatrix} \dfrac{Z_x + Z_y}{2} & \dfrac{Z_x - Z_y}{2} \\ \dfrac{Z_x - Z_y}{2} & \dfrac{Z_x + Z_y}{2} \end{bmatrix} \begin{bmatrix} I_1 \\ I_2 \end{bmatrix} \qquad (3.1.2)$$

A comparison of this result with Eq. (2.1.9) indicates that, from the

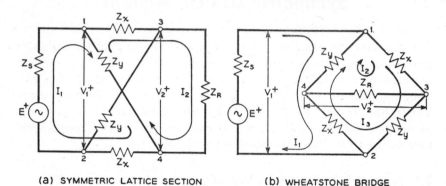

(a) SYMMETRIC LATTICE SECTION   (b) WHEATSTONE BRIDGE

Fig. 3.1.1

standpoint of transmission, the symmetric T ($Z_a = Z_c$, Fig. 2.1.2) and the symmetric lattice are equivalent if

$$\frac{Z_x + Z_y}{2} = Z_a + Z_b \qquad (3.1.3)$$

$$\frac{Z_x - Z_y}{2} = -Z_b \qquad (3.1.4)$$

Hence the symmetric lattice equivalent of the symmetric T is

$$Z_x = Z_a \qquad (3.1.5)$$

$$Z_y = Z_a + 2Z_b \qquad (3.1.6)$$

These last two equations show that the symmetric lattice equivalent of a physical symmetric T is always physical, since the sum of two physically realizable impedances is also physically realizable.

The formulas for the impedances of the symmetric lattice equivalent of any symmetric, passive, reciprocal 4TN can be written immediately from the last two equations and Eqs. (2.1.11). Since $\Delta_{11} = \Delta_{22}$ for symmetric networks, the lattice impedances are

$$Z_x = \frac{\Delta_{11} - \Delta_{12}}{\Delta_{1122}} \tag{3.1.7}$$

$$Z_y = \frac{\Delta_{11} + \Delta_{12}}{\Delta_{1122}} \tag{3.1.8}$$

For symmetric networks, as given by Eq. (2.1.7),

$$\Delta_{11}{}^2 - \Delta_{12}{}^2 = \Delta\Delta_{1122} \tag{3.1.9}$$

so permitting the alternate expressions for the lattice impedances,

$$Z_x = \frac{\Delta}{\Delta_{11} + \Delta_{12}} \tag{3.1.10}$$

$$Z_y = \frac{\Delta}{\Delta_{11} - \Delta_{12}} \tag{3.1.11}$$

The two pairs of Eqs. (3.1.7), (3.1.8) and (3.1.10), (3.1.11) give no indication as to whether the Z_x and Z_y so defined can be realized in physical form. Brief consideration is given next to the problem of physical realizability.

Various degrees of idealization are in use in network theory:

1. *Physical.* All network elements always contain in some degree the full set of components R, L, and C.

2. *Approximately Physical.* The network elements may contain any combination of pure R, L, or C components. This form of idealization is the most widely used.

3. *Brune.* The network elements contain only R or L or C but never any combination of them except parallel and/or series resonators of L and C only. Ideal transformers may be considered components in this idealization.

4. *Reactive.* The network elements contain L or C or a combination of them. No R factors appear. This idealization is the basis of the discussion for most of this book.

The symmetric lattice of Fig. 3.1.1a has a general property of outstanding importance as expressed in the theorem: *For any physically realizable, symmetric, reciprocal, four-terminal network, a Brune symmetric reciprocal lattice can be derived which has identical transmission properties.*[1] The validity of this theorem is demonstrated next.

---

[1] Campbell, G. A., "Physical Theory of the Electric Wave Filter," *Bell System Tech. J.*, April, 1922; Bode, H. W., *Network Analysis and Feedback Amplifier Design*, D. Van Nostrand Company, Inc., New York, 1945, p. 266; Cauer, W., *Theorie der linearen Wechselstromschaltungen*, Edwards Brothers, Inc., Ann Arbor, 1948, pp. 97–98.

Consider the circuit arrangement of Fig. 3.1.2a where an ideal transformer is connected to the output of a physical symmetric 4TN. The ideal transformer forces the voltage relations $V = V_1 = V_2$.

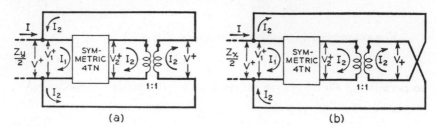

Fig. 3.1.2

These voltage restrictions applied to the equations for the 4TN, i.e., Eq. (2.1.5), which is

$$\begin{bmatrix} I_1 \\ I_2 \end{bmatrix} = \frac{1}{\Delta} \begin{bmatrix} \Delta_{11} & \Delta_{12} \\ \Delta_{12} & \Delta_{22} \end{bmatrix} \begin{bmatrix} V_1 \\ -V_2 \end{bmatrix} \tag{3.1.12}$$

give

$$I_1 = \frac{\Delta_{11} - \Delta_{12}}{\Delta} V \tag{3.1.13}$$

$$I_2 = \frac{\Delta_{12} - \Delta_{22}}{\Delta} V \tag{3.1.14}$$

The total input current is $I_1 - I_2$, so the driving-point impedance is

$$Z_d = \frac{V}{I_1 - I_2} = \frac{1}{2} \frac{\Delta}{\Delta_{11} - \Delta_{12}} \tag{3.1.15}$$

Comparison of this result with that given by Eq. (3.1.11) shows that the driving-point impedance of Fig. 3.1.2a is one-half the diagonal impedance of the symmetric lattice which has the same transmission properties as the symmetric 4TN.

Similarly, the ideal transformer and interconnection of Fig. 3.1.2b forces the voltage relations $V_1 = V$ and $V_2 = -V$. The currents given by the 4TN equations (3.1.12), for these voltage restrictions are

$$I_1 = \frac{\Delta_{11} + \Delta_{12}}{\Delta} V \tag{3.1.16}$$

$$I_2 = \frac{\Delta_{12} + \Delta_{22}}{\Delta} V \tag{3.1.17}$$

and the driving-point impedance is

$$Z_d = \frac{V}{I_1 + I_2} = \frac{1}{2} \frac{\Delta}{\Delta_{11} + \Delta_{12}} \qquad (3.1.18)$$

But this impedance expression represents one-half the series imped-ance of the symmetric lattice which has the same transmission proper-ties as the symmetric 4TN. The driving-point impedance of Fig. 3.1.2b is thus $Z_x/2$ as indicated on the diagram.

The 2TN of Fig. 3.1.2 are nonphysical because of inclusion of the ideal transformer. However, the work of Brune[2] and its extension by Bott and Duffin[3] shows that these are Brune networks. Therefore, if a symmetric lattice is formed by connecting two of the networks of Fig. 3.1.2a in series to form each Z_y, and two of the networks of Fig. 3.1.2b in series to form each Z_x, such a lattice has the transmission properties of the symmetric 4TN and is a Brune network as was to be proved.

Under the appropriate modification of the foregoing proof, the following statement may be made: *a symmetric, reactive, lattice always*

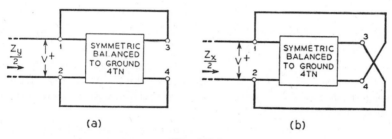

(a)   (b)

Fig. 3.1.3

exists which has the same transmission properties as any symmetric, reactive four-terminal network. This statement is the basis for much of the material presented in the remainder of this book. The design is effected in terms of the symmetric reactive lattice first of all, followed by various modifications depending on the circumstances.

A more general form of the theorem of the preceding discussion is possible for symmetric balanced-to-ground and one-side-grounded networks. Consider the arrangement of Fig. 3.1.3a. Since the voltage between terminals 1 and 3 and between 2 and 4 vanishes if the same voltage is placed across terminals 1–2 and 3–4, the addition of the short circuits shown does not alter the network behavior. Similarly

[2] Brune, O., *J. Math. Phys.*, **10**, 191–236 (1931).
[3] Bott, R. and Duffin, R. J., *J. Appl. Phys.*, **20**, 816 (1949).

the voltages across 1–4 and 2–3 vanish if the same voltage is placed across 1–2 and across 4–3. The driving-point impedances are as shown therefore, since this strapping arrangement is identical, voltage-wise, to Fig. 3.1.2. The impedances obtained from the strapped networks mathematically, by measurement, or by direct use of the so formed 2TN are physical. A physical lattice, therefore, always exists (can actually be constructed) which has the same transmission properties as any *physical* symmetric, balanced-to-ground 4TN.

The symmetric one-side-grounded 4TN has voltage and impedance relations as indicated by Fig. 3.1.4. The short circuit and open

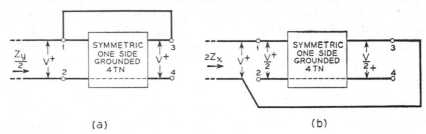

(a)   (b)

Fig. 3.1.4

circuit do not alter the voltage distribution over that of Fig. 3.1.2 except that in Fig. 3.1.4b one-half of V appears across the 4TN terminals oriented as shown. The driving-point impedances are therefore as shown on Fig. 3.1.4. Once again, the 2TN of Fig. 3.1.4, if physical, determine a physical, symmetric lattice with the same transmission properties.

Because of the generality of the symmetric lattice, it forms a useful and frequently used basis for design purposes. If the electrical properties sought can be obtained from a symmetric lattice, or as nearly so as time, expense, and the restrictions of the lattice will allow, there is practical certainty that no other 4TN will meet the electrical requirements better. Then, if the physical form of the final 4TN is to be other than a lattice because of parasitics, unbalance, or whatever reason, the equivalent network, in the form desired, may be computed from the designed lattice. Needless to say, formidable obstacles of one form or another often appear in the path of the completion of the foregoing schedule.

A further and equally important factor in the choice of the symmetric lattice as the basic network for design purposes is the mathematical simplicity with which two completely defining parametric functions can be formed. These two defining functions are one pair of several possible pairs which completely define the symmetric lattice in accordance with the two-parameter requirement deduced in the preceding chapter. These simple parametric functions are defined in the next section.

3.2 General formulas for the image parameters, impedance and transfer, of a symmetric lattice

The image impedance, defined in general for symmetric 4TN by Eq. (2.5.5), may be specialized into the symmetric lattice form by using the determinant of Eq. (3.1.1). From the latter equation

$$\Delta = 2Z_x Z_y (Z_x + Z_y) \tag{3.2.1}$$

and
$$\Delta_{1122} = 2(Z_x + Z_y) \tag{3.2.2}$$

Consequently, from Eq. (2.5.5), the image impedance is

$$Z_I(\omega) = \pm \sqrt{\frac{\Delta}{\Delta_{1122}}} = \pm \sqrt{\frac{2Z_x Z_y (Z_x + Z_y)}{2(Z_x + Z_y)}}$$
$$= \pm \sqrt{Z_x(\omega) Z_y(\omega)} \tag{3.2.3}$$

which has a useful mathematical simplicity.

The transfer function defined in general by Eq. (2.6.2), or alternatively by Eq. (2.7.3), may be specialized for the symmetric lattice as follows: from Eq. (3.1.1),

$$\Delta_{11} = \Delta_{22} = (Z_x + Z_y)^2 \tag{3.2.4}$$

Hence with the aid of Eqs. (3.2.1) and (3.2.2), the transfer function for the symmetric lattice is defined by

$$\frac{\epsilon^{P_I} - \epsilon^{-P_I}}{\epsilon^{P_I} + \epsilon^{-P_I}} = \tanh P_I = \pm \sqrt{\frac{\Delta \Delta_{1122}}{\Delta_{11} \Delta_{22}}} = \frac{\pm 2 \sqrt{Z_x Z_y}}{Z_x + Z_y} \tag{3.2.5}$$

The mathematical simplicity of the image impedance parametric expression of Eq. (3.2.3) is certainly not a characteristic of this last expression. This situation can be remedied, however, by using a parametric relation, ratio function, defined by

$$H(\omega) = \pm \sqrt{Z_x(\omega)/Z_y(\omega)} \tag{3.2.6}$$

Then Eq. (3.2.5) becomes (inverted)

$$\frac{\epsilon^{P_I} + \epsilon^{-P_I}}{\epsilon^{P_I} - \epsilon^{-P_I}} = \frac{H(\omega)}{2} + \frac{1}{2H(\omega)} \tag{3.2.7}$$

from which

$$P_I(\omega) = A_I(\omega) + jB_I(\omega)$$

$$= \ln \frac{1 \pm \sqrt{Z_x(\omega)/Z_y(\omega)}}{1 \mp \sqrt{Z_x(\omega)/Z_y(\omega)}} = \ln \frac{1 + H(\omega)}{1 - H(\omega)} \qquad (3.2.8)$$

An alternative expression, readily derivable from this last equation, relating the ratio function $H(\omega)$ and the transfer function $P_I(\omega)$ is

$$\tanh \frac{P_I(\omega)}{2} = \tanh \left[\frac{A_I(\omega)}{2} + j \frac{B_I(\omega)}{2} \right] = \pm \sqrt{\frac{Z_x(\omega)}{Z_y(\omega)}} = H(\omega)$$

$$(3.2.9)$$

At once from Eq. (3.2.8) the transfer loss in terms of the ratio function $H(\omega)$ is

$$A_I(\omega) = \ln \left| \frac{1 + H(\omega)}{1 - H(\omega)} \right| \qquad (3.2.10)$$

The two simple mathematical relations $Z_I(\omega)$ of Eq. (3.2.3) and $H(\omega)$ of Eq. (3.2.6) thus determine the two parametric relations, image impedance and transfer function, from specified $Z_x(\omega)$ and $Z_y(\omega)$. Conversely, the two independent parametric relations $Z_I(\omega)$ and $H(\omega)$, by their product and ratio, evidently determine the symmatric lattice, and because of their mathematical simplicity, form the basis of the development of this book. This independence of the $Z_I(\omega)$ and $H(\omega)$ functions makes it possible to design for a required transfer function by way of $H(\omega)$ independently of designing for an image impedance requirement.

3.3 Pass and block characteristics of a nondissipative symmetric lattice

As demonstrated in Chapter 1, one of the outstanding properties of reactive 2TN is the appearance of poles and zeros of reactance at certain real frequencies. Any dissipation in the network causes the impedance to depart from a pole or a zero at these frequencies. However, if the dissipation is low, the impedance does not differ much from a pole or a zero at the critical frequencies. For this reason, practical design work can be effected in terms of pure reactance as a first approximation, followed by or in conjunction with corrections for dissipative effects. The design methods presented in this book are based on such a procedure. Consequently the properties of purely reactive lattice networks are given as the next step toward the development of design procedures.

The impedances of the branches of a purely reactive symmetric lattice may be expressed as

$$Z_x(\omega) = \pm j|X_x(\omega)| \quad \text{and} \quad Z_y(\omega) = \pm j|X_y(\omega)|$$

the magnitude and sign depending on the frequency and particular form of 2TN being considered. The particular sign of $Z_x(\omega)$ and of $Z_y(\omega)$ at any particular frequency affects the character of $Z_I(\omega)$ as is next shown.

When the signs of $X_x(\omega)$ and $X_y(\omega)$ are opposite, Eq. (3.2.3) shows that $Z_I(\omega)$ is real; when their signs are alike, $Z_I(\omega)$ is imaginary. A question arises as to the sign to use for $Z_I(\omega)$, since the radical introduces both the plus and minus signs. There is no mathematical or physical reason for rejecting either. Either sign, if consistently used, may be used for analysis. However, practice has shown that it is most convenient to specify $Z_I(\omega)$ as positive if it is real. If it is imaginary, it is convenient to give $Z_I(\omega)$ the same sign as $X_x(\omega)$ and $X_y(\omega)$. Tabulation 3.3.1 shows the relations between the signs of $X_x(\omega)$ and $X_y(\omega)$, and the form of $Z_I(\omega)$.

TABULATION 3.3.1

$Z_x(\omega)$	$Z_y(\omega)$	$Z_I(\omega)$
$+j|X_x(\omega)|$	$+j|X_y(\omega)|$	$0 + jX_I(\omega)$
$+j|X_x(\omega)|$	$-j|X_y(\omega)|$	$R_I(\omega) + j0$
$-j|X_x(\omega)|$	$+j|X_y(\omega)|$	$R_I(\omega) + j0$
$-j|X_x(\omega)|$	$-j|X_y(\omega)|$	$0 + jX_I(\omega)$

Consider next the ratio function parameter $H(\omega)$. When the signs of $X_x(\omega)$ and $X_y(\omega)$ are alike, Eq. (3.2.6) shows that $H(\omega)$ is real. When the signs of $X_x(\omega)$ and $X_y(\omega)$ are opposite $H(\omega)$ is imaginary. Again, some ambiguity of the sign of $H(\omega)$ results from the fact that the radical might be plus or minus from purely mathematical considerations. The choice of sign is resolved by other factors. For example, a negative real value for $H(\omega)$ would mean that $A_I(\omega)$ would be negative real (Eq. 3.2.10). Experience has indicated that $A_I(\omega)$ is most conveniently considered positive; therefore $H(\omega)$ is taken to be positive when it is real. The choice of sign for imaginary values of $H(\omega)$ is also arbitrary. For convenience the sign of $H(\omega)$ should assign a positive slope to imaginary values of $H(\omega)$ expressed as a function of frequency, in direct correspondence with positive slope of reactance with frequency described in Sec. 1.2. Further examination of Eq. (3.2.6) shows that this positive slope condition is satisfied when the sign of $H(\omega)$ is the same as the sign of $X_x(\omega)$. Hence $H(\omega)$ is given the sign of $X_x(\omega)$ for imaginary values of $H(\omega)$.

Tabulation 3.3.2 shows the relations between the signs of $X_x(\omega)$ and $X_y(\omega)$ and the two components of the transfer function, the transfer loss $A_I(\omega)$ (Eq. 3.2.10), and the transfer phase $B_I(\omega)$. Of great importance is the fact that the *transfer loss $A_I(\omega)$ is zero if $X_x(\omega)$ and $X_y(\omega)$ are of opposite sign*, since then $H(\omega)$ is pure imaginary and $1 + H(\omega)$ and $1 - H(\omega)$ are conjugates with a ratio of unity magnitude. A frequency region for which $A_I(\omega) = 0$ is known as a *pass* region or band. All other regions are known as *block* regions or bands. A frequency at the junction of a pass and block region is known as a cutoff frequency and is designated f_0 or ω_0 throughout this book.

TABULATION 3.3.2

$Z_x(\omega)$	$Z_y(\omega)$	$P_I(\omega)$
$+j\|X_x(\omega)\|$	$+j\|X_y(\omega)\|$	$A_I(\omega) \pm jk\pi, \quad k = 0, 1, 2, \ldots$
$+j\|X_x(\omega)\|$	$-j\|X_y(\omega)\|$	$0 + jB_I(\omega)$
$-j\|X_x(\omega)\|$	$+j\|X_y(\omega)\|$	$0 + jB_I(\omega)$
$-j\|X_x(\omega)\|$	$-j\|X_y(\omega)\|$	$A_I(\omega) \pm jk\pi, \quad k = 0, 1, 2, \ldots$

As examples of the significance of the results indicated in Tabulations 3.3.1 and 3.3.2, consider the reactance patterns of Fig. 3.3.1. A block region occurs over frequency ranges for which $X_x(\omega)$ and $X_y(\omega)$ have the same sign, and a pass band occurs wherever these reactances are of opposite sign. As observed in Chapter 1, the reactances have a positive slope with frequency and pass through a succession of zeros and poles. In Fig. 3.3.1a, there is no correlation between the zeros and poles of Z_x and Z_y, and the filter exhibits a multiplicity of pass and block bands. Such a filter is rarely useful. In Fig. 3.3.1b, there are a number of frequencies at which a pole of Z_x is coincident with a zero of Z_y, or at which the reverse is true. Beginning at the left, as the frequency varies through such a point, the signs of the two reactances remain opposite, so that there is no break in the pass region at such a frequency. At ω_0, there is a pole of Z_y, resulting in a change of sign for Z_y with no corresponding change in sign for Z_x. At frequencies above cutoff, ω_0, the two reactances are of the same sign and constitute a block region. In the block region, there is a frequency at which a zero occurs, and a second frequency at which a pole occurs, in both Z_x and Z_y. Accordingly, the signs of the two reactances continue to be the same and the block region is continuous through those frequencies. The pattern of Fig. 3.3.1b applies to a low-pass filter. Similarly, the patterns of Figs. 3.3.1c, d, e, and f, respectively, apply to band-elimination, band-pass, high-pass, and all-pass filters. The all-pass structure is used very extensively as a phase-corrective network.

It is to be noted particularly that while the transfer loss is zero throughout the pass regions, the transfer phase is a function of frequency. Conversely, in the block regions the transfer phase is always an integral multiple of π, but the transfer loss is a function of frequency.

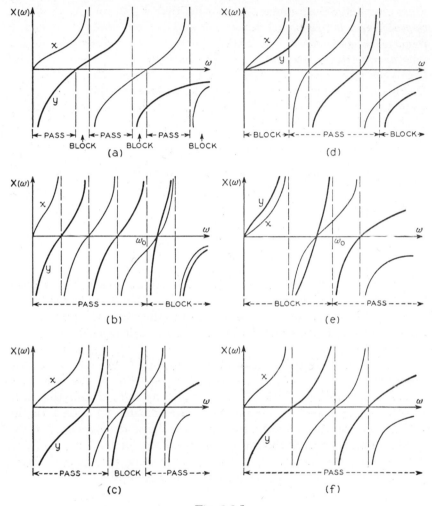

Fig. 3.3.1

3.4 Low-pass network basic for filter design

As is shown in Chapter 10, relatively simple frequency transformations make it possible to change a low-pass design into a high-pass design, or into designs of band-pass or band-elimination filters exhibiting frequency characteristics which are symmetric with respect to the mid-band frequency. Since a low-pass design thereby covers the filters of most general interest, the discussions from this point through Chapter 9 are based on the low-pass (LP) type of filter.

As shown by Tabulation 3.3.2, the branches of a lattice *low-pass* filter must have reactance patterns such that $X_x(\omega)$ and $X_y(\omega)$ are of *opposite sign at frequencies below the cutoff ω_0, and of the same sign at frequencies above the cutoff*. There are no other restrictions on the reactance patterns, so that one of the patterns may be selected arbitrarily as any one of the four classes of 2TN described in Sec. 1.5. However, any such selection uniquely establishes the class of the second pattern. Hence there are four possible low-pass combinations, as shown by Tabulation 3.4.1.

TABULATION 3.4.1

CLASSES OF NETWORKS FOR LOW-PASS

	Z_x	Z_y
1	LL	CL
2	CC	LC
3	LC	CC
4	CL	LL

A feature of Tabulation 3.4.1 is that combinations 3 and 4 are the same as 2 and 1, with Z_x and Z_y interchanged. Reference to the lattice network shows that such an interchange has the effect of interchanging the output terminals, which results in a phase shift of 180°, but has no other effect.

As stated more than once in the foregoing, the design procedures described in this book are based on the properties of the two independent parametric relations: the image impedances and the ratio functions, the latter of which leads to the transfer functions. In the earlier part of this chapter the idea has been developed that the structure basic to these design procedures is the lattice low-pass filter. Accordingly, the remainder of this chapter deals with $Z_I(\omega)$, $H(\omega)$, and $P_I(\omega) = A_I(\omega) + jB_I(\omega)$ for lattice low-pass filters.

3.5 Properties of the impedance functions $Z_I(\omega)$, $Z_I(x)$

The image impedance function of a nondissipative lattice low-pass filter is given by Eq. (3.2.3) as

$$Z_I(\omega) = \pm \sqrt{Z_x(\omega)Z_y(\omega)} \qquad (3.5.1)$$

In most of the subsequent developments of this book it is more convenient to use the so-called normalized frequency x as the independent variable rather than ω, where

$$x = \frac{f}{f_0} = \frac{\omega}{\omega_0} \qquad (3.5.2)$$

While ω_0 could be an arbitrary frequency, it is convenient to specify it as the cutoff of the low-pass filter. By this definition $x = 1$ at cutoff. The normalized image impedance is written

$$Z_I(x) = R_I(x) + jX_I(x) = \pm \sqrt{Z_x(x)Z_y(x)} \qquad (3.5.3)$$

It should be noted that while the same symbolism is retained for convenience, $Z_I(x)$ is not formed from $Z_I(\omega)$ by direct substitution of x for ω, although the change is slight, as shown in Eq. (3.5.5).

Use of the normalized frequency x does not alter the relations between the signs of Z_x and Z_y and the form of Z_I, so the relations of Tabulation 3.3.1 still apply.

At this point it should be observed that $Z_x(\omega)$ and $Z_y(\omega)$ are the impedances of two-terminal networks, described in Chapter 1. These impedances may be expressed as the ratio of two polynomials, as shown in Eq. (1.2.7), as follows:

$$Z_d(\omega) = (j\omega)^{\pm 1}k \left[\frac{(\omega_2{}^2 - \omega^2)(\omega_4{}^2 - \omega^2)\ldots(\omega_m{}^2 - \omega^2)}{(\omega_1{}^2 - \omega^2)(\omega_3{}^2 - \omega^2)\ldots(\omega_n{}^2 - \omega^2)} \right] \qquad (3.5.4)$$

The normalized expression becomes

$$Z_d(x) = (jx\omega_0)^{\pm 1}k \left[\frac{(x_2{}^2 - x^2)(x_4{}^2 - x^2)\ldots(x_m{}^2 - x^2)}{(x_1{}^2 - x^2)(x_3{}^2 - x^2)\ldots(x_n{}^2 - x^2)} \right] \qquad (3.5.5)$$

Factors of the form $(x_j{}^2 - x^2)$ have been used deliberately in preference to the form $(x^2 - x_j{}^2)$ for reasons that appear in the discussion immediately following.

For a low-pass filter, as illustrated by Fig. 3.3.1b, the zeros (or poles) of $Z_x(x)$ are at the same frequencies as the poles (or zeros) of $Z_y(x)$ in the pass band. Accordingly, when the product Z_xZ_y is formed, all the terms containing critical frequencies in the pass band may be canceled, leaving only the terms containing critical frequencies in the block band and one term corresponding to the cutoff; i.e., *the image impedance parametric function is a function of cutoff ω_0 and the block-region critical frequencies but not of the pass-band critical frequencies.*

As an illustration, consider the image impedance of a low-pass filter for which $Z_x(x)$ is of the LL class. Specifically, let the reactances

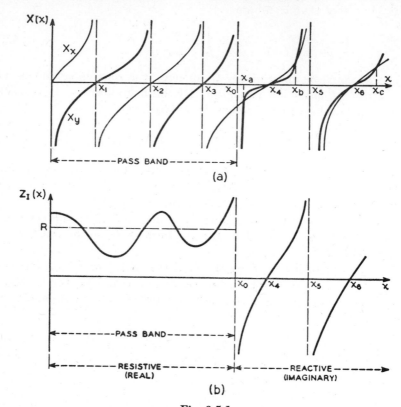

Fig. 3.5.1

$Z_x(x)$ and $Z_y(x)$ take the forms shown in Fig. 3.5.1a. The equations for the impedances are

$$Z_x(x) = jk_x x\omega_0 \frac{(x_2{}^2 - x^2)(x_4{}^2 - x^2)(x_6{}^2 - x^2)}{(x_1{}^2 - x^2)(x_3{}^2 - x^2)(x_5{}^2 - x^2)} \qquad (3.5.6)$$

$$Z_y(x) = -jk_y x\omega_0 \frac{(x_1{}^2 - x^2)(x_3{}^2 - x^2)(x_4{}^2 - x^2)(x_6{}^2 - x^2)}{x^2(x_2{}^2 - x^2)(1 - x^2)(x_5{}^2 - x^2)} \qquad (3.5.7)$$

From these last two equations,

$$Z_I(x) = \pm \sqrt{Z_x(x)Z_y(x)} = \sqrt{k_x k_y}\ \omega_0 \frac{(x_4{}^2 - x^2)(x_6{}^2 - x^2)}{\sqrt{1 - x^2}\ (x_5{}^2 - x^2)} \qquad (3.5.8)$$

The presence of a radical indicates the possibility of either a plus or minus sign. However, as written in Eq. (3.5.8), only the plus sign satisfies the conditions discussed in Sec. 3.3. That is, $Z_I(x)$ is to be positive when real, $(x < 1)$, and is to have a positive slope with frequency when imaginary $(x \geq 1)$. If the expressions are written in the form $(x^2 - x_j{}^2)$ instead of $(x_j{}^2 - x^2)$, it is necessary to use a minus sign for the radical in the pass band and a plus sign in the block band to satisfy these conditions.

If the cutoff is moved so as to fall between x_2 and x_3 of Fig. 3.5.1a the diagonal branch reactance becomes

$$Z_y(x) = -jk_y x\omega_0 \frac{(x_1{}^2 - x^2)(1 - x^2)(x_4{}^2 - x^2)(x_6{}^2 - x^2)}{x^2(x_2{}^2 - x^2)(x_3{}^2 - x^2)(x_5{}^2 - x^2)} \quad (3.5.9)$$

and the image impedance function is

$$Z_I(x) = \sqrt{k_x k_y}\, \omega_0 \frac{\sqrt{1 - x^2}\,(x_4{}^2 - x^2)(x_6{}^2 - x^2)}{(x_3{}^2 - x^2)(x_5{}^2 - x^2)} \quad (3.5.10)$$

These illustrations serve to emphasize the fact that the image impedance is controlled only by the cutoff and the block-band critical frequencies, and is independent of the pass-band critical frequencies.

In general, the design problem is that of making the image impedance approximate the filter terminations as closely as practicable. For most problems, this termination is resistive and constant with frequency. Whatever the desired relationship of $Z_I(x)$ with frequency, functions such as those defined by Eqs. (3.5.8) and (3.5.10) can be shaped by proper selection of the critical frequencies and the multiplying factor. For example, the function of Eq. (3.5.8) contains three critical frequencies. Treating these critical frequencies and the multiplying constant as unknown parameters, it is in general possible to equate $Z_I(x)$ with R, the filter termination, for four different frequencies in the pass band, and obtain a $Z_I(x)$ function which oscillates about the desired characteristic. The resulting $Z_I(x)$ is depicted in Fig. 3.5.1b for $Z_R = R$. Similarly, the function of Eq. (3.5.10) permits five crossings, or one more than the number of critical frequencies. Since these polynomials, $Z_I(x) = R$, are satisfied for at most a number of x values equal to the degree of the polynomial, more crossings of $Z_I(x)$ and the R line are not possible than those indicated in the foregoing.

TABULATION 3.5.1

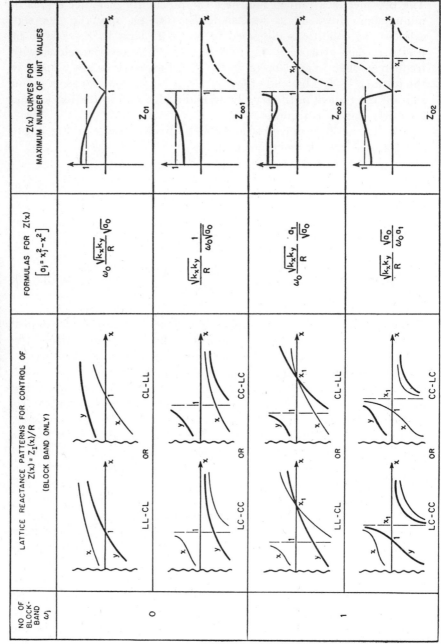

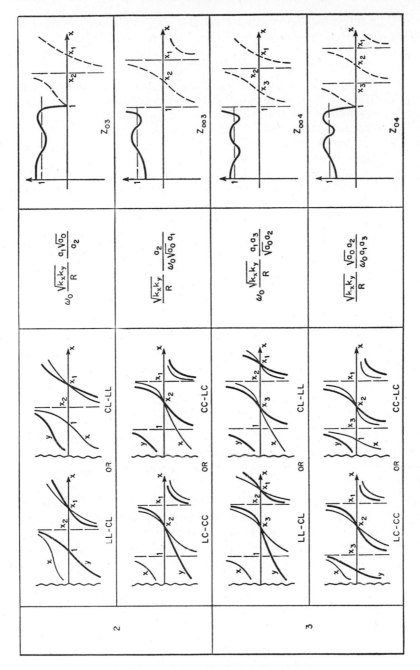

The following list of properties of $Z_I(x)$ condenses the foregoing discussion into a convenient reference form.

PROPERTIES OF $Z_I(x)$

1. The degree of the numerator and denominator of $Z_I(x)$ differ by unity.
2. $Z_I(x)$ is a function of cutoff and the critical frequencies of the block region but not of the pass-band critical frequencies.
3. $Z_I(x)$ is real and positive in the pass band.
4. $Z_I(x)$ has the same form as $Z_x(x)$ and $Z_y(x)$ for $\omega > \omega_0(x > 1)$, pure imaginary and positive slope.
5. The maximum number of real values which may be assigned to $Z_I(x)$ in the pass band is one more than the number of block-region critical frequencies.
6. $Z_I(x)$ has a pole or a zero at cutoff and at infinity.

The relations indicated in Tabulation 3.5.1 also serve to give a general notion of the possibilities for the image impedance function.

3.6. Properties of the ratio function H(x)

The ratio function $H(\omega)$ was introduced in Sec. 3.2 and defined by Eq. (3.2.6) as one of a pair of parametric functions which could be used to evaluate $P_I(\omega)$; it lends itself to analysis more readily than $P_I(\omega)$. Using x, the normalized frequency, as defined by Eq. (3.5.2), Eq. (3.2.6) may be rewritten as

$$H(x) = \pm \sqrt{Z_x(z)/Z_y(x)} \qquad (3.6.1)$$

In contrast with Eq. (3.5.3), in this ratio function the critical frequencies of the pass band are retained, while the critical frequencies of the block band cancel. That such is the case can be deduced from the fact, as illustrated by Fig. 3.3.1b, that the zeros (or poles) of $Z_x(x)$ are at the same frequencies as the zeros (or poles) of $Z_y(x)$ in the block band. Hence these terms will cancel when the ratio is formed.

As particular illustrations of the foregoing statements regarding $H(x)$, consider the reactance patterns of Fig. 3.5.1a. The reactances of the series and diagonal branches are given in Eqs. (3.5.6) and (3.5.7).

The ratio function $H(x)$ formed from these reactances is

$$H(x) = \pm \sqrt{\frac{Z_x(x)}{Z_y(x)}} = j \sqrt{\frac{k_x}{k_y}} \frac{x(x_2{}^2 - x^2) \sqrt{1 - x^2}}{(x_1{}^2 - x^2)(x_3{}^2 - x^2)} \qquad (3.6.2)$$

Similarly, for the reactances given by Eqs. (3.5.6) and (3.5.9),

$$H(x) = j \sqrt{\frac{k_x}{k_y}} \frac{x(x_2{}^2 - x^2)}{(x_1{}^2 - x^2) \sqrt{1 - x^2}} \qquad (3.6.3)$$

Just as in the case of the $Z_I(x)$ function, factors of the form $x_j^2 - x^2$ have been used deliberately in preference to the form $x^2 - x_j^2$ in order to simplify the choice of signs for the radical $\sqrt{1 - x^2}$. As discussed in Sec. 3.3, the real part of $H(x)$ is taken as positive, and the sign of the imaginary part should be such as to result in a positive slope with frequency. Inspection will show that these conditions are satisfied for Eqs. (3.6.2) and (3.6.3) when the positive root is used, and not satisfied for the negative root. The use of factors of the other form yield the result that the sign selected for the radical depends on whether the pass or the block band is under consideration.

Summarizing: $H(x)$ is pure imaginary in the *pass band*, exhibiting a positive slope with frequency (or x) and passing through a succession of poles and zeros. As suggested in Problem 3.13, $H(x)$ exhibits the same general pattern as $Z_x(x)$ up to the cutoff, where $H(x)$ must have a pole or zero regardless of the form of $Z_x(x)$. In the *block band*, $H(x)$ is real and positive. In particular there is a pole of $A_I(x)$ at each frequency for which $H(x) = 1$ in this band (Eq. 3.2.10). Thus arises the useful concept that the filter design problem, one of achieving desired high losses, is that of determining $H(x)$ so that it approximates unity to the degree and over the frequency range indicated by the specific problem, and thus to the outstanding importance of the unit values of $H(x)$ for $x > 1$.

The maximum number of block-band unit values of $H(x)$ that can be obtained is the maximum number of roots obtained by equating $H(x)$ to unity. Inspection of typical equations such as Eqs. (3.6.2) and (3.6.3) and the formulas of Tabulation 3.6.1 indicates that the degree of numerator and denominator are the same. Further, the highest degree is one more than the number of critical frequencies in the pass band, i.e., exactly equal to the undetermined elements of $H(x)$. Hence it follows that the *maximum number of block-band unit values of $H(x)$ possible is one greater than the number of pass-band critical frequencies*, and that specification of this maximum number of unit values of $H(x)$ completely determines $H(x)$.

The curves of Figs. 3.6.1 and 3.6.2b give some indication of the variations possible for $H(x)$ for different locations of its unit values. It will be observed that $H(x)$ assumes its unit value four times in Fig. 3.6.1 and three times in Fig. 3.6.2b. Wherever $H(x) = 1$, $Z_x(x) = Z_y(x)$. However, the inverse is not necessarily true if $Z_x(x)$ and $Z_y(x)$ have a pole or a zero at the same frequency. At such a point $H(x)$ is indeterminate if considered as the ratio of $Z_x(x)$ to $Z_y(x)$, but use of equations of the form of Eqs. (3.6.2), (3.6.3) or of Tabulation 3.6.1 remove the indeterminancy. Further consideration leads to the following conclusions regarding the behavior of $H(x)$ at its block region unit values.

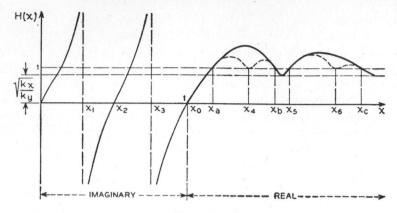

Fig. 3.6.1

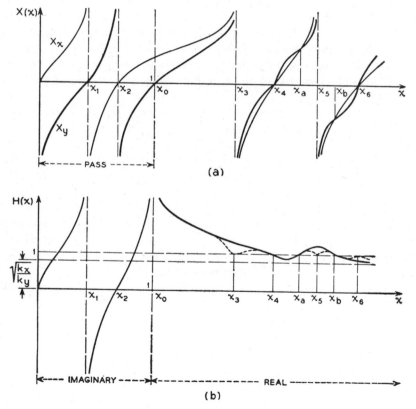

(a)

(b)

Fig. 3.6.2

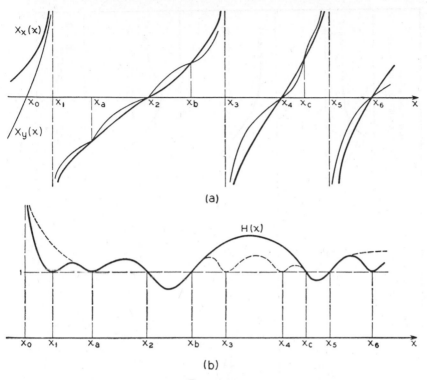

(a)

(b)

Fig. 3.6.3

There are six different forms of the relative behavior of $Z_x(x)$ and $Z_y(x)$ which lead to $H(x) = 1$:

1. $Z_x(x)$ and $Z_y(x)$ may cross off the abscissa—see x_a, x_b, x_c of Fig. 3.5.1a and x_a, x_b of Fig. 3.6.2a.
2. $Z_x(x)$ and $Z_y(x)$ may just "touch" off the abscissa—see x_a of Fig. 3.6.3a.
3. $Z_x(x)$ and $Z_y(x)$ may cross on the abscissa—see x_4, x_6 of Fig. 3.5.1a, x_6 of Fig. 3.6.2a, and x_4, x_6 of Fig. 3.6.3a.
4. $Z_x(x)$ and $Z_y(x)$ may just "touch" on the abscissa—see x_4 of Fig. 3.6.2a and x_2 of Fig. 3.6.3a.
5. $Z_x(x)$ and $Z_y(x)$ may cross at a pole—see x_3, x_5 of Fig. 3.6.2a and x_3 of Fig. 3.6.3a.
6. $Z_x(x)$ and $Z_y(x)$ may just "touch" at a pole—see x_5 of Fig. 3.5.1a and x_5 of Fig. 3.6.3a.

Conditions (1), (2), (4), and (6) are an indication of a unit value of $H(x)$. On the other hand, conditions (3) and (5) may indicate $H(x) = 1$

TABULATION 3.6.1

NO. OF PASS-BAND ω_j	LATTICE REACTANCE PATTERNS FOR CONTROL OF H(x)		FORMULAS FOR H(x) $[a_j = x_j^2 - x^2]$	H(x) CURVES FOR MAXIMUM NUMBER OF UNIT VALUES
0	LL-CL	LC-CC	$\sqrt{\dfrac{k_x}{k_y}}\,\dfrac{jx}{\sqrt{a_0}}$	$H(\infty)<1$ $H_{\infty1}$
0	CL-LL	CC-LC	$\sqrt{\dfrac{k_x}{k_y}}\,\dfrac{\sqrt{a_0}}{jx}$	$H(\infty)>1$ H_{01}
1	LL-CL	LC-CC	$\sqrt{\dfrac{k_x}{k_y}}\,\dfrac{jx\sqrt{a_0}}{a_a}$	$H(\infty)<1$ H_{02}
1	CL-LL	CC-LC	$\sqrt{\dfrac{k_x}{k_y}}\,\dfrac{a_a}{jx\sqrt{a_0}}$	$H(\infty)>1$ $H_{\infty2}$

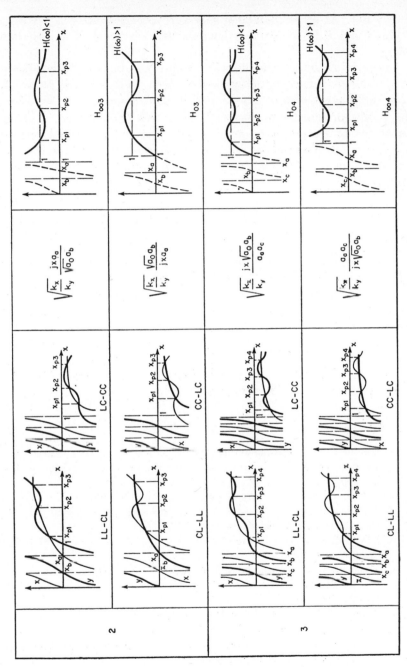

or may not. At other than such special frequencies, the relative sizes of $Z_x(x)$ and $Z_y(x)$ determine whether $H(x)$ is greater or less than unity.

Determination of the limiting values completes the establishment of the pertinent characteristics of $H(x)$. At $x = 1$, i.e., at cutoff, $H(x)$ may have a zero or a pole, and it always has one or the other. This result corresponds to the shift of $\sqrt{a_0}$ (see Tabulation 3.6.1) from numerator to denominator or vice versa as the pass-band critical frequencies are changed by one. As the frequency increases without limit, the fact that the highest degree of numerator and denominator of $H(x)$ are equal leads to

$$\lim_{x \to \infty} H(x) = \sqrt{k_x/k_y} = H(\infty) \qquad (3.6.4)$$

The constants k_x and k_y may be evaluated in various ways, usually indirectly, in terms of the frequencies at which the unit values of $H(x)$ occur, the cutoff frequency, and a value of the image impedance which the 4TN is to present at some particular frequency. Some designs even require that $k_x = k_y$ no matter what the other aspects of the design are. Further discussion of this particular point is given in some of the following material.

The following list of the properties of $H(x)$ and Tabulation 3.6.1 give a brief coverage of the character of $H(x)$.

PROPERTIES OF $H(x)$

1. The numerator and denominator of $H(x)$ are of the same degree.
2. In the pass band, $H(x)$ and $Z_x(x)$ have the same poles and zeros, the same sign, positive slope, and both are pure imaginary.
3. $H(x)$ is real, positive, and never zero in the block region.
4. $H(x)$ is a function of the critical frequencies of the pass band but not those of the block region.
5. Unit values of $H(x)$ in the block region produce poles of $A_I(x)$ at the same frequencies.
6. The maximum possible number of block region unit values of $H(x)$—poles of $A_I(x)$—is one greater than the number of pass-band critical frequencies.
7. At $\omega = 0$ and cutoff, $H(x)$ has a zero or pole, and in the limit as x increases indefinitely $H(x)$ is finite at a value $\sqrt{k_x/k_y}$.
8. The specification of the maximum number of unit values of $H(x)$ completely determines $H(x)$ and so $A_I(x)$.

3.7 Properties of the transfer loss, $A_I(x)$

The transfer function $P_I(x) = A_I(x) + jB_I(x)$ is always considered in terms of its two rectangular components $A_I(x)$ and $B_I(x)$ and never in terms of the square root of the sum of the squares and the corresponding angles as is usual with complex relations. As shown by Eq. (3.2.8), the transfer function is determined by $H(x)$. Indeed, $H(x)$ was more or less invented as a simple auxiliary to ultimate determination of $A_I(x)$ and $B_I(x)$. With the properties of $H(x)$ established, it is convenient next to consider the transfer loss $A_I(x)$ and the transfer phase $B_I(x)$ separately, as is done in this and the next section. Incidentally, the number of parametric relations which are thus used to specify a filter is thereby raised from two—$Z_I(x)$ and $H(x)$—to three (not independent)—$Z_I(x)$, $A_I(x)$, and $B_I(x)$.

The transfer loss $A_I(x)$, defined by Eq. (3.2.10) and repeated here for convenience, is

$$A_I(x) = \ln \left| \frac{1 + H(x)}{1 - H(x)} \right| \tag{3.7.1}$$

In the pass band ($x \le 1$) where $H(x)$ is pure imaginary, $A_I(x) = 0$, since the magnitude of the ratio of conjugate complex numbers is unity, with a logarithm of zero. In the block region ($x > 1$), where $H(x) > 0$ and real, the ratio of Eq. (3.7.1) is always greater than unity, and so $A_I(x) > 0$ for $x > 1$. At cutoff where $H(x)$ has a zero or a pole, the ratio of Eq. (3.7.1) has a magnitude of unity, so $A_I(x) = 0$ at $x = 1$ (cutoff). At intermediate points of the block region wherever $H(x) = 1$ the transfer loss has a pole. At x infinite the transfer loss is finite, provided $k_x \ne k_y$, at a value obtained by substitution of Eq. (3.6.4) into Eq. (3.7.1). If $k_x = k_y$, a pole of transfer loss evidently occurs at x infinite.

Because $H(x)$ does not depend on the block-band critical frequencies but on cutoff and the pass-band critical frequencies, the transfer loss is likewise so dependent. Also *the maximum number of poles of $A_I(x)$ in the block band*, which is the same as the maximum number of unit values of $H(x)$, *is one more than the number of pass-band critical frequencies*. Note further that the transfer loss is not altered by replacing $H(x)$ (see Eq. 3.7.1) by its reciprocal.

The curves of Fig. 3.7.1 indicate some of the possible variations of $A_I(x)$. The minima of $A_I(x)$ are the same (Fig. 3.7.1b) if $H(x)$ deviates from unity in accordance with the reciprocal relation. The $H(x)$ curves of Figs. 3.7.1c and 3.7.1d show the relative insignificance of a block-band unit value, whereas the $A_I(x)$ curve shows the very significant feature of poles at the unit values of $H(x)$.

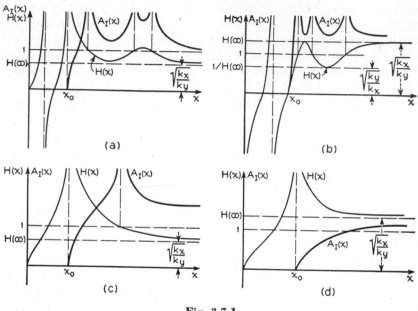

Fig. 3.7.1

For the purposes of reference and emphasis the following summary of the properties of the transfer loss, $A_I(x)$, is given:

PROPERTIES OF $A_I(x)$

1. $A_I(x)$ does not depend on the block-band critical frequencies, but on cutoff and the pass-band critical frequencies.
2. $A_I(x) = 0$ in the pass band ($x \leq 1$), and $A_I(x) > 0$ and real in the block region ($x > 1$).
3. $A_I(1) = 0$; $A_I(x) = \infty$ if $H(x) = 1$; $A_I(\infty)$ is finite if $\sqrt{k_x/k_y} \neq 1$; and $A_I(\infty)$ is infinite if $k_x = k_y$.
4. The maximum number of poles of $A_I(x)$ is one more than the number of pass-band critical frequencies. This maximum number of poles of $A_I(x)$ is aways realizable and the specification of these poles and cutoff determines $A_I(x)$ as well as $H(x)$.
5. $A_I(x)$ is not a function of the class of network but only of the number and location of the critical frequencies.
6. $A_I(x)$ is the same for values of x at which the $H(x)$ values are reciprocals.

7. $A_I(x)$ is completely specified by specification of its maximum number of poles.

3.8 Properties of the transfer phase $B_I(x)$

The second auxiliary parametric relation defined by $H(x)$, namely, the transfer phase, is defined by (Eq. 3.2.8)

$$B_I(x) = \begin{bmatrix} k\pi, & k = 0, \pm 1, \pm 2, \ldots & \text{(block band only)} \\ 2 \tan^{-1} \dfrac{H(x)}{j} & & \text{(pass band only)} \end{bmatrix} \qquad (3.8.1)$$

Based on this definition, it is possible to show that $dB_I(x)/dx$ is positive throughout the pass band. Also the pass-band sign of $B_I(x)$ is that of $H(x)$ directly from Eq. (3.8.1), hence the sign of $B_I(x)$ in the pass band is that of $Z_x(x)$.

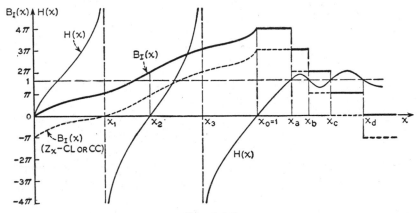

Fig. 3.8.1

Once more based on Eq. (3.8.1), each variation of the purely imaginary ratio function $H(x)$, (pass band) over the interval between any adjacent pair of critical frequencies leads to an increase in $B_I(x)$ of π radians (see Fig. 3.8.1). The number of such intervals is one greater than the number of critical frequencies. Since the number of these intervals is the same as the maximum number of poles of transfer loss possible, the transfer phase of the pass band and the poles of transfer are related by

[maximum possible number of poles of $A_I(x)$]π

$$= \text{total pass-transfer phase increase} \qquad (3.8.2)$$

In the block band, as indicated by Tabulation 3.3.2, $B_I(x)$ has a value of $\pm k\pi$. Furthermore, a "jump" of $\pm k\pi$ ($k > 0$, an integer) radians occurs at each unit value of $H(x)$ as the following argument indicates. First, $H(x)$ changes in magnitude from less than to greater than unity or vice versa at each crossing of $H(x)$ and the unity line. This magnitude variation changes the sign of the ratio of Eq. (3.2.8)

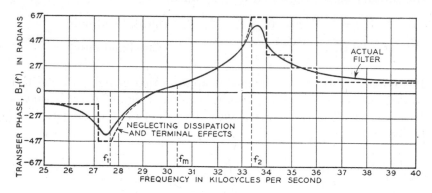

Fig. 3.8.2

and so the sign of $B_I(x)$, i.e., $B_I(x)$ changes by an odd multiple of $\pm\pi$ at each such crossing, since for $k = 0, 1, 2, \ldots$,

$$\ln(-1) = \ln \epsilon^{\pm j(2k+1)\pi} = \pm j(2k+1)\pi$$

If $H(x)$ becomes unity, as at x_1 and x_2 of Fig. 3.6.3b, the change in $B_I(x)$ at such points is an even multiple of $\pm\pi$, since for $k = 0, 1, 2, \ldots$,

$$\ln(+1) = \ln \epsilon^{\pm j2k\pi} = \pm j2k\pi$$

Verification of this fact and an indication of the sign to be used must be obtained from measurement, since mathematically there is no way to establish a sign preference.

Computations and measurements of actual filters indicate that the transfer phase $B_I(x)$ has a negative slope in the block band. A typical illustration of such a measurement is shown by Fig. 3.8.2. The transfer phase discontinuities of 3π at 27.2 and 34.0 kc arise because there are three poles of $A_I(x)$ at each of these frequencies. Further illustrations of the pattern of $B_I(x)$ as associated with the maximum possible number of poles of $A_I(x)$, and as effected by the class of network, are shown by Fig. 3.8.3.

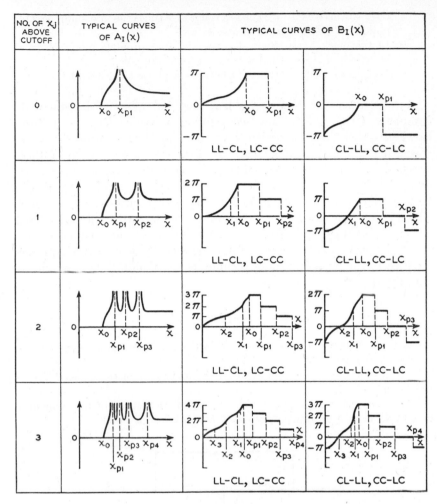

Fig. 3.8.3

The following summary gives compactly the properties of the transfer phase $B_I(x)$:

PROPERTIES OF $B_I(x)$

1. The transfer phase $B_I(x)$ is not a function of the block-band critical frequencies, but of the pass-band critical frequencies and cutoff.
2. In the pass band, the slope of $B_I(x)$ is positive and $B_I(x)$ increases by π radians in the interval between each pair of pass-band critical frequencies.

3. Over the pass band, $B_I(x)$ has a range of π times the maximum possible number of poles of transfer loss $A_I(x)$.
4. In the block band, $B_I(x)$ decreases in discontinuous jumps of $k\pi$ at each pole of $A_I(x)$ where k is the order of the pole.
5. The class of network affects the transfer phase (Fig. 3.8.3.)

In a sense the design problem may be taken as substantially complete at this point. The two defining functions $H(\omega)$ and $Z_I(\omega)$ can be molded with respect to the unity and R lines, respectively, by specifying the appropriate crossings. From the specification of these crossings and cutoff, the critical frequencies in the pass-band for $H(\omega)$ and in the block band for $Z_I(\omega)$, determine $H(\omega)$ and $Z_I(\omega)$, which in turn specify $Z_x(\omega)$ and $Z_y(\omega)$ and so the lattice, pure-reactance filter. There is just one difficulty. Determining the critical frequencies from the line crossings leads to sets of simultaneous nonlinear equations which for practical purposes cannot be solved. The next chapter is devoted to the presentation of techniques for avoiding these nonlinear equations.

Problems

3.1 (a) Determine the symmetrical lattice equivalent of the symmetrical π network of Fig. P.2.17c.

(b) Determine the symmetrical lattice equivalent of the bridged-T network of Fig. P.3.1.

(c) Show that $\Delta_{11} = \Delta_{22}$ is both necessary and sufficient for symmetry of a 4TN. Do not use the equivalent T network in this proof.

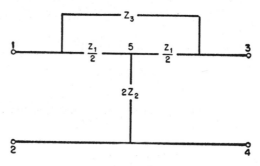

Fig. P.3.1

3.2 Show the equivalence of Fig. P.3.2 by connecting two equivalent T networks in cascade. Then find the equivalent T for this network, after which determine the lattice equivalent of the resulting T.

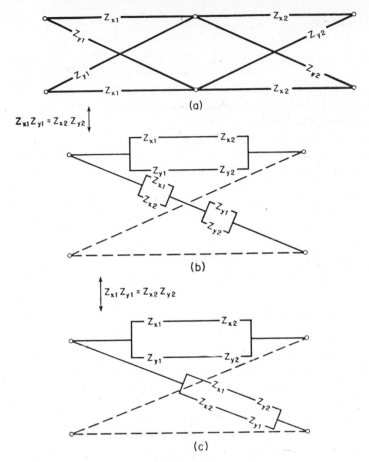

Fig. P.3.2

3.3 Formulas for the single lattice equivalent to a tandem connection of two lattices may be obtained by application of the formulas of Chapter 2. Thus, from the impedance matrix of Fig. P.3.2a,

$$\Delta_{11} = (Z_{x1}+Z_{y1})(Z_{x2}+Z_{y2})(Z_{x1}Z_{x2}+Z_{x2}Z_{y1}+4Z_{x2}Z_{y2}+Z_{x1}Z_{y2}+Z_{y1}Z_{y2})$$

$$\Delta_{12} = -(Z_{x1}+Z_{y1})(Z_{x2}+Z_{y2})(Z_{x2}Z_{y1}-Z_{y1}Z_{y2}-Z_{x1}Z_{x2}+Z_{x1}Z_{y2})$$

$$\Delta_{1122} = 2(Z_{x1}+Z_{y1})(Z_{x2}+Z_{y2})(Z_{x1}+Z_{x2}+Z_{y1}+Z_{y2})$$

Show that these relations are correct.

Substitution of these results into the lattice formulas (3.1.7) and (3.1.8), under the restriction that $Z_{x1}Z_{y1} = Z_{x2}Z_{y2}$, leads to

$$Z_{y0} = \frac{\Delta_{11} + \Delta_{12}}{\Delta_{1122}} = \frac{(Z_{x1} + Z_{y2})(Z_{x2} + Z_{y1})}{(Z_{x1} + Z_{y2}) + (Z_{x2} + Z_{y1})}$$

or alternatively $$Z_{y0} = \frac{Z_{x1}Z_{x2}}{Z_{x1} + Z_{x2}} + \frac{Z_{y1}Z_{y2}}{Z_{y1} + Z_{y2}}$$

and to $$Z_{x0} = \frac{\Delta_{11} - \Delta_{12}}{\Delta_{1122}} = \frac{(Z_{x1} + Z_{x2})(Z_{y1} + Z_{y2})}{(Z_{x1} + Z_{x2}) + (Z_{y1} + Z_{y2})}$$

Show that the last three formulas are correct and that thereby the lattice equivalents of Fig. P.3.2 are correct.

3.4 (a) Prove, by using Kirchhoff's voltage law and the requirement of balance and symmetry, that the voltages V_{13} and V_{24} of Fig. 3.1.3a both vanish if $V_{12} = V_{34}$. Consider the external short circuits as removed for this proof.

(b) Also prove that the voltages V_{14} and V_{23} of Fig. 3.1.3b vanish for such a network if $V_{12} = -V_{34}$. Consider all short circuits as having been removed.

3.5 (a) Prove that the voltage V_{13} of Fig. 3.1.4a, with the external short circuit removed, vanishes if $V_{12} = V_{34}$.

(b) Prove that a voltage $2V$ across terminals 1 and 3 of Fig. 3.1.4b makes $V_{12} = V$ and $V_{34} = -V$.

3.6 Show that Eq. (3.2.5) is correct as given.

3.7 Derive Eqs. (3.2.8), (3.2.9), and (3.2.10). Show $A_I(x)$ is not altered if $H(x)$ is replaced by its reciprocal.

3.8 (a) Plot curves of transfer loss $A_I(x)$ and transfer phase $B_I(x)$ versus x for the symmetric lattice $Z_x(\omega) = 2 + j\omega \times 10^{-3}$ and $Z_y(\omega) = 4 + j(0.1\omega - 10^6/2.5\omega)$.

(b) Repeat part (a) except that the resistances are both to be considered zero.

3.9 If $Z_x(\omega)$ is made of a series resonant component in series with two parallel resonant components, sketch the lattice network and curves to represent the 6 types of pass patterns of Fig. 3.3.1. Assume $Z_y(\omega)$ has a minimum of two parallel resonant components.

3.10 Consider $Z_x(\omega)$ successively as a coil (no internal poles or zeros), then with one internal pole, an internal pole and zero, internal pole-zero-pole, etc. Also consider $Z_y(\omega)$ a capacitor (no internal poles or zeros), then with an internal zero, an internal zero and pole internal zero-pole-zero, etc. Label each of these $Z_x(\omega)$ and $Z_y(\omega)$ impedance types. Make a table of the particular combinations which will form a low-pass filter and which will form an all-pass network.

3.11 Differentiate the expression for $Z_I(x)$ as given by Eq. (3.5.3) with respect to x. Use the positive square root. Show thereby that this derivative is positive for $x > 1$ (block region).

3.12 Plot the curve of $Z_I(x)$ for the low-pass lattice of Fig. P.3.12.

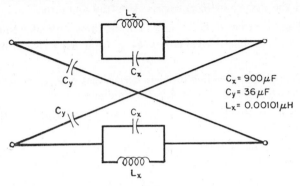

$$C_x = 900\,\mu F$$
$$C_y = 36\,\mu F$$
$$L_x = 0.00101\,\mu H$$

Fig. P.3.12

3.13 (a) Show by direct differentiation that $[dH(x)/dx] > 0$ in the pass band. Make use of the fact that $H(x)$ and $Z_x(x)$ have the same sign, which is opposite that of $Z_y(x)$.

(b) Prove that $[dB_I(x)/dx] < 0$ in the pass band.

3.14 Let $H(\infty) = 1.1$. Plot a curve of $H(x)$ on the basis of two critical frequencies of the pass band. Locate the unit values of $H(x)$ in the block region so that the maximum value of $H(x) = 1.1$ and the minimum value is 0.9 except near cutoff, where $H(x) = 0$. Determine the lowest value of x for which $H(x) = 0.9$. Trial and error should be used to solve this problem.

3.15 Suppose that $\omega_0 = 1000$ and $\omega_1 = 700$. Plot $H(x)$ and the corresponding $A_I(x)$ vs x curve. By guessing and plotting, relocate x_1 so that two poles of $A_I(x)$ occur and so that the minima of $A_I(x)$ are all the same. Let $\sqrt{k_x/k_y} = 0.9$.

3.16 Show that $\sqrt{k_x/k_y} = 1$ for a constant-k, low-pass lattice filter: $Z_x = j\omega L/2$, $Z_y = j\omega L/C + 1/j\omega C$, $L = 2R/\omega_0$, $C = 1/\omega_0 R$. For this filter a pole of $A_I(x)$ occurs at infinite x.

3.17 Show that $\sqrt{k_x/k_y} = m$ for an m-derived, low-pass, lattice filter which is defined by: $Z_x = j\omega Rm/\omega_0$, $Z_y = R\omega_0/j\omega m + j(\omega R/m\omega_0)$. This filter does not have a pole of $A_I(x)$ at infinite x. Determine the location of the pole of $A_I(x)$.

3.18 By definition

$$A_I(x) = 20 \log \left| \frac{1 + H(x)}{1 - H(x)} \right| \quad \text{decibels}$$

Determine $H(x)$ for an *LL-CL* network which corresponds to two poles of $A_I(x)$. Locate these poles so that $A_I(x)$ is not less than 20 db except as it drops off near cutoff. The between-pole minimum should likewise be 20 db. Also locate the value of x at the first up frequency from cutoff at which $A_I(x) = 20$ db. Plot the $A_I(x)$ and $H(x)$ curves. Use trial and error.

3.19 Plot a curve of $B_I(x)$ vs x. Locate three critical frequencies uniformly in the pass band. Evaluate $\sqrt{k_x/k_y}$ from $A_I(\infty) = 20$ db. Plot the $A_I(x)$ curve also.

3.20 Repeat the preceding problem except that $\sqrt{k_x/k_y}$ is to be evaluated from requiring that $B_I(x)$ at $x = \frac{3}{8}$ is $3\pi/2$ radians.

3.21 Plot the functions $Z_x(x)$, $Z_y(x)$, $A_I(x)$, and $B_I(x)$ for the low-pass lattice of Fig. P.3.12.

3.22 Plot curves of $H(x)$, $A_I(x)$, and $B_I(x)$ if

$$H(x) = j2.15 \, \frac{x_1^2 - x^2}{x \, \sqrt{x^2 - 1}}, \quad \omega_0 = 100{,}000, \quad \omega_1 = 103{,}510$$

CHAPTER FOUR

Classification of Component Networks
and Location of Control Frequencies
for Low-Pass Lattice (Reactive)

The discussion in the foregoing parts of this book are largely an exposition of the general properties of the 4TN of interest in filter design. In the preceding chapter attention is directed more specifically toward the properties of low-pass structures. In the present chapter the discussion is centered entirely on the low-pass lattice. A general classification of reactive 2TN combinations which form a low-pass filter is presented in terms of the location of the critical frequencies. Consideration is also given to methods of locating the critical frequencies to produce particular variations of transfer loss $A_I(\omega)$, transfer phase $B_I(\omega)$, and image impedance $Z_I(\omega) = RZ(\omega)$.

4.1 Classification of reactive two-terminal networks

There is not even a remote possibility of exhibiting, or indicating how to exhibit, all the physical forms which reactive 2TN may take. Even if specific characteristics are required of the network, it is not possible to indicate or determine all the physical forms possible. For example, inductors may be connected in endless combinations to give a particular driving-point inductance across two terminals. The totality of reactive 2TN therefore is evidently somewhat extensive.

On the other hand, based on the poles and zeros of a reactive 2TN, an orderly arrangement of minimum element networks of increasing complexity is possible. These networks, in terms of series or parallel resonators, are represented in Fig. 4.1.1 along with their reactance patterns. All possible reactance patterns, and so essentially all possible reactive 2TN, are exhibited by this tabulation or extensions thereof.

85

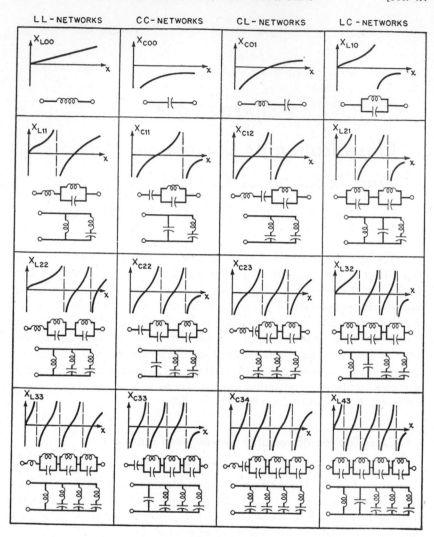

Fig. 4.1.1

The classification of the networks of Fig. 4.1.1 is under two headings: (a) the columns are ordered into the LL, CC, CL, and LC classes; (b) such symbolisms as X_{L00}, X_{C12}, etc. are used to indicate, respectively, reactances behaving as L at $\omega = 0$ (zero at $\omega = 0$) with no internal poles or zeros, behaving as C at $\omega = 0$ (pole at $\omega = 0$) with one internal pole and two internal zeros, etc.

4.2 Combinations of reactive 2TN which form a low-pass filter

Corresponding to the classification of 2TN of Fig. 4.1.1, lattice 4TN which have low-pass characteristics may likewise be classified, i.e., in terms of interconnection of minimum-element, reactive 2TN. The low-pass classification based on the networks of Fig. 4.1.1, is shown in Tabulation 4.2.1. The ordered pair designation $X_{Lij}X_{Cpq}$ indicates a 4TN lattice network with X_{Lij} in the series branch (Z_x) and X_{Cpq} in the lattice branch (Z_y).

TABULATION 4.2.1

COMBINATIONS OF 2TN PRODUCING LOW-PASS LATTICE 4TN WITH
$B_I(\omega) = 0$ AT $\omega = 0$

	No. of control frequencies	ω_0 appears in series branch	ω_0 appears in lattice branch
I	0	$X_{L10}X_{C00}$	$X_{L00}X_{C01}$
II	1	$X_{L11}X_{C01}$	$X_{L10}X_{C11}$
III	2	$X_{L21}X_{C11}$	$X_{L11}X_{C12}$
IV	3	$X_{L22}X_{C12}$	$X_{L21}X_{C22}$
V	4	$X_{L32}X_{C22}$	$X_{L22}X_{C23}$

1. The number of control frequencies is equal to one less than the total number of poles and zeros.
2. The control frequencies may be apportioned in any manner between the pass and block bands.
3. The branch containing ω_0 must have one more critical frequency than the other branch.
4. The two columns shown on the right in the tabulation, for any given number of control frequencies, specify lattices which have the same transfer loss and phase.
4. By interchanging the 2TN used in the series and lattice branches, lattices are obtained which have the same transfer loss as the original 4TN and which have a transfer phase different by 180° from the original 4TN.

The network diagrams and reactance patterns of Fig. 4.2.1 illustrate a particular case, row IV of Tabulation 4.2.1. By means of such patterns for the various network combinations of Tabulation 4.2.1, extensions thereof, and use of Tabulations 3.5.1 and 3.6.1, the following information may be deduced merely by sketches:

1. The general form of the symmetric reactive lattice.

2. The possible allocation of pass- and block-band control frequencies, a particular one of which the designer must choose.

3. The general form of the $H(x)$ and $Z_I(x)$ curves established by this choice. Tabulation 4.2.2 presents some of this information for reference purposes. This tabulation is stated in terms of the maximum number or unit values of $Z(x)$ and $H(x)$. On the basis of Tabulation 4.2.2, the next topic for consideration is taken as that of establishing the properties of the $Z(x)$ and $H(x)$ functions.

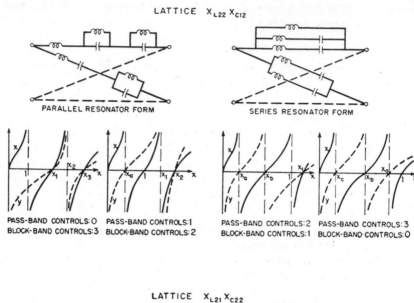

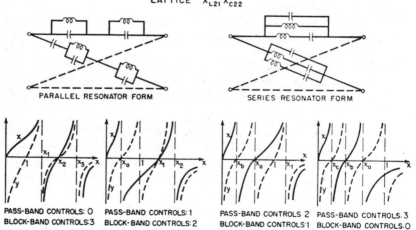

Fig. 4.2.1

TABULATION 4.2.2

THE $Z(x)$ AND $H(x)$ FUNCTIONS ASSOCIATED WITH LOW-PASS LATTICES
(See Tabulations 3.5.1 and 3.6.1 for H_{0i}, $H_{\infty i}$, Z_{0i}, $Z_{\infty i}$ curves)

Pass-band Controls	Block-band Controls	$X_{L10}X_{C00}$	$X_{C00}X_{L10}$	$X_{L00}X_{C01}$	$X_{C01}X_{L00}$
0	0	$Z_{\infty1}, H_{\infty1}$	$Z_{\infty1}, H_{01}$	$Z_{01}, H_{\infty1}$	Z_{01}, H_{01}
		$X_{L11}X_{C01}$	$X_{C01}X_{L11}$	$X_{L10}X_{C11}$	$X_{C11}X_{L10}$
0	1	$Z_{\infty2}, H_{\infty1}$	$Z_{\infty2}, H_{01}$	$Z_{02}, H_{\infty1}$	Z_{02}, H_{01}
1	0	Z_{01}, H_{02}	$Z_{01}, H_{\infty2}$	$Z_{\infty1}, H_{02}$	$Z_{\infty1}, H_{\infty2}$
		$X_{L21}X_{C11}$	$X_{C11}X_{L21}$	$X_{L11}X_{C12}$	$X_{C12}X_{L11}$
0	2	$Z_{\infty3}, H_{\infty1}$	$Z_{\infty3}, H_{01}$	$Z_{03}, H_{\infty1}$	Z_{03}, H_{01}
1	1	Z_{02}, H_{02}	$Z_{02}, H_{\infty2}$	$Z_{\infty2}, H_{02}$	$Z_{\infty2}, H_{\infty2}$
2	0	$Z_{\infty1}, H_{\infty3}$	$Z_{\infty1}, H_{03}$	$Z_{01}, H_{\infty3}$	Z_{01}, H_{03}
		$X_{L22}X_{C12}$	$X_{C12}X_{L22}$	$X_{L21}X_{C22}$	$X_{C22}X_{L21}$
0	3	$Z_{\infty4}, H_{\infty1}$	$Z_{\infty4}, H_{01}$	$Z_{04}, H_{\infty1}$	Z_{04}, H_{01}
1	2	Z_{03}, H_{02}	$Z_{03}, H_{\infty2}$	$Z_{\infty3}, H_{02}$	$Z_{\infty3}, H_{\infty2}$
2	1	$Z_{\infty2}, H_{\infty3}$	$Z_{\infty2}, H_{03}$	$Z_{02}, H_{\infty3}$	Z_{02}, H_{03}
3	0	Z_{01}, H_{04}	$Z_{01}, H_{\infty4}$	$Z_{\infty1}, H_{04}$	$Z_{\infty1}, H_{\infty4}$
		$X_{L32}X_{C22}$	$X_{C22}X_{L32}$	$X_{L22}X_{C23}$	$X_{C23}X_{L22}$
0	4	$Z_{\infty5}, H_{\infty1}$	$Z_{\infty5}, H_{01}$	$Z_{05}, H_{\infty1}$	Z_{05}, H_{01}
1	3	Z_{04}, H_{02}	$Z_{04}, H_{\infty2}$	$Z_{\infty4}, H_{02}$	$Z_{\infty4}, H_{\infty2}$
2	2	$Z_{\infty3}, H_{\infty3}$	$Z_{\infty3}, H_{03}$	$Z_{03}, H_{\infty3}$	Z_{03}, H_{03}
3	1	Z_{02}, H_{04}	$Z_{02}, H_{\infty4}$	$Z_{\infty2}, H_{04}$	$Z_{\infty2}, H_{\infty4}$
4	0	$Z_{\infty1}, H_{\infty5}$	$Z_{\infty1}, H_{05}$	$Z_{01}, H_{\infty5}$	Z_{01}, H_{05}

4.3 The properties of the impedance functions $Z_{01}(x)$ and $Z_{\infty1}(x)$

Considerable convenience arises in design procedures from the use of what is here designated the impedance function defined by

$$Z(x) = \frac{Z_I(x)}{R} \qquad (4.3.1)$$

where R is a positive, real constant, customarily the terminating resistance of the network. In addition to the use of $Z(x)$, years of experience have indicated that a real convenience arises from introducing a parameter, the design resistance R_0, also a positive real constant defined by

$$Z(0) = \frac{R_0}{R} \qquad (4.3.2)$$

Since the impedance function is of interest only in the pass band, the characteristics of $Z(x)$ are considered only in the pass band $(0 \leq x \leq 1)$. The design problem is usually that of making $Z(x)$ approximate unity in the pass band to whatever extent the designer finds expedient. This problem is considered next.

The $Z_{01}(x)$ function as a modification, in accordance with Eq. (4.3.2), of the formula of Tabulation 3.5.1 is

$$Z_{01}(x) = \frac{R_0}{R} \sqrt{1 - x^2} \qquad (4.3.3)$$

The properties of this function may be determined from consideration of its derivative and its limiting values. The derivative is negative

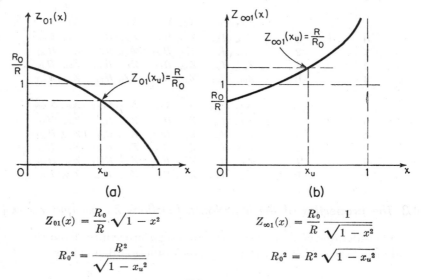

$$Z_{01}(x) = \frac{R_0}{R} \sqrt{1 - x^2}$$

$$R_0{}^2 = \frac{R^2}{\sqrt{1 - x_u{}^2}}$$

$$Z_{\infty 1}(x) = \frac{R_0}{R} \frac{1}{\sqrt{1 - x^2}}$$

$$R_0{}^2 = R^2 \sqrt{1 - x_u{}^2}$$

Fig. 4.3.1

for $0 < x < 1$, which means that $Z_{01}(x)$ decreases as x increases in the pass band. Furthermore, $Z_{01}(0) = R_0/R$ and $Z_{01}(1) = 0$. This impedance function, which is shown of Fig. 4.3.1a, is the well-known constant-k type.

The approximation to unity in the pass band of this impedance function is not good. Some improvement over the useful part of the pass band is possible by making the design resistance R_0 larger than the termination R, and it is convenient to make R the geometric mean of $Z_{01}(0)$ and $Z_{01}(x_u)$, that is, $1 = \sqrt{Z_{01}(0)Z_{01}(x_u)}$, where x_u is the last useful frequency. Under this restriction and in terms of the impedance function,

$$Z_{01}(x_u) = \frac{1}{Z_{01}(0)} = \frac{R}{R_0} = \frac{R_0}{R}\sqrt{1 - x_u^2} \qquad (4.3.4)$$

or

$$R_0^2 = \frac{R^2}{\sqrt{1 - x_u^2}} \qquad (4.3.5)$$

The impedance function $Z_{\infty 1}(x)$ as taken from Tabulation 3.5.1 and modified in accordance with Eq. (4.3.2) is

$$Z_{\infty 1}(x) = \frac{R_0}{R}\frac{1}{\sqrt{1 - x^2}} \qquad (4.3.6)$$

and is illustrated by Fig. 4.3.1b. If x_u is established for geometric mean variation, over $0 \le x \le x_u$, of $Z_{\infty 1}(x)$, then

$$R_0^2 = R^2\sqrt{1 - x_u^2} \qquad (4.3.7)$$

The impedance functions of Fig. 4.3.1 are completely determined, therefore, by a specified x_u in the range $0 \le x_u \le 1$, or directly by a choice of R_0.

4.4 The properties of the impedance functions $Z_{02}(x)$ and $Z_{\infty 2}(x)$

The impedance function $Z_{02}(x)$ given by the fourth row of Tabulation 3.5.1 modified to correspond to Eq. (4.3.2) is

$$Z_{02}(x) = \frac{R_0}{R}\frac{x_1^2\sqrt{1 - x^2}}{x_1^2 - x^2} \qquad (4.4.1)$$

Examination of the derivative of this function shows that $Z_{02}(x)$ may have one of two forms, depending on the location of the control frequency x_1:

Case 1. When $x_1 \ge \sqrt{2}$, then $Z_{02}(x)$ has a maximum equal to R_0/R at $x = 0$ and decreases as x increases for all $0 < x < 1$. This pattern of variation is illustrated by curve 1 of Fig. 4.4.1a, but since it is the same as the variation of Fig. 4.3.1a it is not discussed further.

Case 2. When $1 < x_1 < \sqrt{2}$, then $Z_{02}(x)$ has a minimum at $x = 0$ and a maximum at x_m, where

$$x_m = \sqrt{2 - x_1^2} \qquad (4.4.2)$$

The maximum of $Z_{02}(x)$ is

$$Z_{02}(x_m) = \frac{R_0}{R} \frac{x_1{}^2}{2\sqrt{x_1{}^2 - 1}} > \frac{R_0}{R} \qquad (4.4.3)$$

This impedance function is illustrated by curve 2 of Fig. 4.4.1a.

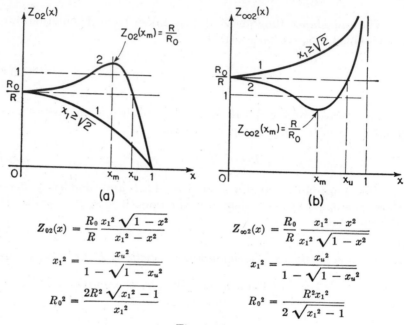

$$Z_{02}(x) = \frac{R_0}{R} \frac{x_1{}^2 \sqrt{1 - x^2}}{x_1{}^2 - x^2} \qquad\qquad Z_{\infty 2}(x) = \frac{R_0}{R} \frac{x_1{}^2 - x^2}{x_1{}^2 \sqrt{1 - x^2}}$$

$$x_1{}^2 = \frac{x_u{}^2}{1 - \sqrt{1 - x_u{}^2}} \qquad\qquad x_1{}^2 = \frac{x_u{}^2}{1 - \sqrt{1 - x_u{}^2}}$$

$$R_0{}^2 = \frac{2R^2 \sqrt{x_1{}^2 - 1}}{x_1{}^2} \qquad\qquad R_0{}^2 = \frac{R^2 x_1{}^2}{2\sqrt{x_1{}^2 - 1}}$$

Fig. 4.4.1

Based on a geometric-mean variation of $Z_{02}(x)$ over $0 \le x \le x_u$, giving the desired approximation to unity (see Fig. 4.4.1a),

$$Z_{02}(x_u) = Z_{02}(0) = \frac{R_0}{R} = \frac{R_0}{R} \frac{x_1{}^2 \sqrt{1 - x_u{}^2}}{x_1{}^2 - x_u{}^2} \qquad (4.4.4)$$

$$Z_{02}(x_m) = \frac{R}{R_0} = \frac{R_0}{R} \frac{x_1{}^2}{2\sqrt{x_1{}^2 - 1}} \qquad (4.4.5)$$

At once from Eq. (4.4.4),

$$x_1{}^2 = \frac{x_u{}^2}{1 - \sqrt{1 - x_u{}^2}} \qquad (4.4.6)$$

and from Eq. (4.4.5),

$$R_0{}^2 = \frac{2R^2\sqrt{x_1{}^2 - 1}}{x_1{}^2} \tag{4.4.7}$$

Therefore, specification of x_u, for geometric-mean variation of $Z_{02}(x)$ over $0 \le x \le x_u$, determines the block-band control frequency x_1 as

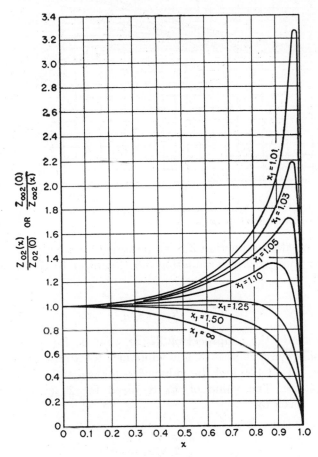

Fig. 4.4.2. Impedance function and reciprocal impedance function for reactive lattice network.

well as the design resistance R_0. The impedance function is thus fully determined by a choice of x_u.

The curves of Figs. 4.4.2 and 4.4.3 show $Z_{02}(x)$ for various values of x_1. Note that these curves do not correspond exactly with the curve of Fig. 4.4.1a, but are altered by division by $Z_{02}(0)$ to facilitate locating the curves on one sheet.

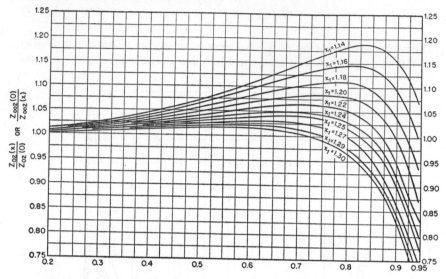

Fig. 4.4.3. Impedance function and reciprocal impedance function for reactive lattice network.

The impedance function $Z_{\infty 2}(x)$, obtained by modifying the equation of the third row of Tabulation 3.5.1, subject to the condition of Eq. (4.3.2), is

$$Z_{\infty 2}(x) = \frac{R_0}{R} \frac{x_1{}^2 - x^2}{x_1{}^2 \sqrt{1 - x^2}} \qquad (4.4.8)$$

which is exactly the reciprocal of $Z_{02}(x)$, that is, Eq. (4.4.1), except for the multiplying constant. The value of x for a minimum of $Z_{\infty 2}(x)$ is given by Eq. (4.4.2) and the value of x_1 for which $Z_{\infty 2}(x_u) = Z_{\infty 2}(0)$ by Eq. (4.4.6). The value of R_0 required for $Z_{\infty 2}(x_m) = 1/Z_{\infty 2}(0) = R_0/R$ is given by

$$R_0{}^2 = \frac{R x_1{}^2}{2 \sqrt{x_1{}^2 - 1}} \qquad (4.4.9)$$

Specification of x_u therefore determines x_1 and R_0 and so $Z_{\infty 2}(x)$ for geometric-mean variation of $Z_{\infty 2}(x)$ over $0 \le x \le x_u$.

The curves of Figs. 4.4.2 and 4.4.3 are for the reciprocal of $Z_{\infty 2}(x)$ exclusive of the multiplying constant R_0/R.

The curves for $Z_{02}(x)$ and $Z_{\infty 2}(x)$ shown by curves 2 of Figs. 4.4.1a and 4.4.1b are the well-known m-derived impedance functions. Note that these impedance functions arise naturally from the existence of one block-band control frequency rather than from the more orthodox and much more involved concepts of the usual m derivation.

Attention is next directed to consideration of the function $H(x)$. Further treatment of $Z(x)$, in the manner of the preceding two sections, leads to algebraic difficulties which make the process and results both of doubtful value.

4.5 The properties of the ratio functions $H_{01}(x)$ and $H_{\infty 1}(x)$

The ratio function $H_{01}(x)$, obtained by modifying the equation of the second row of Tabulation 3.6.1, is

$$H_{01}(x) = \frac{\sqrt{x^2 - 1}}{mx} \qquad (m > 0) \quad (4.5.1)$$

where m is a constant to be determined. This constant is placed in the denominator to make the results conform with the usual m-derived pattern. The ratio functions are of interest in the block band only in the usual case.

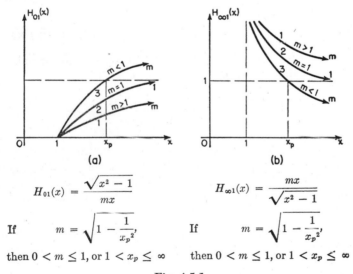

$$H_{01}(x) = \frac{\sqrt{x^2 - 1}}{mx}$$

If $\quad m = \sqrt{1 - \dfrac{1}{x_p^2}},$

then $0 < m \leq 1$, or $1 < x_p \leq \infty$

$$H_{\infty 1}(x) = \frac{mx}{\sqrt{x^2 - 1}}$$

If $\quad m = \sqrt{1 - \dfrac{1}{x_p^2}},$

then $0 < m \leq 1$, or $1 < x_p \leq \infty$

Fig. 4.5.1

The details of a study of this function $H_{01}(x)$ are so simple that only the high points need mentioning. The sketch of Fig. 4.5.1a indicates the limiting values and indicates that $0 < m < 1$ insures one unit value of $H_{01}(x)$ in the block band. The $m > 1$ condition is not used although it is available.

The ratio function $H_{\infty 1}(x)$ is (modification of the first row of Tabulation 3.6.1), in terms of the m parameter,

$$H_{\infty 1}(x) = \frac{mx}{\sqrt{x^2 - 1}} \qquad (m > 0) \quad (4.5.2)$$

where the m parameter is not held in the denominator as is R_0 in the $Z(x)$ relations because of convenience in subsequent developments.

The sketch of Fig. 4.5.1b indicates the characteristics of $H_{\infty 1}(x)$, as, of course, the exact reciprocal of $H_{01}(x)$. Note that for each function, $0 < m < 1$ corresponds to one unit value, and for each function, by setting either Eq. (4.5.1) or (4.5.2) to unity,

$$m = \sqrt{1 - 1/x_p{}^2} \qquad (4.5.3)$$

The specification of the m parameter, directly or by way of x_p, completely determines the ratio functions $H_{01}(x)$ and $H_{\infty 1}(x)$.

The curves 2 of Figs. 4.5.1a and 4.5.1b are the so-called constant-k variation, and the curves 3 are the m-derived type. Note the simplicity of the m-derived result here as compared with the usual approach.

4.6 The properties of the ratio functions $H_{02}(x)$ and $H_{\infty 2}(x)$

The ratio function $H_{02}(x)$, a modification of the formula of the third row of Tabulation 3.6.1, is

$$H_{02}(x) = \frac{mx\sqrt{x^2 - 1}}{x^2 - x_a{}^2} \qquad (4.6.1)$$

From the derivative of this function, two cases of discussion arise:

Case 1. When $x_a \leq 1/\sqrt{2}$, then $H_{02}(x)$ has a maximum equal to m at $x = \infty$ and decreases as x decreases for all $1 < x < \infty$. There is one possible unit value which exists only if $m > 1$ (see Figs. 4.6.1a and 4.5.1a).

Case 2. When $1 > x_a > 1/\sqrt{2}$, then $H_{02}(x)$ has a minimum at $x = \infty$ and a maximum at x_m, where

$$x_m = \frac{x_a}{\sqrt{2x_a{}^2 - 1}} \qquad (4.6.2)$$

from which $$H_{02}(x_m) = \frac{m}{2x_a\sqrt{1 - x_a{}^2}} > m \qquad (4.6.3)$$

This last inequality results from $1 > 2x_a \sqrt{1 - x_a{}^2} > 0$ for $1 > x_a > 1/\sqrt{2}$. Equation (4.6.3) shows that $H_{02}(x_m) > 1$ if and only if $m > 2x_a \sqrt{1 - x_a{}^2}$ and $H_{02}(x)$ can have two unit values, since $H_{02}(\infty)$

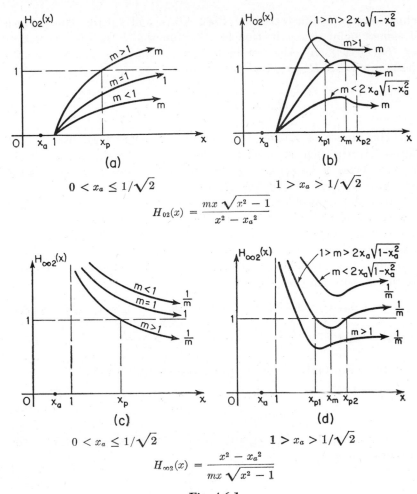

(a)

$$0 < x_a \leq 1/\sqrt{2}$$

(b)

$$1 > x_a > 1/\sqrt{2}$$

$$H_{02}(x) = \frac{mx \sqrt{x^2 - 1}}{x^2 - x_a{}^2}$$

(c)

$$0 < x_a \leq 1/\sqrt{2}$$

(d)

$$1 > x_a > 1/\sqrt{2}$$

$$H_{\infty 2}(x) = \frac{x^2 - x_a{}^2}{mx \sqrt{x^2 - 1}}$$

Fig. 4.6.1

$= m$, if and only if $m < 1$; hence for two unit values of $H_{02}(x)$, $1 > m > 2x_a \sqrt{1 - x_a{}^2}$. Alternatively, the method of Problem 4.12 may be used to establish this last inequality. These relations are shown in Fig. 4.6.1b. The parameter m is fixed so that $m < 1$ permits the maximum number of unit values of $H(x)$.

The ratio function $H_{\infty 2}(x)$, which is exactly the reciprocal of $H_{02}(x)$, is

$$H_{\infty 2}(x) = \frac{x^2 - x_a^2}{mx\sqrt{x^2 - 1}} \qquad (4.6.4)$$

This function is illustrated on Figs. 4.6.1c and 4.6.1d. The pattern of salient point determination for this function is so similar to that for $H_{02}(x)$ that only the results are given. Thus Eq. (4.6.2) specifies the minimum of $H_{\infty 2}(x)$, Fig. 4.6.1d, and

$$H_{\infty 2}(x_m) = \frac{2x_a\sqrt{1 - x_a^2}}{m} \qquad (4.6.5)$$

The ranges of x_a and m, now established and as displayed in Fig. 4.6.1, are such as to specify the pattern of behavior of all the possible forms of $H_{02}(x)$ and $H_{\infty 2}(x)$; further, fixing x_a and m fixes the two ratio functions $H_{02}(x)$ and $H_{\infty 2}(x)$.

In a design problem, x_{p1} and x_{p2} the two values of x at which $H_{02}(x) = 1$ or $H_{\infty 2}(x) = 1$, are usually known, rather than m and x_a. Hence it is desirable to express m and x_a in terms of x_{p1} and x_{p2} or parameters easily obtained from x_{p1} and x_{p2}. This relationship may be realized in simple mathematical form by introducing the parameters m_1 and m_2 through the relations

$$m_1 = \sqrt{1 - 1/x_{p1}^2} \quad \text{and} \quad m_2 = \sqrt{1 - 1/x_{p2}^2} \qquad (4.6.6)$$

so that $\quad x_{p1}^2 = \dfrac{1}{1 - m_1^2} \quad$ and $\quad x_{p2}^2 = \dfrac{1}{1 - m_2^2} \qquad (4.6.7)$

Then from Eq. (4.6.1) or its reciprocal set equal to unity,

$$mm_1 x_{p1}^2 + x_a^2 = x_{p1}^2$$
$$mm_2 x_{p2}^2 + x_a^2 = x_{p2}^2 \qquad (4.6.8)$$

On subtracting these last equations and using relations (4.6.6), the parameter m is

$$m = \frac{m_1 + m_2}{1 + m_1 m_2} < 1 \qquad (4.6.9)$$

and solving either of Eqs. (4.6.8) for x_a and using this last equation,

$$x_a = \frac{1}{\sqrt{1 + m_1 m_2}} > \frac{1}{\sqrt{2}} \qquad (4.6.10)$$

for m_1 and m_2 determined from Eqs. (4.6.6). Note that x_{p1} and x_{p2} may be chosen arbitrarily in the block band and the m and x_a of Eqs.

(4.6.9) and (4.6.10) determine $H_{02}(x)$ and $H_{\infty 2}(x)$ such that these functions have two unit values.

Since the parameters m_1 and m_2 determine $H_{02}(x)$ and $H_{\infty 2}(x)$, they also determine x_m, $H_{02}(x_m)$, and $H_{\infty 2}(x_m)$. Thus using the values for m and x_a specified by Eqs. (4.6.9) and (4.6.10), Eqs. (4.6.2), (4.6.3), and (4.6.5) become, in terms of the two auxiliary parameters m_1 and m_2,

$$x_m = \frac{1}{\sqrt{1 - m_1 m_2}}$$

$$H_{02}(x_m) = \frac{m_1 + m_2}{2\sqrt{m_1 m_2}}, \quad H_{\infty 2}(x_m) = \frac{2\sqrt{m_1 m_2}}{m_1 + m_2} \tag{4.6.11}$$

It is of at least academic interest to set the maximum value of $H_{02}(x)$ [minimum of $H_{\infty 2}(x)$] equal to the reciprocal of $H(\infty)$. Such an $H(x)$ function assures that the minima of the transfer loss are all the same over the entire useful block band, namely, "flat loss." For this condition, from Eqs. (4.6.3), (4.6.5), and (4.6.11) on setting $H(x_m) = 1/H(\infty)$,

$$m^2 = 2x_a \sqrt{1 - x_a{}^2} = \frac{2\sqrt{m_1 m_2}}{1 + m_1 m_2} \tag{4.6.12}$$

Note that m and x_a are not independent parameters for this "flat loss" condition. The next section deals with this aspect of $A_I(x)$.

4.7 Properties of the transfer loss $A_I(x)$ determined by $H_{01}(x)$ and $H_{\infty 1}(x)$

Once the properties of the ratio function are determined, the characteristics of the transfer loss in the block band

$$A_I(x) = \ln \left| \frac{1 + H(x)}{1 - H(x)} \right| \tag{4.7.1}$$

follow readily. At once from this last equation, $A_I(x)$ is the same for $H(x)$ and its reciprocal. Thus the function $H_{01}(x)$ and $H_{\infty 1}(x)$ specify the same transfer loss function. It follows from Fig. 4.5.1 that when $m < 1$, then $A_I(x)$ has a pole at x_p, when $m = 1$, then $A_I(x)$ has a pole at ∞, and when $m > 1$, then $A_I(x)$ has no pole. At cutoff ($x = 1$), then $A_I(x) = 0$ and for $x = \infty$, then $A_I(\infty) = \ln (1 + m)/(1 - m)$. These relationships are shown in Fig. 4.7.1. Curve 3 is the transfer loss of the

TABULATION 4.7.1
TRANSFER LOSS, $A_I(x)$, IN DECIBELS, NONDISSIPATIVE LOW PASS

$m =$	.140	.197	.240	.275	.305	.332	.356	.378	.398	.417	.450	.480	.507	.531	.553	.600	.639	.672
$x_p =$	1.01	1.02	1.03	1.04	1.05	1.06	1.07	1.08	1.09	1.10	1.12	1.14	1.16	1.18	1.20	1.25	1.30	1.35
x																		
1.010	∞	15.5	11.7	9.8	8.7	7.9	7.2	6.8	6.4	6.1	5.6	5.2	4.9	4.7	4.5	4.1	3.9	3.7
1.015	20.1	23.1	15.6	12.7	11.0	9.9	9.1	8.5	8.0	7.6	7.0	6.5	6.1	5.8	5.6	5.1	4.8	4.5
1.020	15.5	∞	20.2	15.7	13.4	11.9	10.8	10.1	9.4	8.9	8.2	7.6	7.1	6.8	6.5	5.9	5.5	5.3
1.025	13.2	25.4	27.2	19.0	15.8	13.8	12.5	11.5	10.8	10.2	9.3	8.6	8.1	7.6	7.3	6.7	6.2	5.9
1.030	11.7	20.2	∞	23.3	18.4	15.9	14.2	13.0	12.1	11.4	10.3	9.5	8.9	8.4	8.1	7.4	6.8	6.5
1.035	10.6	17.5	28.7	30.0	21.5	18.0	15.9	14.5	13.4	12.6	11.3	10.4	10.0	9.2	8.8	8.0	7.4	7.0
1.040	9.8	15.7	23.3	∞	25.7	20.6	17.8	16.0	14.8	13.8	12.3	11.3	10.5	10.0	9.5	8.6	8.0	7.5
1.045	9.2	14.4	20.4	31.2	32.2	23.5	19.9	17.7	16.1	15.0	13.3	12.2	11.3	10.7	10.1	9.2	8.5	8.0
1.050	8.7	13.4	18.4	25.7	∞	27.5	22.4	19.4	17.6	16.2	14.3	13.0	12.1	11.4	10.8	9.7	9.0	8.5
1.055	8.2	12.5	17.0	22.6	33.1	34.0	25.2	21.4	19.1	17.5	15.3	13.9	12.9	12.1	11.4	10.3	9.5	8.9
1.060	7.9	11.9	15.9	20.6	27.5	∞	29.1	23.8	20.9	18.9	16.4	14.8	13.6	12.7	12.0	10.8	10.0	9.4
1.065	7.5	11.3	15.0	19.0	24.4	34.8	35.5	26.6	22.8	20.4	17.5	15.6	14.4	13.4	12.7	11.3	10.5	9.8
1.070	7.2	10.8	14.2	17.8	22.4	29.1	∞	30.5	25.1	22.1	19.5	16.6	15.1	14.1	13.3	11.9	10.9	10.3
1.075	7.0	10.4	13.6	16.9	20.7	25.9	36.2	36.9	27.9	24.0	20.0	17.5	15.9	14.8	13.9	12.4	11.4	10.7
1.080	6.8	10.1	13.0	16.0	19.4	23.8	30.5	∞	31.7	26.2	21.1	18.5	16.7	15.5	14.5	12.9	11.8	11.1
1.085	6.6	9.7	12.5	15.3	18.4	22.1	27.3	37.4	38.0	29.0	22.6	19.5	17.6	16.2	15.1	13.4	12.2	11.5
1.090	6.4	9.4	12.1	14.8	17.6	20.9	25.1	31.7	∞	32.8	24.2	20.6	18.4	16.9	15.8	13.9	12.7	11.8
1.095	6.2	9.2	11.7	14.2	16.8	19.8	23.4	28.4	38.6	39.0	26.0	21.7	19.3	17.6	16.4	14.4	13.1	12.2
1.100	6.1	8.9	11.4	13.8	16.2	18.9	22.1	26.2	32.8	∞	28.2	23.0	20.2	18.4	17.0	14.9	13.5	12.6
1.110	5.8	8.5	10.8	13.0	15.2	17.5	20.1	23.2	27.2	33.7	34.7	26.0	22.2	20.0	18.4	15.9	14.4	13.4
1.12	5.6	8.2	10.3	12.3	14.3	16.4	19.5	21.1	24.2	28.2	∞	29.9	24.6	21.7	19.8	17.0	15.2	14.1
1.13	5.4	7.9	9.9	11.8	13.6	15.5	17.5	19.6	22.1	25.1	35.5	36.3	27.5	23.7	21.4	18.0	16.1	14.8
1.14	5.2	7.6	9.5	11.3	13.0	14.8	16.6	18.5	20.6	23.0	29.9	∞	31.4	26.0	23.1	19.1	17.0	15.6
1.15	5.1	7.4	9.2	10.9	12.5	14.1	15.8	17.5	19.4	21.4	26.7	37.0	37.7	28.8	25.0	20.3	17.8	16.3
1.16	4.9	7.1	8.9	10.5	12.1	13.6	15.1	16.7	18.4	20.2	24.6	31.4	∞	32.7	27.3	21.5	18.8	17.1
1.17	4.8	7.0	8.7	10.2	11.7	13.1	14.6	16.1	17.6	19.2	23.0	28.2	38.4	39.0	30.0	22.8	19.7	17.8
1.18	4.7	6.8	8.4	10.0	11.4	12.7	14.1	15.5	16.9	18.4	21.7	26.0	32.7	∞	33.9	24.3	20.7	18.6
1.19	4.6	6.6	8.3	9.7	11.1	12.4	13.7	15.0	16.3	17.7	20.7	24.3	29.5	39.6	40.2	25.9	21.7	19.4
1.20	4.5	6.5	8.1	9.5	10.8	12.0	13.3	14.5	15.8	17.0	19.8	23.1	27.3	33.9	∞	27.8	22.8	20.3
1.21	4.4	6.4	7.9	9.3	10.5	11.7	12.9	14.1	15.3	16.5	19.1	22.0	25.6	30.6	40.8	29.9	24.0	21.1
1.22	4.3	6.2	7.8	9.1	10.3	11.5	12.6	13.8	14.9	16.0	18.4	21.1	24.3	28.4	35.0	32.7	25.3	22.0
1.23	4.3	6.1	7.6	8.9	10.1	11.2	12.3	13.4	14.5	15.6	17.9	20.3	23.2	26.7	31.7	36.5	26.7	22.9
1.24	4.2	6.0	7.5	8.7	9.9	11.0	12.1	13.1	14.2	15.2	17.4	19.7	22.3	25.4	29.5	42.7	28.2	23.9
1.25	4.1	5.9	7.4	8.6	9.7	10.8	11.9	12.9	13.9	14.9	16.9	19.1	21.5	24.3	27.8	∞	30.0	25.0
1.30	3.9	5.5	6.8	8.0	9.0	10.0	10.9	11.8	12.7	13.5	15.2	17.0	18.8	20.7	22.8	30.0	∞	32.0
1.35	3.7	5.3	6.5	7.5	8.5	9.4	10.3	11.1	11.8	12.6	14.1	15.6	17.1	18.6	20.3	25.0	32.0	∞
1.40	3.5	5.0	6.2	7.2	8.1	9.0	9.7	10.5	11.2	11.9	13.3	14.6	15.9	17.3	18.6	22.3	26.8	33.8
1.45	3.4	4.9	6.0	6.9	7.8	8.6	9.4	10.1	10.7	11.4	12.7	13.9	15.1	16.3	17.4	20.7	24.1	28.5
1.50	3.3	4.7	5.8	6.7	7.6	8.3	9.0	9.7	10.4	11.0	12.2	13.3	14.4	15.5	16.6	19.3	22.3	25.7
1.55	3.2	4.6	5.6	6.5	7.3	8.1	8.8	9.4	10.0	10.6	11.8	12.8	13.9	14.9	15.9	18.4	21.0	23.8
1.60	3.2	4.5	5.5	6.4	7.2	7.9	8.6	9.2	9.8	10.3	11.4	12.5	13.5	14.4	15.4	17.7	20.0	22.5
1.65	3.1	4.4	5.4	6.3	7.0	7.7	8.4	9.0	9.6	10.1	11.2	12.1	13.1	14.0	14.9	17.1	19.3	21.5
1.70	3.0	4.3	5.3	6.2	6.9	7.6	8.2	8.8	9.4	9.9	10.9	11.9	12.8	13.7	14.5	16.6	18.6	20.7
1.75	3.0	4.3	5.2	6.1	6.8	7.5	8.1	8.6	9.2	9.7	10.7	11.6	12.5	13.4	14.2	16.2	18.1	20.0
1.80	3.0	4.2	5.2	6.0	6.7	7.3	7.9	8.5	9.1	9.6	10.5	11.5	12.3	13.1	13.9	15.8	17.7	19.5
1.85	2.9	4.2	5.1	5.9	6.6	7.2	7.8	8.4	8.9	9.4	10.4	11.3	12.1	12.9	13.7	15.5	17.3	19.0
1.90	2.9	4.1	5.0	5.8	6.5	7.2	7.8	8.3	8.8	9.3	10.2	11.1	11.9	12.7	13.5	15.3	17.0	18.6
1.95	2.9	4.1	5.0	5.8	6.4	7.1	7.7	8.2	8.7	9.2	10.1	11.0	11.8	12.6	13.3	15.0	16.7	18.3
2.00	2.8	4.0	4.9	5.7	6.4	7.0	7.6	8.1	8.6	9.1	10.0	10.9	11.7	12.4	13.1	14.8	16.4	18.0
2.10	2.8	4.0	4.9	5.6	6.3	6.9	7.5	8.0	8.5	9.0	9.8	10.7	11.4	12.1	12.8	14.5	16.0	17.5
2.2	2.8	3.9	4.8	5.5	6.2	6.8	7.4	7.9	8.4	8.8	9.7	10.5	11.2	11.9	12.6	14.2	15.7	17.1
2.3	2.7	3.9	4.7	5.5	6.1	6.7	7.3	7.8	8.3	8.7	9.6	10.3	11.1	11.8	12.4	14.0	15.4	16.8
2.4	2.7	3.8	4.7	5.4	6.1	6.6	7.2	7.7	8.2	8.6	9.4	10.2	10.9	11.6	12.3	13.8	15.2	16.5
2.5	2.7	3.8	4.7	5.4	6.0	6.6	7.1	7.6	8.1	8.5	9.4	10.1	10.8	11.5	12.1	13.6	15.0	16.2
2.6	2.7	3.8	4.6	5.3	6.0	6.5	7.1	7.6	8.0	8.4	9.3	10.0	10.7	11.4	12.0	13.5	14.8	16.1
2.7	2.7	3.7	4.6	5.3	5.9	6.5	7.0	7.5	8.0	8.4	9.2	9.9	10.6	11.3	11.9	13.3	14.7	15.9
2.8	2.6	3.7	4.6	5.3	5.9	6.4	7.0	7.5	7.9	8.3	9.1	9.9	10.6	11.2	11.8	13.3	14.5	15.7
2.9	2.6	3.7	4.5	5.2	5.9	6.4	6.9	7.4	7.9	8.3	9.1	9.8	10.5	11.1	11.7	13.2	14.4	15.6
3.0	2.6	3.7	4.5	5.2	5.8	6.4	6.9	7.4	7.8	8.2	9.0	9.8	10.4	11.1	11.7	13.1	14.3	15.5
3.1	2.6	3.7	4.5	5.2	5.8	6.4	6.9	7.3	7.8	8.2	9.0	9.7	10.4	11.0	11.6	13.0	14.2	15.4
3.2	2.6	3.7	4.5	5.2	5.8	6.3	6.8	7.3	7.8	8.2	9.0	9.7	10.3	11.0	11.6	12.9	14.2	15.3
3.3	2.6	3.7	4.5	5.2	5.8	6.3	6.8	7.3	7.7	8.2	8.9	9.6	10.3	10.9	11.5	12.9	14.1	15.2
3.4	2.6	3.6	4.5	5.1	5.8	6.3	6.8	7.3	7.7	8.1	8.9	9.6	10.3	10.9	11.5	12.8	14.0	15.2
3.5	2.6	3.6	4.4	5.1	5.7	6.3	6.8	7.2	7.7	8.1	8.9	9.6	10.2	10.8	11.4	12.8	14.0	15.1
3.6	2.6	3.6	4.4	5.1	5.7	6.3	6.8	7.2	7.7	8.1	8.8	9.5	10.2	10.8	11.4	12.7	13.9	15.0
3.7	2.6	3.6	4.4	5.1	5.7	6.2	6.7	7.2	7.6	8.0	8.8	9.5	10.2	10.8	11.4	12.7	13.9	15.0
3.8	2.5	3.6	4.4	5.1	5.7	6.2	6.7	7.2	7.6	8.0	8.8	9.5	10.1	10.8	11.3	12.7	13.9	14.9
3.9	2.5	3.6	4.4	5.1	5.7	6.2	6.7	7.2	7.6	8.0	8.8	9.5	10.1	10.7	11.3	12.6	13.8	14.9
4.0	2.5	3.6	4.4	5.1	5.7	6.2	6.7	7.2	7.6	8.0	8.8	9.5	10.1	10.7	11.3	12.6	13.8	14.9
4.5	2.5	3.6	4.4	5.0	5.6	6.2	6.6	7.1	7.5	7.9	8.7	9.4	10.0	10.6	11.2	12.5	13.6	14.7
5.0	2.5	3.5	4.3	5.0	5.6	6.1	6.6	7.1	7.5	7.9	8.6	9.3	10.0	10.5	11.1	12.4	13.5	14.6
5.5	2.5	3.5	4.3	5.0	5.6	6.1	6.6	7.0	7.5	7.9	8.6	9.3	9.9	10.5	11.1	12.3	13.5	14.5
6.0	2.5	3.5	4.3	5.0	5.6	6.1	6.6	7.0	7.4	7.8	8.6	9.2	9.9	10.5	11.0	12.3	13.4	14.4
8.0	2.5	3.5	4.3	4.9	5.5	6.1	6.5	7.0	7.4	7.8	8.5	9.2	9.8	10.4	10.9	12.2	13.3	14.3
∞	2.5	3.5	4.2	4.9	5.5	6.0	6.5	6.9	7.3	7.7	8.4	9.1	9.7	10.3	10.8	12.0	13.1	14.1

TABULATION 4.7.1

TRANSFER LOSS, $A_I(x)$, IN DECIBELS, NONDISSIPATIVE LOW PASS

$m =$	.700	.724	.745	.764	.781	.809	.832	.850	.866	.891	.909	.923	.934	.943	.958	.968	1.00
$x_p =$	1.40	1.45	1.50	1.55	1.60	1.70	1.80	1.90	2.00	2.20	2.40	2.60	2.80	3.00	3.50	4.00	∞
x																	
1.010	3.5	3.4	3.3	3.2	3.2	3.0	3.0	2.9	2.8	2.8	2.7	2.7	2.6	2.6	2.6	2.5	2.5
1.015	4.3	4.2	4.1	4.0	3.9	3.7	3.6	3.5	3.5	3.4	3.3	3.3	3.2	3.2	3.1	3.1	3.0
1.020	5.0	4.9	4.7	4.6	4.5	4.3	4.2	4.1	4.0	3.9	3.8	3.8	3.7	3.7	3.6	3.6	3.5
1.025	5.7	5.4	5.3	5.1	5.0	4.8	4.7	4.6	4.5	4.4	4.3	4.2	4.2	4.1	4.1	4.0	3.9
1.030	6.2	6.0	5.8	5.6	5.5	5.3	5.2	5.0	4.9	4.8	4.7	4.6	4.6	4.5	4.4	4.4	4.2
1.035	6.7	6.5	6.3	6.1	6.0	5.7	5.6	5.4	5.3	5.2	5.1	5.1	4.9	4.9	4.8	4.7	4.6
1.040	7.2	6.9	6.7	6.5	6.4	6.2	6.0	5.8	5.7	5.5	5.4	5.3	5.3	5.2	5.1	5.1	4.9
1.045	7.7	7.4	7.2	6.9	6.8	6.5	6.3	6.2	6.1	5.9	5.7	5.7	5.6	5.5	5.4	5.4	5.2
1.050	8.1	7.8	7.6	7.3	7.2	6.9	6.7	6.5	6.4	6.2	6.1	6.0	5.9	5.8	5.7	5.7	5.5
1.055	8.5	8.2	7.9	7.7	7.5	7.2	7.0	6.8	6.7	6.5	6.4	6.3	6.2	6.1	6.0	5.9	5.7
1.060	9.0	8.6	8.3	8.1	7.9	7.6	7.3	7.2	7.0	6.8	6.6	6.5	6.4	6.4	6.3	6.2	6.0
1.065	9.4	9.0	8.7	8.4	8.2	7.9	7.6	7.5	7.3	7.1	6.9	6.8	6.7	6.6	6.5	6.5	6.2
1.070	9.7	9.4	9.0	8.8	8.6	8.2	7.9	7.8	7.6	7.4	7.2	7.1	7.0	6.9	6.8	6.7	6.5
1.075	10.1	9.7	9.4	9.1	8.9	8.5	8.2	8.0	7.9	7.6	7.4	7.3	7.2	7.1	7.0	6.9	6.7
1.080	10.5	10.1	9.7	9.4	9.2	8.8	8.5	8.3	8.1	7.9	7.7	7.6	7.5	7.4	7.2	7.2	6.9
1.085	10.9	10.4	10.0	9.7	9.5	9.1	8.8	8.6	8.4	8.1	7.9	7.8	7.7	7.6	7.5	7.4	7.1
1.090	11.2	10.7	10.4	10.0	9.8	9.4	9.1	8.8	8.6	8.4	8.2	8.0	7.9	7.8	7.7	7.6	7.3
1.095	11.6	11.1	10.7	10.3	10.1	9.6	9.3	9.1	8.9	8.6	8.4	8.2	8.1	8.0	7.9	7.8	7.5
1.100	11.9	11.4	11.0	10.6	10.3	9.9	9.6	9.3	9.1	8.8	8.6	8.4	8.3	8.2	8.1	8.0	7.7
1.110	12.6	12.0	11.6	11.2	10.9	10.4	10.1	9.8	9.6	9.2	9.0	8.9	8.7	8.6	8.5	8.4	8.1
1.12	13.3	12.7	12.2	11.8	11.4	10.9	10.5	10.2	10.0	9.7	9.4	9.3	9.1	9.0	8.9	8.8	8.4
1.13	13.9	13.3	12.7	12.3	11.9	11.4	11.0	10.7	10.4	10.1	9.8	9.6	9.5	9.4	9.2	9.1	8.8
1.14	14.6	13.9	13.3	12.8	12.5	11.9	11.5	11.1	10.9	10.5	10.2	10.0	9.9	9.8	9.6	9.5	9.1
1.15	15.3	14.5	13.9	13.4	13.0	12.3	11.9	11.5	11.3	10.9	10.6	10.4	10.2	10.1	9.9	9.8	9.4
1.16	15.9	15.1	14.4	13.9	13.5	12.8	12.3	11.9	11.7	11.2	10.9	10.7	10.6	10.4	10.2	10.1	9.7
1.17	16.6	15.7	15.0	14.4	13.9	13.2	12.7	12.3	12.0	11.6	11.3	11.1	11.0	10.8	10.5	10.4	10.0
1.18	17.3	16.3	15.5	14.9	14.4	13.7	13.1	12.7	12.4	11.9	11.6	11.4	11.2	11.1	10.8	10.7	10.3
1.19	17.9	16.9	16.0	15.4	14.9	14.1	13.5	13.1	12.8	12.3	11.9	11.7	11.5	11.4	11.1	11.0	10.5
1.20	18.6	17.4	16.6	15.9	15.4	14.5	13.9	13.5	13.1	12.6	12.3	12.0	11.8	11.7	11.4	11.3	10.8
1.21	19.3	18.1	17.1	16.4	15.8	14.9	14.3	13.8	13.5	12.9	12.6	12.3	12.1	12.0	11.8	11.5	11.1
1.22	20.0	18.7	17.7	16.9	16.3	15.4	14.7	14.2	13.8	13.3	12.9	12.6	12.4	12.3	12.0	11.8	11.3
1.23	20.7	19.3	18.2	17.4	16.8	15.8	15.1	14.6	14.2	13.6	13.2	12.9	12.7	12.5	12.3	12.1	11.6
1.24	21.5	19.9	18.8	17.9	17.2	16.2	15.5	14.9	14.5	13.9	13.5	13.2	13.0	12.8	12.5	12.3	11.8
1.25	22.3	20.7	19.3	18.4	17.7	16.6	15.8	15.3	14.8	14.2	13.8	13.5	13.3	13.1	12.8	12.6	12.0
1.30	26.8	24.1	22.3	21.0	20.0	18.6	17.7	17.0	16.4	15.7	15.2	14.8	14.5	14.3	14.0	13.8	13.1
1.35	33.8	28.5	25.7	23.8	22.5	20.7	19.5	18.6	18.0	17.1	16.5	16.1	15.7	15.5	15.1	14.9	14.1
1.40	∞	35.4	30.0	27.2	25.3	22.8	21.3	20.3	19.5	18.5	17.7	17.2	16.9	16.6	16.1	15.9	15.1
1.45	35.4	∞	36.8	31.4	28.5	25.2	23.2	21.9	21.0	19.7	18.9	18.4	18.0	17.7	17.1	16.8	15.9
1.50	30.0	36.8	∞	38.2	32.8	27.8	25.3	23.6	22.5	21.0	20.1	19.5	19.0	18.6	18.1	17.7	16.7
1.55	27.2	31.4	38.2	∞	39.4	30.9	27.5	25.5	24.1	22.3	21.3	20.5	20.0	19.6	19.0	18.6	17.5
1.60	25.3	28.5	32.8	39.4	∞	35.0	30.0	27.4	25.7	23.6	22.4	21.6	21.0	20.5	19.8	19.4	18.2
1.65	23.9	26.6	29.8	33.9	40.6	41.6	32.1	29.5	27.4	25.0	23.5	22.6	21.9	21.4	20.6	20.2	18.9
1.70	22.8	25.2	27.8	30.9	35.0	∞	37.2	32.0	29.3	26.3	24.7	23.6	22.9	22.3	21.5	21.0	19.5
1.75	22.0	24.1	26.4	28.9	32.1	42.8	43.7	35.0	31.4	27.8	25.8	24.6	23.8	23.2	22.2	21.7	20.1
1.80	21.3	23.2	25.3	27.5	30.0	37.2	∞	39.0	33.8	29.3	27.0	25.6	24.7	24.0	23.0	22.4	20.7
1.85	20.8	22.5	24.4	26.4	28.5	34.0	44.4	45.5	36.8	30.9	28.2	26.7	25.6	24.9	23.8	23.1	21.3
1.90	20.3	21.9	23.6	25.5	27.4	32.0	39.0	∞	40.8	32.7	29.5	27.7	26.6	25.7	24.5	23.8	21.8
1.95	19.9	21.4	23.0	24.7	26.5	30.5	35.9	46.4	47.2	34.7	30.9	28.8	27.5	26.6	25.2	24.4	22.4
2.00	19.5	21.0	22.5	24.1	25.7	29.3	33.8	40.8	∞	37.0	32.3	29.9	28.5	27.5	25.9	25.1	22.9
2.10	18.9	20.3	21.7	23.1	24.5	27.6	31.1	35.5	42.4	43.8	35.6	32.3	30.4	29.2	27.3	26.4	23.9
2.2	18.4	19.7	21.0	22.3	23.6	26.3	29.3	32.7	37.0	∞	39.8	35.0	32.5	30.9	28.7	27.6	24.8
2.3	18.0	19.3	20.5	21.7	22.9	25.4	28.0	30.9	34.2	45.3	46.5	38.1	34.8	32.8	30.1	28.8	25.6
2.4	17.7	18.9	20.1	21.3	22.4	24.7	27.0	29.5	32.3	39.8	∞	42.4	37.4	34.8	31.6	30.0	26.5
2.5	17.5	18.6	19.7	20.9	21.9	24.1	26.3	28.5	31.0	36.9	48.1	48.9	40.5	37.0	33.0	31.2	27.2
2.6	17.2	18.4	19.5	20.5	21.6	23.6	25.6	27.7	29.9	35.0	42.4	∞	44.6	40.5	34.7	32.5	28.0
2.7	17.0	18.1	19.2	20.2	21.2	23.2	25.1	27.1	29.1	33.6	39.4	51.2	51.2	42.6	36.2	33.7	28.7
2.8	16.9	18.0	19.0	20.0	21.0	22.9	24.7	26.6	28.5	32.5	37.4	44.6	∞	46.6	37.8	34.9	29.3
2.9	16.7	17.8	18.8	19.8	20.7	22.6	24.4	26.1	27.9	31.6	35.9	41.5	52.0	53.2	39.7	36.2	30.0
3.0	16.6	17.7	18.6	19.6	20.5	22.3	24.0	25.7	27.5	30.9	34.8	39.5	46.6	∞	41.8	37.5	30.6
3.1	16.5	17.5	18.5	19.4	20.4	22.1	23.8	25.4	27.1	30.4	33.9	38.1	43.5	54.2	44.2	38.9	31.2
3.2	16.4	17.4	18.4	19.3	20.2	21.9	23.6	25.1	26.7	29.9	33.2	36.9	41.5	48.6	47.1	40.4	31.8
3.3	16.3	17.3	18.3	19.2	20.1	21.7	23.3	24.9	26.4	29.4	32.6	36.0	39.9	45.4	51.1	42.0	32.4
3.4	16.2	17.2	18.2	19.1	19.9	21.6	23.2	24.7	26.1	29.1	32.0	35.2	38.8	43.3	57.8	43.8	32.9
3.5	16.1	17.1	18.1	19.0	19.8	21.5	23.0	24.5	25.9	28.7	31.6	34.7	37.8	41.8	∞	45.8	33.4
3.6	16.1	17.1	18.0	18.9	19.7	21.3	22.8	24.3	25.7	28.5	31.2	34.0	37.1	40.6	58.5	48.1	33.9
3.7	16.0	17.0	17.9	18.8	19.6	21.2	22.7	24.2	25.5	28.2	30.9	33.5	36.4	39.6	52.7	51.1	34.5
3.8	16.0	16.9	17.8	18.7	19.5	21.1	22.6	24.0	25.4	28.0	30.5	33.1	35.8	38.8	49.4	55.1	34.9
3.9	15.9	16.9	17.8	18.6	19.5	21.0	22.5	23.9	25.2	27.8	30.3	32.8	35.3	38.1	47.3	61.7	35.4
4.0	15.9	16.8	17.7	18.6	19.4	21.0	22.4	23.8	25.1	27.6	30.0	32.5	34.9	37.5	45.8	∞	35.8
4.5	15.7	16.7	17.5	18.3	19.1	20.6	22.0	23.3	24.6	26.9	29.1	31.3	33.4	35.5	41.3	49.1	38.0
5.0	15.6	16.5	17.3	18.2	18.9	20.4	21.7	23.0	24.2	26.4	28.5	30.5	32.4	34.3	39.1	44.5	39.8
5.5	15.5	16.4	17.2	18.0	18.8	20.2	21.6	22.8	24.0	26.1	28.1	30.0	31.8	33.5	37.8	42.2	41.5
6.0	15.4	16.3	17.2	17.9	18.7	20.1	21.4	22.6	23.8	25.9	27.8	29.6	31.3	33.0	36.9	40.8	43.1
8.0	15.3	16.1	17.0	17.7	18.5	19.8	21.1	22.3	23.4	25.4	27.2	28.9	30.4	31.9	35.2	38.2	48.1
∞	15.1	15.9	16.7	17.5	18.2	19.5	20.7	21.8	22.9	24.8	26.5	28.0	29.3	30.6	33.4	35.8	∞

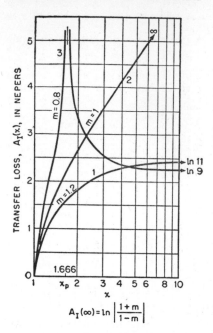

$$A_I(\infty) = \ln \left| \frac{1+m}{1-m} \right|$$

Fig. 4.7.1

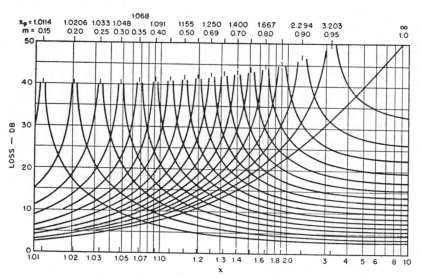

Fig. 4.7.2. Transfer loss, $A_I(x)$, in decibels:

$$x_p = \omega_p/\omega_0, \qquad m = \sqrt{1 - (1/x_p^2)}.$$

m-derived structure, and curve 2 is the transfer loss of the constant-k structure. Curve 1 is not ordinarily useful for practical filter design.

From Eq. (4.5.3), m approaches zero as x_p approaches cutoff. Thus the steepness of the transfer function near cutoff increases as x_p approaches unity, but at the expense of the high-frequency loss. The family of curves of Fig. 4.7.2 and the set of numbers given by Tabulation 4.7.1 indicate the manner of variation of the transfer loss. These curves and set of numbers are useful for estimation purposes in filter design, and are discussed further in connection with presentation of design techniques of following chapters.

4.8 Properties of the transfer loss $A_I(x)$ determined by $H_{02}(x)$ and $H_{\infty 2}(x)$

The ratio functions $H_{02}(x)$ and $H_{\infty 2}(x)$ define the same transfer loss function. They may define the transfer loss characteristics of Fig. 4.7.1, but are rarely used to do so. Instead, these functions are designed to have characteristics which specify two poles of $A_I(x)$, in correspondence with the $H(x)$ of case 2 of Sec. 4.6.

The specification of the poles x_{p1} and x_{p2} determines the properties of $A_I(x)$. Thus at the boundaries of the block region, Eqs. (4.7.1), (4.6.1), and (4.6.9),

$$A_I(1) = 0$$

$$A_I(\infty) = \ln\left|\frac{1+m}{1-m}\right| = \ln\left|\frac{(1+m_1)(1+m_2)}{(1-m_1)(1-m_2)}\right| \qquad (4.8.1)$$

The minimum loss between the poles is determined by $H(x_m)$ and Eq. (4.7.1). This loss may be expressed in terms of: (1) the pass-band control frequency x_a and the parameter m; (2) the poles of $A_I(x)$, x_{p1}, and x_{p2}; or (3) the two parameters m_1 and m_2, by employing the equations of the preceding section.

4.9 Properties of the transfer phase $B_I(x)$ determined by $H_{01}(x)$ and $H_{\infty 1}(x)$

As indicated in the preceding chapter, the transfer phase $B_I(x)$ has the value of $\pm k\pi$ in the block band, and in the pass band,

$$B_I(x) = 2\tan^{-1}\frac{H(x)}{j} \qquad (4.9.1)$$

When $H(x)$ is replaced by its reciprocal, the resultant transfer phase differs from that in Eq. (4.9.1) by $\pm 180°$. The networks of any group in Tabulation 4.2.1 all have the same transfer phase. An examination of the transfer phase characteristic at $x = 0$ indicates whether $B_I(0) = 0$ or $B_I(0) = \pm\pi$.

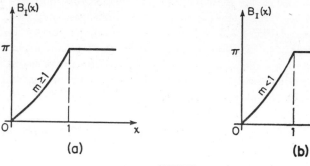

$B_I(x) = 2 \tan^{-1} mx/\sqrt{1 - x^2}$. Determined by $H_{\infty 1}(x)$.

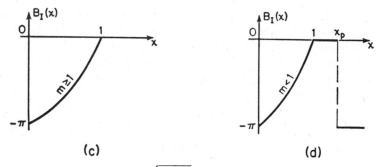

$B_I(x) = 2 \tan^{-1} \sqrt{1 - x^2}/mx$. Determined by $H_{01}(x)$.

Fig. 4.9.1

In the pass band the transfer phase determined by $H_{\infty 1}(x)$ (see Eq. 4.5.2) is

$$B_I(x) = 2 \tan^{-1} \frac{H_{\infty 1}(x)}{j} = 2 \tan^{-1} \frac{mx}{\sqrt{1 - x^2}} \qquad (4.9.2)$$

According to this equation, in the pass band, $B_I(x)$ increases from $B_I(0) = 0$ to $B_I(1) = \pi$.

In the block band, $B_I(x) = \pi$ when $m \geq 1$, but jumps from π to 0 at x_p for $m < 1$. (See Sec. 3.8.) This pattern of behavior is shown in Figs. 4.9.1a and 4.9.1b. The transfer phase characteristic determined by $H_{01}(x)$ is shown in Fig. 4.9.1c and 4.9.1d. Families of curves, for various values of m or x_p, of pass-band transfer phase are shown on Fig. 4.9.2.

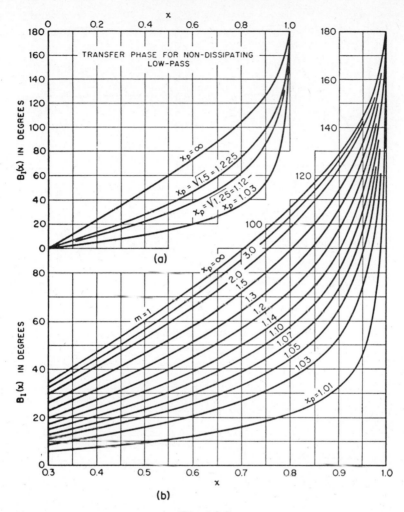

Fig. 4.9.2

4.10 Properties of the transfer phase $B_I(x)$ determined by $H_{02}(x)$ and $H_{\infty 2}(x)$

The transfer phase in the pass band is, as determined by $H_{02}(x)$ of Eq. (4.6.1),

$$B_I(x) = 2 \tan^{-1} \frac{H_{02}(x)}{j} = 2 \tan^{-1} \frac{mx \sqrt{1-x^2}}{x_a{}^2 - x^2} \qquad (4.10.1)$$

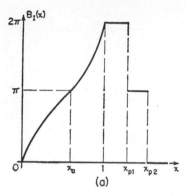 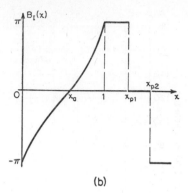

(a)   (b)

$$B_I(x) = 2 \tan^{-1} \frac{mx \sqrt{1 - x^2}}{x_a^2 - x^2} \qquad\qquad B_I(x) = 2 \tan^{-1} \frac{x_a^2 - x^2}{mx \sqrt{1 - x^2}}$$

Determined by $H_{02}(x)$.   Determined by $H_{\infty 2}(x)$.

Fig. 4.9.3

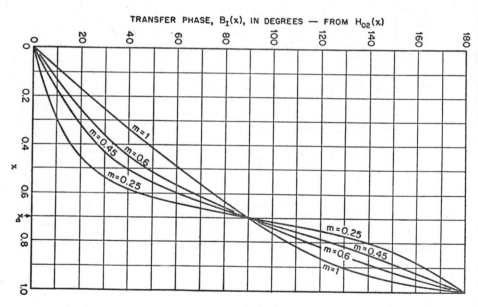

Fig. 4.9.4

From this equation, $B_I(0) = 0$, $B_I(x_a) = \pi$, and $B_I(1) = 2\pi$, as shown on Figs. 4.9.3a and 4.9.4. In the block band, the transfer phase jumps from 2π to π at x_{p1}, and from π to 0 at x_{p2}. The transfer phase characteristic determined by $H_{\infty 2}(x)$ is shown in Fig. 4.9.3b.

4.11 Element values for the $X_{L10}X_{C00}$, $X_{C00}X_{L10}$, $X_{L00}X_{C01}$, $X_{C01}X_{L00}$ networks

Specification of the functions $Z(x)$ and $H(x)$, in the proper form, specifies the series and cross arms of a symmetric lattice by the formulas

$$Z_x(x) = RZ(x)H(x) \tag{4.11.1}$$

$$Z_y(x) = \frac{RZ(x)}{H(x)} \tag{4.11.2}$$

The functions $Z_{\infty 1}(x)$ and $H_{\infty 1}(x)$, for the $X_{L10}X_{C00}$ network (indicated by Tabulation 4.2.2) are, from Eqs. (4.3.6) and (4.5.2),

$$Z_{\infty 1}(x) = \frac{R_0}{R} \frac{1}{\sqrt{1 - x^2}} \tag{4.11.3}$$

$$H_{\infty 1}(x) = m \frac{x}{\sqrt{x^2 - 1}} \tag{4.11.4}$$

Therefore, for the $X_{L10}X_{C00}$ network,

$$Z_x(x) = \frac{mR_0}{j(x - 1/x)} = \frac{1}{1/(mR_0/jx) + 1/jmR_0x} \tag{4.11.5}$$

$$Z_y(x) = \frac{R_0}{jmx} = \frac{1}{jmx/R_0} \tag{4.11.6}$$

Instead of the parameters R_0 and m, however, it is necessary to specify the L and C parameters in order to fix the network. In turn, in order to specify the L and C parameters, it is necessary to change the independent variable from x to ω. The additional parameter ω_0 is thereby introduced from $x = \omega/\omega_0$.

Equations (4.11.5) and (4.11.6) expressed in terms of ω are

$$Z_x(\omega) = \frac{1}{1/(m\omega_0 R_0/j\omega) + 1/(jmR_0\omega/\omega_0)} = \frac{1}{1/(1/j\omega C_1) + 1/j\omega L_1} \tag{4.11.7}$$

$$Z_y(\omega) = \frac{1}{jm\omega/R_0\omega_0} = \frac{1}{j\omega C_a} \tag{4.11.8}$$

These equations are evidently those for a parallel resonator, $Z_x(\omega)$, and for a capacitor, $Z_y(\omega)$. The element values are therefore as given on Fig. 4.11.1a. These element-value parameters in turn determine the parameters m, R_0, and ω_0 as shown on this figure.

The element-value parameters for the $X_{L00}X_{C01}$ and $X_{C01}X_{L00}$ networks may be deduced as in the foregoing and are not considered here beyond exhibiting the relations by Fig. 4.11.1b.

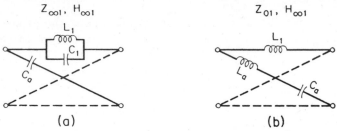

$$Z_{\infty 1}, \ H_{\infty 1} \qquad\qquad\qquad Z_{01}, \ H_{\infty 1}$$

(a)   (b)

No controls, one pole of $A_I(x)$:   No controls, one pole of $A_I(x)$:
($Z_{\infty 1}$, H_{01} on interchange of Z_x and Z_y)   (Z_{01}, H_{01} on interchange of Z_x and Z_y)

$L_1 = mR_0/\omega_0$	$m = \sqrt{C_a/C_1}$	$L_1 = mR_0/\omega_0$	$m = \sqrt{L_1/L_a}$
$C_1 = 1/\omega_0 R_0 m$	$\omega_0 = 1/\sqrt{L_1 C_1}$	$L_a = R_0/m\omega_0$	$\omega_0 = 1/\sqrt{L_a C_a}$
$C_a = m/\omega_0 R_0$	$R_0 = \sqrt{L_1/C_a}$	$C_a = m/R_0\omega_0$	$R_0 = \sqrt{L_1/C_a}$

Fig. 4.11.1

4.12 Element values for the $X_{L11}X_{C01}$, $X_{C01}X_{L11}$, $X_{L10}X_{C11}$, $X_{C11}X_{L10}$ networks

The functions $Z_{\infty 2}(x)$ and $H_{\infty 1}(x)$, which determine the $X_{L11}X_{C01}$ and $X_{C01}X_{L11}$ networks (Tabulation 4.2.2) with one block-band control, are, from Eqs. (4.4.8) and (4.5.2),

$$Z_{\infty 2}(x) = \frac{R_0}{R}\frac{x_1^2 - x^2}{x_1^2 \sqrt{1 - x^2}} \tag{4.12.1}$$

$$H_{\infty 1}(x) = m\frac{x}{\sqrt{x^2 - 1}} \tag{4.12.2}$$

The impedances of the series and cross arms of the lattice $X_{L11}X_{C01}$ are, from Eqs. (4.11.1) and (4.11.2),

$$Z_x(x) = j\frac{mR_0}{x_1^2}x\left(1 + \frac{1 - x_1^2}{x^2 - 1}\right) \tag{4.12.3}$$

$$Z_y(x) = j\frac{R_0}{mx_1^2}x\left(1 - \frac{x_1^2}{x^2}\right) \tag{4.12.4}$$

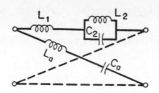

$Z_{\infty2}, H_{\infty1}$ **Z_{01}, H_{02}**

One $Z_I(\omega)$ control, one pole of $A_I(\omega)$:   No $Z_I(\omega)$ controls, two poles of $A_I(\omega)$:
($Z_{\infty2}, H_{01}$ on interchange of Z_x and Z_y)   ($Z_{01}, H_{\infty2}$ on interchanging Z_x and Z_y)

$$L_1 = \frac{m\omega_0 R_0}{\omega_1^2} \qquad m = \sqrt{\frac{L_1}{L_a}} \qquad\qquad L_1 = \frac{mR_0}{\omega_0} \qquad m = \sqrt{\frac{L_1}{L_a}}$$

$$L_2 = \frac{mR_0(\omega_1^2 - \omega_0^2)}{\omega_0\omega_1^2} \qquad \omega_0 = \frac{1}{\sqrt{L_2 C_2}} \qquad L_2 = \frac{mR_0(\omega_0^2 - \omega_a^2)}{\omega_0\omega_a^2} \qquad \omega_0 = \sqrt{\frac{L_1 + L_2}{L_1 L_2 C_2}}$$

$$L_a = \frac{\omega_0 R_0}{m\omega_1^2} \qquad R_0 = \frac{\sqrt{L_1 L_2 C_2}}{C_a \sqrt{L_a}} \qquad L_a = \frac{R_0}{m\omega_0} \qquad R_0 = \sqrt{\frac{L_1 + L_2}{C_a}}$$

$$C_2 = \frac{\omega_1^2}{m\omega_0 R_0(\omega_1^2 - \omega_0^2)} \qquad \omega_1 = \frac{1}{\sqrt{L_a C_a}} \qquad C_2 = \frac{\omega_0}{mR_0(\omega_0^2 - \omega_a^2)} \qquad \omega_a = \frac{1}{\sqrt{L_a C_2}} = \frac{1}{\sqrt{L_a C_a}}$$

$$C_a = \frac{m}{\omega_0 R_0} \qquad\qquad\qquad\qquad C_a = \frac{m\omega_0}{R_0 \omega_a^2}$$

(a)

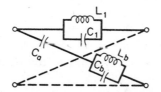

$Z_{02}, H_{\infty1}$ **$Z_{\infty1}, H_{02}$**

One $Z_I(\omega)$ control, one pole of $A_I(\omega)$:   No $Z_I(\omega)$ controls, two poles of $A_I(\omega)$:
(Z_{02}, H_{01} on interchanging Z_x and Z_y)   ($Z_{\infty1}, H_{\infty2}$ on interchanging Z_x and Z_y)

$$C_1 = \frac{\omega_0}{mR_0\omega_1^2} \qquad m = \sqrt{\frac{L_1 C_a}{L_b(C_a + C_b)}} \qquad C_1 = \frac{1}{m\omega_0 R_0} \qquad m = \frac{1}{C_1}\sqrt{\frac{L_b C_b C_a}{L_1}}$$

$$C_a = \frac{m}{\omega_0 R_0} \qquad \omega_0 = \frac{1}{\sqrt{L_b(C_a + C_b)}} \qquad C_a = \frac{m\omega_0}{R_0 \omega_a^2} \qquad \omega_0 = \frac{1}{\sqrt{L_b C_b}}$$

$$C_b = \frac{m\omega_0}{R_0(\omega_1^2 - \omega_0^2)} \qquad R_0 = \sqrt{\frac{L_1}{C_a}} \qquad C_b = \frac{m\omega_0}{R_0(\omega_0^2 - \omega_a^2)} \qquad R_0 = \sqrt{\frac{L_1}{C_a}}$$

$$L_1 = \frac{mR_0}{\omega_0} \qquad \omega_1 = \frac{1}{\sqrt{L_b C_b}} = \frac{1}{\sqrt{L_1 C_1}} \qquad L_1 = \frac{m\omega_0 R_0}{\omega_a^2} \qquad \omega_a = \frac{1}{\sqrt{L_1 C_1}}$$

$$L_b = \frac{R_0(\omega_1^2 - \omega_0^2)}{m\omega_0\omega_1^2} \qquad\qquad\qquad L_b = \frac{R_0(\omega_0^2 - \omega_a^2)}{m\omega_0^3}$$

(b)

Fig. 4.12.1

In terms of the independent variable ω, these last two equations are

$$Z_x(\omega) = j\,\frac{mR_0\omega_0}{\omega_1{}^2}\,\omega\left(1 + \frac{\omega_0{}^2 - \omega_1{}^2}{\omega^2 - \omega_0{}^2}\right) \tag{4.12.5}$$

$$= j\omega L_1 + j\omega\,\frac{-1/C_2}{\omega^2 - 1/L_2C_2}$$

$$Z_y(\omega) = j\,\frac{R_0\omega_0}{m\omega_1{}^2}\,\omega\left(1 - \frac{\omega_1{}^2}{\omega^2}\right) = j\omega L_a + \frac{1}{j\omega C_a} \tag{4.12.6}$$

In turn these equations specify the element-value parameters in terms of the parameters m, R_0, ω_0, ω_1 and vice versa as on Figs. 4.12.1a and 4.12.1b.

The element-value parameters for all the other entries of the second main entry of Tabulation 4.2.2 are given on Fig. 4.12.1. The technique of determining these relations is precisely as in the foregoing.

4.13 Location of H(x) and Z(x) control frequencies, general

The pattern of impedance function variation set in the discussion of Secs. 4.3 and 4.4, namely, geometric mean variation with respect to unity, has been found the most convenient all purpose form. This convenience is manifested in mathematical simplification and entirely satisfactory control of the deviation of the impedance function from unity, or, $Z_I(x)$ from R.

A pattern of less deviation over a wider portion of the pass band as the number of block-band control frequencies is increased, is exhibited by $Z(x)$ under geometric mean variation. Thus in terms of the sketch of $Z(x)$ of Fig. 4.13.1, as the number of block-band controls, x_1, x_2, x_3, ... increases, the deviation of $Z(x)$ from unity decreases, and x_{uz} approaches unity.

The algebraic treatment of Sec. 4.4 becomes extremely difficult for two and practically impossible for more than two block-band control frequencies. The next section is devoted to an alternative and, in so far as use is concerned, not very complicated technique for locating the $Z(x)$ block-band controls such that the pass band variation of $Z(x)$ is as illustrated by Fig. 4.13.1 (geometric mean).

Reference to Tabulations 3.5.1 and 3.6.1 shows that replacing x by $1/x$ in any $Z(x)$ leads to one of the $H(x)$ functions except for the precise form of the constant multiplier. Consequently, if $H(x)$ varies as indicated on Fig. 4.13.1 (geometric mean with respect to unity and so "flat loss") any technique which may be used to determine the control frequencies for geometric mean variation of $Z(x)$ may also be used to establish the control frequencies for "flat loss" variation of $H(x)$.

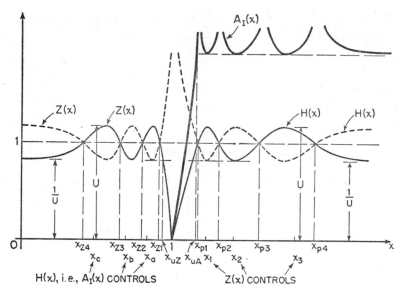

Fig. 4.13.1

4.14 Location of control frequencies for geometric-mean variation of image impedance

The geometric-mean variation with respect to unity, discussed in foregoing parts of this chapter, is often designated as the Tschebyscheff approximation. Because of the utility of this type of functional variation, much work has been done on establishing a means of locating the control frequencies and unit values of $H(x)$ and $Z(x)$ to specify a geometric mean variation.[1]

The method used is that of making a change in the independent variable, in the $H(x)$ and $Z(x)$ functions, in the form

$$x = k \operatorname{sn} F(\Phi, x_u) \tag{4.14.1}$$

---

[1] Cauer, W., *Siebschaltungen*, V.D.I. Verlag, G.m.b.H., Berlin, 1931; "Ein Interpolations Problem mit Funktionen mit positive Realteil," *Math. Z.*, Vol. 38, No. 1, November 1933; *Theorie der linearen Wechselstromschaltungen*, Edwards Brothers, Inc., Ann Arbor, 1948.

where k is a positive constant,

$$F(\Phi, x_u) = \int_0^{\Phi} \frac{d\psi}{\sqrt{1 - x_u{}^2 \sin^2 \psi}} \qquad (4.14.2)$$

is the elliptic integral of the first kind, and sn $F(\Phi, x_u)$ is designated the elliptic sine of $F(\Phi, x_u)$. The auxiliary relation

$$x = k \sin \Phi = k \operatorname{sn} F(\Phi, x_u) \qquad (4.14.3)$$

defines the sn function and evidently suggests the term elliptic sine. Since tables of numerical values of sn $F(\Phi, x_u)$ are available, the transformation of Eq. (4.14.1) differs in no respect from $x = k \sin \Phi$, $x = k \cos \Phi$, etc. except that of familiarity.

First note the ranges of correspondence of the several variables of Eqs. (4.14.1), (4.14.2), and (4.14.3):

$$0 \le x \le k \text{ corresponds to} \begin{bmatrix} 0 \le \Phi \le \dfrac{\pi}{2} \\ 0 \le \operatorname{sn} F(\Phi, x_u) \le 1 \\ 0 \le F(\Phi, x_u) \le K \end{bmatrix} \qquad (4.14.4)$$

where

$$K = K(x_u) = F\left(\frac{\pi}{2}, x_u\right) = \int_0^{\pi/2} \frac{d\psi}{\sqrt{1 - x_u{}^2 \sin^2 \psi}} \qquad (4.14.5)$$

It has been proved that location of points, according to specific patterns of uniformity, on the $F(\Phi, x_u)$ scale in the range of $0 \le F(\Phi, x_u) \le K$, followed by transferrence of these points to the x scale by way of Eq. (4.14.1), specifies the geometric-mean variation of $Z(x)$ over the range $0 \le x \le x_u$. The pattern of this uniform location is indicated by Fig. 4.14.1.

Consider first the location of the unit values of $Z(x)$, that is, x_{Zi} of Fig. 4.14.1. The transformation of Eq. (4.14.1), with $k = x_u$, is used for this situation, i.e.,

$$x = x_u \operatorname{sn} F(\Phi, x_u) \qquad (4.14.6)$$

On the F scale, the unit values of $Z(x)$ occur at uniformly located points. These points are located with half intervals at each end and full intervals between for $0 \le F(\Phi, x_u) \le K$. Or in general for n the number of block band controls

$$x_{Zi} = x_u \operatorname{sn} \frac{2(n - i) + 3}{2(n + 1)} K \qquad (1 \le i \le n + 1) \quad (4.14.7)$$

specifies the location of these unit values of $Z(x)$ on the x scale for geometric-mean variation over $0 \leq x \leq x_u$.

The $Z(x)$ control frequencies of the block region are located by way of sn $F(\Phi, x_u)$ but in a slightly different manner than the unit values of $Z(x)$. In the first place the range of $F(\Phi, x_u)$, $0 \leq F(\Phi, x_u) \leq K$, is

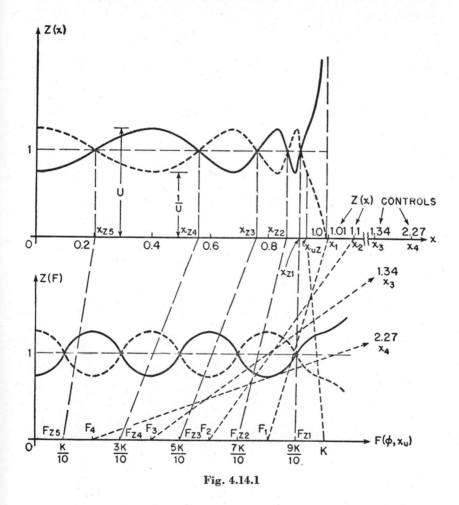

Fig. 4.14.1

divided into $n + 1$ equal intervals where n is the number of $Z(x)$ controls (Fig. 4.14.1). The points so located, n in number, are then transferred to the x scale (pass band) by way of Eq. (4.14.1) with $k = 1$ after which they are transferred to the block region by way of reciprocals. The whole pattern then is

$$x_{n+1-i} = \frac{1}{\text{sn}\,[iK/(n+1)]} \quad (1 \leq i \leq n) \quad (4.14.8)$$

which locates the $Z(x)$ controls for geometric-mean variation of $Z(x)$ over $0 \leq x \leq x_u$.

Example 4.14.1

Locate the $Z(x)$ control and $Z(x) = 1$ frequencies for a low-pass filter with cutoff at $f_0 = 48.5$ kc and with $f_u = 46.88$ kc. This filter is to have two impedance control frequencies.

TABULATION 4.14.1

VALUES OF sn(Kn) FOR θ GIVEN AT HEAD OF COLUMN

θ / n	55	60	65	70	75	80	81	82	83	84	85
1/16	.1265	.1340	.1432	.1553	.1714	.1945	.2005	.2076	.2153	.2244	.2349
1/14	.1444	.1530	.1633	.1771	.1954	.2216	.2284	.2363	.2450	.2552	.2670
1/12	.1682	.1782	.1902	.2059	.2269	.2571	.2647	.2737	.2837	.2954	.3090
1/10	.2011	.2128	.2272	.2456	.2700	.3054	.3145	.3250	.3366	.3499	.3654
1/8	.2498	.2639	.2815	.3038	.3333	.3752	.3862	.3982	.4118	.4274	.4457
1/7	.2835	.2999	.3195	.3439	.3768	.4226	.4344	.4475	.4625	.4792	.4987
1/6	.3286	.3464	.3687	.3961	.4321	.4825	.4955	.5095	.5255	.5434	.5642
3/16	.3668	.3862	.4102	.4397	.4782	.5316	.5451	.5599	.5764	.5948	.6161
1/5	.3891	.4094	.4342	.4648	.5048	.5594	.5731	.5883	.6051	.6239	.6452
3/14	.4142	.4352	.4610	.4929	.5339	.5899	.6037	.6191	.6356	.6547	.6560
1/4	.4749	.4975	.5250	.5590	.6018	.6591	.6730	.6881	.7048	.7234	.7439
2/7	.5319	.5558	.5845	.6191	.6624	.7187	.7323	.7470	.7629	.7802	.7993
3/10	.5539	.5779	.6067	.6414	.6846	.7402	.7536	.7679	.7832	.8000	.8185
5/16	.5724	.5967	.6255	.6602	.7032	.7579	.7709	.7848	.7997	.8160	.8337
1/3	.6025	.6268	.6556	.6900	.7323	.7851	.7976	.8107	.8250	.8401	.8570
5/14	.6352	.6596	.6879	.7216	.7623	.8128	.8246	.8369	.8502	.8643	.8794
3/8	.6587	.6826	.7106	.7347	.7833	.8316	.8428	.8546	.8669	.8801	.8942
2/5	.6900	.7134	.7406	.7724	.8099	.8552	.8654	.8763	.8876	.8994	.9121
5/12	.7098	.7327	.7593	.7900	.8261	.8692	.8790	.8892	.8996	.9108	.9224
3/7	.7236	.7461	.7720	.8020	.8369	.8785	.8878	.8975	.9075	.9181	.9290
7/16	.7335	.7557	.7812	.8106	.8448	.8851	.8940	.9033	.9131	.9232	.9337
1/2	.7972	.8165	.8384	.8632	.8913	.9231	.9299	.9369	.9441	.9515	.9591
9/16	.8502	.8662	.8840	.9038	.9256	.9495	.9545	.9596	.9467	.9699	.9751
4/7	.8570	.8724	.8897	.9088	.9298	.9526	.9573	.9622	.9670	.9719	.9769
7/12	.8656	.8805	.8970	.9151	.9349	.9564	.9609	.9654	.9699	.9744	.9790
3/5	.8773	.8911	.9066	.9233	.9417	.9613	.9654	.9694	.9735	.9776	.9817
5/8	.8935	.9061	.9197	.9346	.9508	.9678	.9713	.9748	.9783	.9817	.9852
9/14	.9045	.9158	.9283	.9420	.9565	.9719	.9750	.9781	.9812	.9842	.9873
2/3	.9176	.9277	.9388	.9507	.9634	.9766	.9793	.9819	.9845	.9871	.9897
11/16	.9283	.9373	.9471	.9577	.9687	.9799	.9825	.9848	.9871	.9893	.9914
7/10	.9343	.9426	.9518	.9614	.9717	.9822	.9843	.9864	.9884	.9904	.9924
5/7	.9407	.9484	.9567	.9655	.9748	.9842	.9861	.9880	.9898	.9916	.9933
3/4	.9553	.9613	.9676	.9744	.9815	.9886	.9900	.9914	9928	.9941	.9953
11/14	.9676	.9720	.9767	.9817	.9869	.9921	.9930	.9940	.9950	.9959	.9968
4/5	.9719	.9757	.9799	.9842	.9888	.9932	.9941	.9949	.9958	.9965	.9973
13/16	.9754	.9788	.9824	.9863	.9902	.9941	.9949	.9956	.9964	.9970	.9977
5/6	.9807	.9834	.9863	.9893	.9924	.9954	.9960	.9966	.9972	.9977	.9982
6/7	.9859	.9879	.9900	.9922	.9945	.9967	.9972	.9976	.9980	.9984	.9988
7/8	.9892	.9908	.9923	.9941	.9959	.9975	.9979	.9982	.9985	.9988	.9991
9/10	.9931	.9941	.9952	.9963	.9974	.9985	.9987	.9989	.9990	.9992	.9994

*$\sin\theta = x_u$

θ	x_u
55	.81915
60	.86603
65	.90631
70	.93969
75	.96593
80	.98481
81	.98769
82	.99027
83	.99255
84	.99452
85	.99619

* Elliptic sines are tabulated in terms of θ as defined by $\sin \theta = x_u$ rather than directly in terms of x_u.

Solution

By definition

$$x_u = \frac{\omega_u}{\omega_0} = \frac{f_u}{f_0} = \frac{46.88}{48.5} = 0.966$$

and from Eq. (4.14.8) for $n = 2$,

$$x_1 = \frac{1}{\text{sn } 2K/3}, \qquad x_2 = \frac{1}{\text{sn } K/3}$$

Then from Tabulation 4.14.1 (see footnote of tabulation) corresponding to $\theta = \sin^{-1} x_u = \sin^{-1} 0.966 = 75°$

$$x_1 = \frac{1}{0.9634}, \qquad f_1 = \frac{48.5}{0.9634} = 50.4 \text{ kc}$$

$$x_2 = \frac{1}{0.7320}, \qquad f_2 = \frac{48.5}{0.7320} = 66.3 \text{ kc}$$

The critical frequencies for $Z(x)$, from Eq. (4.14.7) and Tabulation 4.14.1 are

$$x_{Z3} = x_u \text{ sn } K/6 = 0.966(0.4321) = 0.4174,$$
$$f_{Z3} = 48.5(0.4174) = 20.24 \text{ kc}$$
$$x_{Z2} = x_u \text{ sn } 3K/6 = 0.966(0.8913) = 0.8610,$$
$$f_{Z2} = 48.5(0.8610) = 41.76 \text{ kc}$$
$$x_{Z1} = x_u \text{ sn } 5K/6 = 0.966(0.9924) = 0.9586,$$
$$f_{Z1} = 48.5(0.9586) = 46.62 \text{ kc}$$

The usual approach to the design problem is not, however, in terms of a known number of control frequencies, but in terms of a specified deviation of $Z(x)$ from unity over a specific range of frequency, i.e., ω_u and the deviation are specified and the number and location of the control frequencies are sought.

The parameters ω_0, ω_u, and U are related in accordance with the set of formulas of Tabulation 4.14.2 or an easy extension thereof. Curves corresponding to these formulas are given in Fig. 4.14.2. The curves are useful in choosing the number of control frequencies from specified deviation and ω_u. The particular requirement which is tentatively set at the start of a design cannot ordinarily be met exactly, because control frequencies occur in integral numbers only. The curves of Fig. 4.14.2 serve to help in the choice of the number of control frequencies, then the formulas of Tabulation 4.14.2 may be used to compute the precise deviation specified by U after the number of control frequencies is chosen. This additional computation determines $Z(0)$ and so R_0/R of the $Z(x)$ function, i.e., the specification of the $Z(x)$ function is thereby completed.

TABULATION 4.14.2

Number of $Z(x)$ control
frequencies
geometric-mean deviation $\sqrt{1 - 1/U^4}$*

0	K
1	$x_{uz}{}^2 \dfrac{1}{x_1{}^4}$
2	$x_{uz}{}^3 \dfrac{1}{x_2{}^4}$
3	$x_{uz}{}^4 \dfrac{1}{(x_1 x_3)^4}$
4	$x_{uz}{}^5 \dfrac{1}{(x_2 x_4)^4}$
5	$x_{uz}{}^6 \dfrac{1}{(x_1 x_3 x_5)^4}$
6	$x_{uz}{}^7 \dfrac{1}{(x_2 x_4 x_6)^4}$
7	$x_{uz}{}^8 \dfrac{1}{(x_1 x_3 x_5 x_7)^4}$

$$* U = \left[\begin{array}{l} Z(0) = R_0/R \text{ if } Z(0) > 1 \\ 1/Z(0) = R/R_0 \text{ if } Z(0) < 1 \end{array} \right.$$

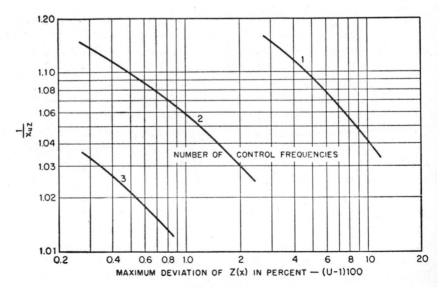

Fig. 4.14.2

4.15 Location of control frequencies and poles of flat transfer loss

The realization of a flat loss transfer function requires geometric-mean variation of $H(x)$ (Fig. 4.13.1). The crossings of $H(x)$ and the unity line, and so the poles of $A_I(x)$, as well as the pass band $A_I(x)$ control frequencies may be located uniformly on an F scale in a manner similar to the treatment of $Z(x)$ of the preceding section.

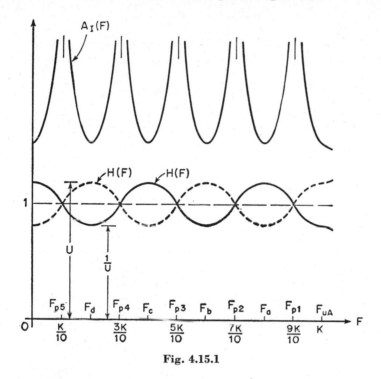

Fig. 4.15.1

The pass-band control frequencies are distributed uniformly on the F scale over the range $0 \leq F \leq K$ (see F_a, F_b, F_c, and F_d of Fig. 4.15.1). The formula for the transformation from the F scale to x scale values of these control frequencies is, for n controls.

$$x_{n+1-i} = \operatorname{sn} \frac{iK}{n+1} \qquad (1 \leq i \leq n) \quad (4.15.1)$$

The poles of $A_I(x)$, i.e., unit values of $H(x)$, transfer from the block region to the pass band and then to the F scale, first by a reciprocal to the pass band, and then through an elliptic sine transformation. The poles of $A_I(x)$, when located on the F scale, appear in the same pattern of uniformity (half intervals at the beginning and end of $0 \leq F \leq K$) as do the unit values of $Z(x)$ (see Fig. 4.15.1). The formula which specifies the complete transformation from the uniformly located poles of $A_I(x)$ on the F scale to the pass band of the x scale is

$$x_{p[2(n-i)+3]} = \frac{1}{(1/x_{uA}) \operatorname{sn}[(2i-1)K/2(n+1)]} \quad (1 \leq i \leq n+1) \quad (4.15.2)$$

The design approach to the location of transfer-loss controls is to specify x_{uA} and the minimum loss above x_{uA}, and from these two values

TABULATION 4.15.1

Number of $A_I(x)$ control frequencies, flat loss	$\sqrt{1 - 1/U_A{}^4}$*
0	K
1	$\dfrac{1}{x_{uA}{}^2} x_a{}^4$
2	$\dfrac{1}{x_{uA}{}^3} x_b{}^4$
3	$\dfrac{1}{x_{uA}{}^4} x_a{}^4 x_c{}^4$
4	$\dfrac{1}{x_{uA}{}^5} x_b{}^4 x_d{}^4$
5	$\dfrac{1}{x_{uA}{}^6} x_a{}^4 x_c{}^4 x_e{}^4$
6	$\dfrac{1}{x_{uA}{}^7} x_b{}^4 x_d{}^4 x_f{}^4$
7	$\dfrac{1}{x_{uA}{}^8} x_a{}^4 x_c{}^4 x_e{}^4 x_g{}^4$

$$* \; U_A = H(\infty) = \frac{\epsilon^{A_I(\infty)} + 1}{\epsilon^{A_I(\infty)} - 1}, \quad \text{or} \quad A_I(\infty) = \ln\left|\frac{1 + U_A}{1 - U_A}\right|$$

$A_I(x)$ decibels $= 8.686 A_I(x)$ nepers

to determine the number and location of the poles of $A_I(x)$ and the control frequencies. In this connection the formulas of Tabulation 4.15.1 are useful. The curves of Fig. 4.15.2 are a graphical representation of the formulas of this tabulation. The curves are useful for determining the number of control frequencies required to maintain any desired flat loss above x_{uA}.

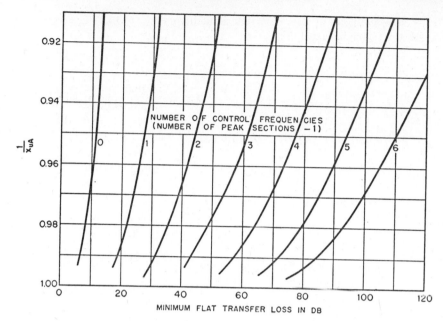

Fig. 4.15.2

Example 4.15.1 .

A low-pass filter is to maintain a flat transfer loss of not less than 80 db above 53.12 kc. Cutoff is at $f_0 = 48.5$ kc. Determine the pass-band control frequencies and the poles of transfer loss.

Solution

The value of $1/x_{uA}$ is

$$\frac{1}{x_{uA}} = \frac{\omega_0}{\omega_{uA}} = \frac{f_0}{f_{uA}} = \frac{48.5}{53.12} = 0.913$$

From the curves of Fig. 4.15.2, four control frequencies are required to keep the transfer loss above 80 db. Entering Tabulation 4.14.1 corresponding to

$$\Theta = \sin^{-1}\frac{1}{x_{uA}} = \sin^{-1} 0.913 = 65.9°$$

and $n = 4$, the control frequencies are, from Eq. (4.15.1),

$$x_a = \operatorname{sn} 4K/5 = 0.981, \quad f_a = 48.5(0.981) = 47.58 \text{ kc}$$
$$x_b = \operatorname{sn} 3K/5 = 0.910, \quad f_b = 48.5(0.910) = 44.13 \text{ kc}$$
$$x_c = \operatorname{sn} 2K/5 = 0.746, \quad f_c = 48.5(0.746) = 36.18 \text{ kc}$$
$$x_d = \operatorname{sn} K/5 = 0.440, \quad f_d = 48.5(0.440) = 21.34 \text{ kc}$$

The five poles of $A_I(x)$ are determined from Eq. (4.15.2) in accordance with the following schedule:

$$x_{p1} = \frac{1}{0.913 \ \text{sn} \ (9K/10)} = \frac{1}{0.913(0.995)},$$

$$f_{p1} = \frac{48.5}{0.913(0.995)} = 53.4 \ \text{kc}$$

$$x_{p2} = \frac{1}{0.913 \ \text{sn} \ (7K/10)} = \frac{1}{0.913(0.954)},$$

$$f_{p2} = \frac{48.5}{0.913(0.954)} = 55.6 \ \text{kc}$$

$$x_{p3} = \frac{1}{0.913 \ \text{sn} \ (5K/10)} = \frac{1}{0.913(0.843)},$$

$$f_{p3} = \frac{48.5}{0.913(0.843)} = 63.0 \ \text{kc}$$

$$x_{p4} = \frac{1}{0.913 \ \text{sn} \ (3K/10)} = \frac{1}{0.913(0.614)},$$

$$f_{p4} = \frac{48.5}{0.913(0.614)} = 86.5 \ \text{kc}$$

$$x_{p5} = \frac{1}{0.913 \ \text{sn} \ (K/10)} = \frac{1}{0.913(0.231)},$$

$$f_{p5} = \frac{48.5}{0.913(0.231)} = 230.0 \ \text{kc}$$

Note incidentally, either from the curves of Fig. 4.15.2 or from the formulas of Tabulation 4.15.1, that this filter with four $A_I(x)$ controls will produce a flat loss of 89 db.

Once the number and location of the control frequencies of $A_I(x)$ are known, the flat loss which the filter will exhibit may be computed. From this flat loss $U = H(\infty)$ can be computed (see Tabulation 4.15.1 for the formula). The factor $\sqrt{k_x k_y}$ (or m) of $H(x)$ as given in Tabulation 3.6.1 can then be computed to complete the determination of the ratio function $H(x)$ and so, of course, the transfer loss $A_I(x)$.

4.16 Determination of lattice which has a specified transfer loss and image impedance

This section includes an example of determination of the symmetric lattice which will exhibit a specified image impedance and transfer loss characteristic. In a sense this example epitomizes all the preceding work of this book. The type of image impedance variation considered here is the geometric-mean variety. The transfer loss considered here is flat. A more general type of transfer loss is considered in the next section and in a subsequent chapter.

Example 4.16.1

Determine the symmetric lattice which has the following properties:

1. $f_0 = 48.5$ kc; $f_{uZ} = 46.88$ kc; $f_{uA} = 53.12$ kc;
   $x_{uZ} = f_{uZ}/f_0 = 0.966$; $1/x_{uA} = f_0/f_{uA} = 0.913$
2. $Z_I(x)$ must not differ from 600 ohms more than 2 per cent over the range $0 < x < x_{uZ}$.
3. $A_I(x)$ must not be less than 80 db over the range $x_{uA} \leq x$.

Solution

The number of control frequencies for the image impedance may be determined from Fig. 4.14.2 with $1/x_{uZ} = 1/0.966 = 1.0352$ and 2 per cent deviation. The chart indicates that 2 control frequencies must be used. These control frequencies have already been located in Example 4.14.1 as $f_1 = 50.4$ kc and $f_2 = 66.3$ kc. Use of the formula x_{uZ}^3/x_2^4 from Tabulation 4.14.2 or directly from Fig. 4.14.2 establishes the factor U as $U = 1.0175$. Further, if the lattice is to be such as to exhibit a pole of $Z(x)$ at cutoff, the three crossings of $Z_{\infty3}(x)$ and the unity line make $Z(0) = 1/U = 0.9828$ (see Fig. 4.16.1). The design resistance is specified then by $R_0 = RZ(0) = 589.68$ ohms. Incidentally note that the maximum deviation of $Z_{\infty3}(x)$ from unity, and so of $Z_I(x)$ from the terminating resistance $R = 600$ ohms, is, from the value of U, 1.75 per cent.

Consider the transfer loss next. Reference to Fig. 4.15.2 with $1/x_{uA} = 0.913$ shows that three control frequencies are not sufficient to give an 80 db flat transfer loss. Four control frequencies therefore must be used. These four control frequencies will bring the flat transfer loss to over 89 db, as the curves of Fig. 4.15.2 show.

The control frequencies are given in Example 4.15.1 as $f_a = 47.58$ kc, $f_b = 44.13$ kc, $f_c = 36.18$ kc, $f_d = 21.34$ kc, and are indicated on Fig. 4.16.1. These four control frequencies specify five poles of $A_I(x)$. These poles are given in Example 4.15.1 as $f_{p1} = 53.4$ kc, $f_{p2} = 55.6$ kc, $f_{p3} = 63.1$ kc, $f_{p4} = 86.5$ kc, $f_{p5} = 230$ kc. These poles are shown on Fig. 4.16.1.

From the equation at the bottom of Tabulation 4.15.1, the value of U_A may be obtained after first converting the 89 db to its equivalent value of 10.246 nepers. The result is $U_A = 1.00007262$. For the reactance patterns of Fig. 4.16.1, the ratio function has a pole at cutoff, i.e., $H(1) = \infty$. The five crossing of $H(x)$ and the unity line require, therefore, that $H(\infty) = 1/U_A$, which from the value of U_A already computed gives $H(\infty) = 0.999927386$.

One form of the network is given on Fig. 4.16.1. The element values of this network are computed next. First the reactance functions are

$$Z_x(\omega) = -j\omega k_x \frac{(\omega^2 - \omega_c^2)(\omega^2 - \omega_a^2)(\omega^2 - \omega_1^2)}{(\omega^2 - \omega_d^2)(\omega^2 - \omega_b^2)(\omega^2 - \omega_0^2)(\omega^2 - \omega_2^2)}$$

$$Z_y(\omega) = -j\omega k_y \frac{(\omega^2 - \omega_d^2)(\omega^2 - \omega_b^2)(\omega^2 - \omega_1^2)}{\omega^2(\omega^2 - \omega_c^2)(\omega^2 - \omega_a^2)(\omega^2 - \omega_2^2)}$$

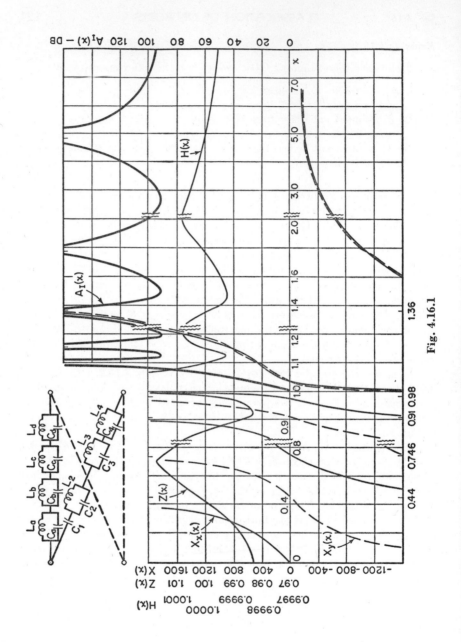

Fig. 4.16.1

122

From these functions,

$$H(\omega) = \sqrt{\frac{Z_x(\omega)}{Z_y(\omega)}} = \sqrt{\frac{k_x}{k_y}} \frac{\omega(\omega^2 - \omega_c^2)(\omega^2 - \omega_a^2)}{\sqrt{\omega^2 - \omega_0^2}\,(\omega^2 - \omega_d^2)(\omega^2 - \omega_b^2)}$$

from which

$$H(\infty) = \sqrt{\frac{k_x}{k_y}} = \frac{1}{U_A} = 0.999927386$$

and

$$Z(\omega) = \frac{\sqrt{k_x k_y}}{R} \frac{\omega_1^2 - \omega^2}{\sqrt{\omega_0^2 - \omega^2}\,(\omega_2^2 - \omega^2)}$$

from which

$$Z(0) = \frac{1}{U} = \frac{\sqrt{k_x k_y}}{R} \frac{\omega_1^2}{\omega_0 \omega_2^2} = 0.9828$$

The constants k_x and k_y are thereby determined as

$$k_x = \sqrt{k_x k_y} \sqrt{\frac{k_x}{k_y}} = \frac{R \omega_0 \omega_2^2}{U_A U \omega_1^2} = 3.109373 \times 10^8$$

$$k_y = \sqrt{k_x k_y} \sqrt{\frac{k_y}{k_x}} = \frac{U_A R \omega_0 \omega_2^2}{U \omega_1^2} = 3.109825 \times 10^8$$

Comparison of Eq. (1.5.29) and the foregoing equation for $Z_x(\omega)$ shows that $k_x = 1/C_\infty$. The element values of the series arm of the lattice are then from Eq. (1.5.30), in farads and henries,

$$C_a = \frac{(\omega_d^2 - \omega_b^2)(\omega_d^2 - \omega_0^2)(\omega_d^2 - \omega_2^2)}{k_x(\omega_d^2 - \omega_c^2)(\omega_d^2 - \omega_a^2)(\omega_d^2 - \omega_1^2)} = 1.114 \times 10^{-8}$$

$$L_a = \frac{1}{C_a \omega_d^2} = 0.197$$

$$C_b = \frac{(\omega_b^2 - \omega_d^2)(\omega_b^2 - \omega_0^2)(\omega_b^2 - \omega_2^2)}{k_x(\omega_b^2 - \omega_c^2)(\omega_b^2 - \omega_a^2)(\omega_b^2 - \omega_1^2)} = 3.972 \times 10^{-8}$$

$$L_b = \frac{1}{C_b \omega_b^2} = 0.0129$$

$$C_c = \frac{(\omega_0^2 - \omega_d^2)(\omega_0^2 - \omega_b^2)(\omega_0^2 - \omega_2^2)}{k_x(\omega_0^2 - \omega_c^2)(\omega_0^2 - \omega_a^2)(\omega_0^2 - \omega_1^2)} = 2.912 \times 10^{-7}$$

$$L_c = \frac{1}{C_c \omega_0^2} = 1.460 \times 10^{-3}$$

$$C_d = \frac{(\omega_2^2 - \omega_d^2)(\omega_2^2 - \omega_b^2)(\omega_2^2 - \omega_0^2)}{k_x(\omega_2^2 - \omega_c^2)(\omega_2^2 - \omega_a^2)(\omega_2^2 - \omega_1^2)} = 5.192 \times 10^{-9}$$

$$L_d = \frac{1}{C_d \omega_2^2} = 4.381 \times 10^{-2}$$

Comparison of Eq. (1.5.19) and the foregoing equation for $Z_y(\omega)$ indicates that $k_y = 1/C_\infty$. Then from Eq. (1.5.21), C_1 of the lattice arm of the network of Fig. 4.16.1 is

$$C_1 = \frac{\omega_c{}^2\omega_a{}^2\omega_2{}^2}{k_y\omega_d{}^2\omega_b{}^2\omega_1{}^2} = 1.859 \times 10^{-8}$$

Then from Eq. (1.5.20) the other element values of the lattice arm are

$$C_2 = \frac{\omega_c{}^2(\omega_c{}^2 - \omega_a{}^2)(\omega_c{}^2 - \omega_2{}^2)}{k_y(\omega_c{}^2 - \omega_d{}^2)(\omega_c{}^2 - \omega_b{}^2)(\omega_c{}^2 - \omega_1{}^2)} = 1.849 \times 10^{-8}$$

$$L_2 = \frac{1}{\omega_c{}^2 C_2} = 4.132 \times 10^{-2}$$

$$C_3 = \frac{\omega_a{}^2(\omega_a{}^2 - \omega_c{}^2)(\omega_a{}^2 - \omega_2{}^2)}{k_y(\omega_a{}^2 - \omega_d{}^2)(\omega_a{}^2 - \omega_b{}^2)(\omega_a{}^2 - \omega_1{}^2)} = 1.101 \times 10^{-7}$$

$$L_3 = \frac{1}{\omega_a{}^2 C_3} = 4.713 \times 10^{-3}$$

$$C_4 = \frac{\omega_2{}^2(\omega_2{}^2 - \omega_c{}^2)(\omega_2{}^2 - \omega_a{}^2)}{k_y(\omega_2{}^2 - \omega_d{}^2)(\omega_2{}^2 - \omega_b{}^2)(\omega_2{}^2 - \omega_1{}^2)} = 5.196 \times 10^{-9}$$

$$L_4 = \frac{1}{\omega_2{}^2 C_4} = 4.378 \times 10^{-2}$$

4.17 Transfer loss, nonflat

A flat loss transfer function has no, or little, practical utility. All communication systems are designed in terms of a finite band of frequencies and there is little interest in the response of the system outside of the total frequency range of the transmitted signals. For example, there is no point in maintaining a high transfer loss far above the highest frequency which must be blocked by a low-pass filter. Indeed it is desirable not to do so since the filter can be structurally simplified and so made less expensive if high loss is not maintained for very high frequencies.

Location of the poles for a flat transfer loss may be useful on occasions as a first estimate, to be followed by trial and error relocation of these poles to the positions which specify the desired loss. Following the location of the poles of $A_I(x)$ by whatever means it may be accomplished, the pass-band control frequencies, up to four in number, may be determined from the formulas of Tabulation 4.17.1. These formulas serve to handle fairly elaborate situations. In a subsequent chapter, at filter with more than five poles of $A_I(x)$ is designed, thus indicating an alternative method of handling designs even more elaborate than can be treated by way of Tabulation 4.17.1 or any method presented in the preceding discussion.

TABULATION 4.17.1

FORMULAS FOR THE CONTROL FREQUENCIES OF LOW-PASS
FILTERS WITH NO TO FIVE POLES OF TRANSFER LOSS

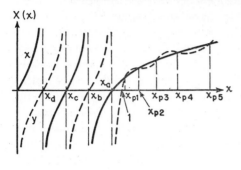 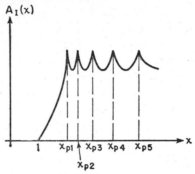

$$m_n = \sqrt{1 - 1/x_{pn}^2} \quad (n = 1,2,3,4,5)$$

$$k \text{ peaks: } (m_{k+j} = 0, j = 1, 2, \ldots, k + j \leq 5)$$

$$A = m_1 + m_2 + m_3 + m_4 + m_5$$

$$B = m_1m_2 + m_1m_3 + m_1m_4 + m_1m_5 + m_2m_3 + m_2m_4 + m_2m_5$$
$$+ m_3m_4 + m_3m_5 + m_4m_5$$

$$C = m_1m_2m_3 + m_1m_2m_4 + m_1m_2m_5 + m_1m_3m_4 + m_1m_3m_5$$
$$+ m_1m_4m_5 + m_2m_3m_4 + m_2m_3m_5 + m_2m_4m_5 + m_3m_4m_5$$

$$D = m_1m_2m_3m_4 + m_1m_2m_3m_5 + m_1m_2m_4m_5$$
$$+ m_1m_3m_4m_5 + m_2m_3m_4m_5$$

$$E = m_1m_2m_3m_4m_5$$

$$x_a^2 = \frac{2}{B + \sqrt{B^2 - 4D} + 2} \qquad x_c^2 = \frac{2}{B - \sqrt{B^2 - 4D} + 2}$$

$$x_b^2 = \frac{2A}{C + \sqrt{C^2 - 4AE} + 2A} \qquad x_d^2 = \frac{2A}{C - \sqrt{C^2 - 4AE} + 2A}$$

4.18 Cascading of lattice networks to form filters

The design of communication systems is based largely on designing four-terminal networks with various electrical properties and then combining these 4TN in useful ways. Even in the design of the component 4TN, many of the desired results are obtained by interconnecting 4TN having various characteristics. Filter design is certainly no exception to the general situation.

It is common practice to cascade simple 4TN with simple electrical characteristics, to form 4TN with elaborate electrical properties and high over-all structural complexity. The basic reason for this forming of complex 4TN in terms of interconnection of simple ones is largely a matter of forming the physical systems so that they can be controlled with sufficient precision that mathematical predictions of behavior and measured behavior correspond to a high degree of accuracy. The more elaborate the electric network the greater are the uncontrollable and unpredictable parasitics—capacitive, inductive, and dissipative. Shielding and, where possible, incorporation of inevitable parasitics into the network design help in overcoming these difficulties to some extent. The residue, however, is always troublesome if an elaborate network is built as, say, a single lattice rather than a combination of simple lattices which can be electrically separated from each other except for specifically desired relationships.

In terms of what is presented in the preceding chapters, it is possible to form a 4TN with a low-pass transfer loss of practically any pattern desired by cascading simple lattice structures. These simple lattice structures must have the same pass band and block region, of course. Unfortunately they must also have the same image impedance if mathematical predictions are to be practical in complexity and accuracy. As seen in the preceding discussions, as the image impedance is made to approximate more nearly the terminating resistance R, the number of block-band controls increases. This increase in turn requires incorporation of more network elements and so more expense in realizing the network. The next two chapters present the means of reducing the complexity of the component 4TN rather effectively where the filter can be used in ladder rather than lattice form. If the lattice must be used, some added complexity for impedance control is unavoidable.

Problems

4.1 Make a series of diagrams similar to those of Fig. 4.2.2 for a group VIII of an extension of the network combinations of Tabulation 4.2.1.

4.2 Establish the properties of Eq. (4.3.3) which are indicated in the discussion following this equation.

4.3 Verify the first two entries in Tabulation 4.2.2 by means of reactance sketches, location of control frequencies, etc.

4.4 Show that the formulas for $Z_{02}(x)$ and $Z_{\infty 2}(x)$ as given on Fig. 4.4.1 are correct.

4.5 Discuss in full detail, proving each conclusion, case 1 of Sec. 4.4.

4.6 From the derivative of Eq. (4.4.1) show that for $1 < x_1 < \sqrt{2}$ the minima are at $x = 0$ and $x = 1$, and the maximum is located by Eq. (4.4.2).

4.7 Prove that Eq. (4.4.8) has the properties indicated in Sec. 4.4.

4.8 Establish the general pattern of location of the parameter m in numerator or denominator of $H(x)$ such that $H(\infty) = m$ or $1/m$ and such that $m < 1$ allows the maximum number of unit values of $H(x)$.

4.9 The parameter m of Fig. 4.5.1 can be expressed in terms of the two C parameters of the $X_{L10}X_{C00}$ network. Show how.

4.10 The parameter R_0 may be expressed in terms of the element values of, say, the $X_{L10}X_{C00}$ network. Show how.

4.11 Show that if $1 > x_a > 1/\sqrt{2}$ then $1 > 2x_a \sqrt{1 - x_a^2} > 0$, and hence that $H(x_m) > m$ as indicated by Eqs. (4.6.3).

4.12 Show, by equating Eq. (4.6.1) to unity, that the value of x which satisfies this formula is real for $1 > x_a > 1/\sqrt{2}$ if and only if $1 > m > 2x_a \sqrt{1 - x_a^2}$.

4.13 Equations (4.6.8) define x_{p1} and x_{p2} in terms of m and x_a implicitly. Obtain formulas for these poles of transfer loss explicitly from Eqs. (4.6.8). (a) Establish an inequality pattern for x_a and m so that x_{p1} and x_{p2} are real and greater than 1. (b) Repeat part (a) but for only x_{p1} or x_{p2} real and so only one pole of $A_I(x)$ rather than two. (c) Repeat to establish the inequality relations of x_a and m so that neither x_{p1} nor x_{p2} is real.

4.14 Establish the formulas for m_1 and m_2 in terms of x_a and m.

4.15 Suppose that cutoff ω_0 is 5×10^5, $H(x_m) = 1.5$, $L_1 = 10$ μh, $x_{p1} = 1.2$, and $x_{p2} = 1.4$. Determine the element values of the $X_{L11}X_{C01}$ network.

4.16 The ratio function is to vary so that the maximum value and limiting value $(x = \infty)$ are reciprocals, $1/m$ and m respectively (Fig. 4.6.1b). (a) If $x_{p1} = 1.2$ and $x_{p2} = 1.3$, determine x_a and m, m_1 and m_2. Sketch the block region curve of $H(x)$ for the $X_{L10}X_{C11}$ and $X_{C01}X_{L11}$ networks. (b) If $x_u = 0.4$ and $m = 0.8$, determine x_{p1} and x_{p2}. Sketch the $H(x)$ function for the $X_{C11}X_{L10}$ and $X_{L11}X_{C01}$ networks.

4.17 A "flat" transfer loss of 20 db is desired from a lattice, $A_I(x_m) = A_I(\infty)$. Determine the location of the two poles of $A_I(x)$ and the location of the pass-band control frequency. Determine the first useful frequency x_u, where $A_I(x_u) = A_I(x_m)$.

4.18 Plot a family of curves of $B_I(x)$ for the networks $X_{C01}X_{L00}$ and $X_{C00}X_{L10}$. Use the m values 0.8, 0.9, 1.0, 1.1, and 1.2. Plot for the pass band only.

4.19 Plot a family of curves of $B_I(x)$ for the networks $X_{L11}X_{C01}$ and $X_{L10}X_{C11}$. Let $x_a = 0.8$, $m = 0.8$, 0.9, 1.0, 1.1, and 1.2. Plot for the pass band only.

4.20 Determine element value formulas for the $X_{C00}X_{L10}$ and $X_{C01}X_{L00}$ networks by the method of Sec. 4.11.

4.21 Determine element value formulas for the $X_{C01}X_{L11}$ network for the control frequency in the pass band and in the block band by the method of Sec. 4.12.

4.22 Determine the element values of the lattice network, $X_{L11}X_{C01}$ type, which has two poles of $A_I(x)$. The minimum flat loss is 20 db, $\omega_0 = 500,000$, $R_0 = 500$ ohms. Find x_u for both the transfer loss and the impedance function.

4.23 The poles of $A_I(x)$ are located at $x_{p1} = 1.1$, $x_{p2} = 1.5$, $X_{C11}X_{L10}$ network, $R_0 = 100$ ohms, and $\omega_0 = 10^6$. Determine the element values of the network. Plot $A_I(x)$. Find x_u for both the $A_I(x)$ and $Z(x)$ functions.

4.24 Plot the integrand $1/\sqrt{1 - x_u{}^2 \sin^2 \phi}$ over the range of ϕ, $0 \le \phi \le \pi$ for $x_u = 0.9$. Integrate this result graphically (area under curve) and deduce that values of $F(\phi, x_u)$ for $0 \le \phi \le \pi/2$ and a particular x_u are sufficient to determine $F(\phi, x_u)$ for that particular x_u and all values of ϕ. Note that the integrand is periodic but that $F(\phi, x_u)$ is not periodic, i.e., does not repeat but continues to increase in value.

4.25 Consider the relation $y = \sin x$. Show that the transformation of variable $x = az + b$ shifts and shrinks any particular period of the original function. Show how this change may be interpreted as a transfer of unaltered ordinates to different abscissa positions.

4.26 Suppose $x_u = \omega_u/\omega_0 = 0.99$. Locate the $Z(x)$ block-band controls and the $Z(x) = 1$ frequencies of the pass band of a low-pass filter with four control frequencies for geometric-mean variation of $Z(x)$. The cutoff is at $\omega_0 = 100,000$. Establish the impedance function $Z(x)$ where $Z(1) = 0$.

4.27 If the maximum deviation must not be less than $U - 1 = 0.4$ and if $\omega_0 = 3 \times 10^6$ and $\omega_{uZ} = 2.82 \times 10^6$, determine the location of the critical $[Z(x) = 1]$ and control frequencies of $Z(x)$. Establish the impedance function $Z(x)$ when $Z(1) = \infty$.

4.28 A low-pass filter is to maintain a flat loss value above $\omega_{uA} = 2.82 \times 10^6$ of not less than 90 db. Cutoff is at $\omega_0 = 3 \times 10^6$. Determine the pass-band control frequencies and the poles of $A_I(x)$. Establish the ratio function $H(x)$ if $H(1) = 0$.

4.29 Determine the element values of the lattice network which has the properties required in Example 4.16.1, with $Z(1) = 0$ and $H(1) = 0$.

4.30 Determine the three lattice networks which may be cascaded to produce the same image impedance and transfer loss as the one specified by Example 4.16.1. One network should exhibit the poles at $f_{p1} = 53.4$ kc and $f_{p2} = 55.6$ kc, a second lattice the poles at $f_{p3} = 63.0$ kc and $f_{p4} = 86.5$ kc, and the third lattice the pole at $f_{p5} = 230.0$ kc.

4.31 Determine the five lattice networks which when cascaded will exhibit the same transfer loss and image impedance as specified in Example 4.16.1.

4.32 Determine the parallel resonator type, symmetric lattice fixed by $H_{\infty 4}(x)$, $Z_{\infty 2}(x)$, $x_{p1} = 1.03$, $x_{p2} = 1.05$, $x_{p3} = 1.10$, $x_{p4} = 1.11$, $(U - 1)100 = 2.0$, $x_{uZ} = 0.925$.

CHAPTER FIVE

Some Aspects of Ladder-Lattice Equivalents

The lattice network is not always the most convenient form in which to build a filter network. The ladder is more convenient than the lattice, other things being equal, because, as the discussions of this and the next chapter show, fewer network elements are required to build the ladder. Also a ladder network may be constructed in unbalanced form and so fits naturally into unbalanced systems such as are employed widely in communication networks.

Ladder networks, as exemplified by π, T, or bridged-T networks or cascaded arrangements thereof, are the most commonly used alternatives to the lattice network. For this reason the only ladder networks considered in this book are those which may be formed by cascading the elementary ladder sections, namely, T or π, or the so-called half sections ⌐ or ⌐ formed by splitting a T or π along its center, or line of symmetry.

This chapter is a discussion of the aspects of ladder networks which have been found particularly useful in practice.

5.1 Symmetric lattice equivalent of a symmetric ladder

Ladder networks in unbalanced form (essentially such structures are three-terminal networks) are the only type considered here. The discussion of Sec. 3.1 and its associated diagrams of Fig. 3.1.4 present the pattern for establishing a symmetric lattice which has the same transmission property as any ladder network. The equivalent lattice is physical if the ladder is physical. The fact that $Z_y/2$ and $2Z_x$ (not Z_y and Z_x) are determined by Fig. 3.1.4 is easily compensated for as indicated by Fig. 5.1.1, namely, by proper multiplication or division of the element values by 2.

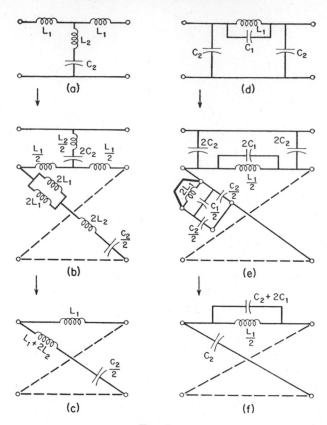

Fig. 5.1.1

5.2 *Alteration of a symmetric lattice by removal of a series impedance*

Since a symmetric lattice is balanced to ground, the pattern of Fig. 3.1.3 may be used on a 4TN such as illustrated by Fig. 5.2.1. Application of the diagram of Fig. 3.1.3b to Fig. 5.2.1b specifies the arrangement of Figs. 5.2.1c and e. Application of the diagram of Fig. 3.1.3a to Fig. 5.2.1b specifies the arrangement of Figs. 5.2.1d and f. These results of Figs. 5.2.1e and f combined as in Fig. 5.2.1g specify a symmetric lattice with the same transmission properties as the symmetric 4TN of Fig. 5.2.1a, i.e., a series impedance may be removed from all the elements of the symmetric lattice and placed in series externally in the manner of Fig. 5.2.1a. Also such an external imped-

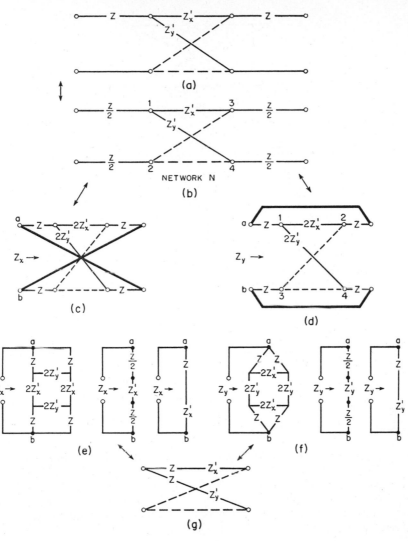

Fig. 5.2.1

ance as in Fig. 5.2.1a may be absorbed into the lattice as in Fig. 5.2.1g without altering the transmission properties.

Example 5.2.1

Determine a T network equivalent to the symmetric lattice shown in Fig. 5.2.2a.

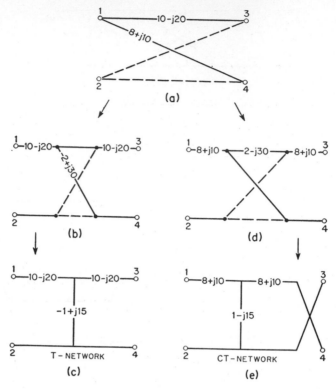

Fig. 5.2.2

Solution

The series removal of $10 - j20$ from each lattice element in accordance with Fig. 5.2.1 gives the network of Fig. 5.2.2.b. The parallel combination of the remaining lattice arms gives the nonphysical T network of Fig. 5.2.2c.

Alternatively, removal of $8 + j10$ from in series with each element of the lattice (Fig. 5.2.2d) and combination of the resulting parallel impedances gives the physical CT network of Fig. 5.2.2e.

5.3 Removal of shunt impedance from a lattice

Consider a common impedance in parallel with both Z'_x and Z'_y of a symmetric lattice as in Fig. 5.3.1f. Application of the equivalences of Fig. 3.1.3 applied to Fig. 5.3.1a as indicated by the sequence of transformations of Fig. 5.3.1 indicates that the common parallel impedance may be removed from the lattice and such an impedance

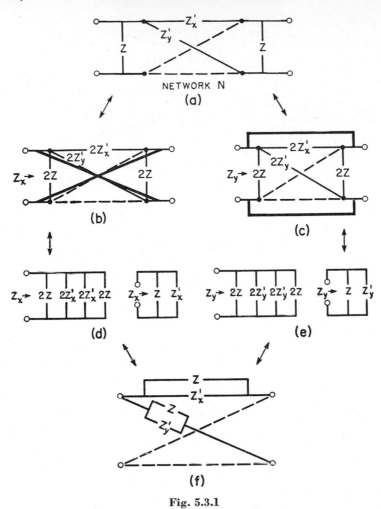

Fig. 5.3.1

placed in parallel with the input and output terminals without affecting the transmission properties of the network.

5.4 Symmetric ladder equivalent of a symmetric lattice

The two networks of Figs. 5.4.1e and 5.4.1g, and the manner of deducing them as equivalent to the network of Fig. 5.4.1a, indicate one way in which the removal of shunt and series impedances from a lattice may be used to establish ladder equivalents.

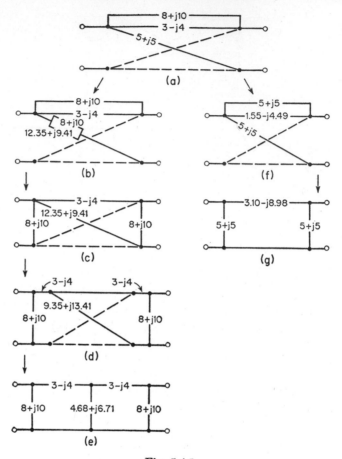

Fig. 5.4.1

5.5 Constant-k ladder section

Probably the most widely known of the various ladder sections is the constant-k or prototype as it is sometimes called. Mention is made of this section in Chapter 4. The basic properties of the constant-k section are: no image impedance or transfer loss controls with a pole of transfer loss at infinity. The reactance patterns, the curves of $Z(x)$, $B_I(x)$, $A_I(x)$, and the corresponding lattice are shown by Figs. 5.5.1a, b, c, e, f, and g. The ladder equivalents follow at once as shown of Figs. 5.5.1d and h if use is made of the equivalences described in Secs. 5.2 and 5.3 with the element values taken directly from Figs. 4.11.1a and b for $m = 1$.

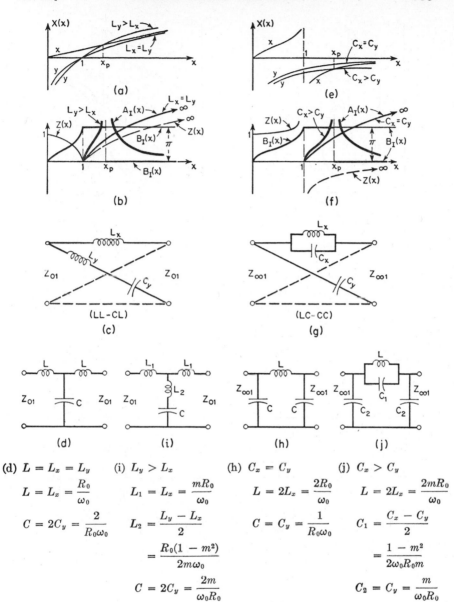

(d) $L = L_x = L_y$ (i) $L_y > L_x$ (h) $C_x = C_y$ (j) $C_x > C_y$

$$L = L_x = \frac{R_0}{\omega_0}$$ $$L_1 = L_x = \frac{mR_0}{\omega_0}$$ $$L = 2L_x = \frac{2R_0}{\omega_0}$$ $$L = 2L_x = \frac{2mR_0}{\omega_0}$$

$$C = 2C_y = \frac{2}{R_0\omega_0}$$ $$L_2 = \frac{L_y - L_x}{2}$$ $$C = C_y = \frac{1}{R_0\omega_0}$$ $$C_1 = \frac{C_x - C_y}{2}$$

$$= \frac{R_0(1 - m^2)}{2m\omega_0}$$ $$= \frac{1 - m^2}{2\omega_0 R_0 m}$$

$$C = 2C_y = \frac{2m}{\omega_0 R_0}$$ $$C_2 = C_y = \frac{m}{\omega_0 R_0}$$

Fig. 5.5.1

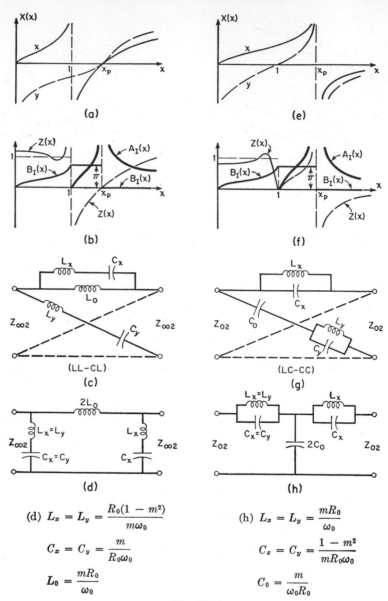

(a)

(b)

(c) (LL–CL)

(d)

(e)

(f)

(g) (LC–CC)

(h)

(d) $L_x = L_y = \dfrac{R_0(1 - m^2)}{m\omega_0}$

$C_x = C_y = \dfrac{m}{R_0\omega_0}$

$L_0 = \dfrac{mR_0}{\omega_0}$

(h) $L_x = L_y = \dfrac{mR_0}{\omega_0}$

$C_x = C_y = \dfrac{1 - m^2}{mR_0\omega_0}$

$C_0 = \dfrac{m}{\omega_0 R_0}$

Fig. 5.6.1

Alternatively, if $L_y > L_x$ of Fig. 5.5.1c and $C_x > C_y$ of Fig. 5.5.1g, the pole of transfer loss occurs at some frequency x_p other than at $x = \infty$. The ladder equivalents for such inductor and capacitor relations are shown by Figs. 5.5.1i and 5.5.1j. These two ladder sections do not appear in the usual classifications: constant-k, m-derived, etc. For lack of a better title the designation *peak section* is used here.

5.6 M-derived ladder section

The filter section designated as m-derived is well known and widely used. This section in lattice form has one image impedance control, no transfer loss controls, with one pole of transfer loss. The curves and diagrams of Fig. 5.6.1 give the salient features of the two m-derived filters. The element values are determined from the formulas given on Fig. 4.12.1b and a for the special case of $\omega_1 = \omega_p$, i.e., coincidence of the pole of transfer loss and the one impedance control frequency, and the transformations of Tabulation 1.6.1 are also required to establish Fig. 5.6.1d.

5.7 Lattice equivalent of certain 4TN: half-section technique

Important ladder-lattice (symmetric) equivalents may be established in terms of measurements or computations on half sections. These equivalents divide naturally into two groups on the basis of symmetry.

First consider balanced 4TN which are physically, or perhaps better structurally, symmetric. The interior nodes or junctions of such a network occur in integral multiples of 4, as indicated by Fig. 5.7.1b for a possible node group. Such a 4TN may be rotated about either axis of symmetry without affecting either its physical appearance or its electrical properties. A symmetric lattice is an example of such a network. A second group of these equivalences deals with unbalanced networks which may have only their input and output interchanged without affecting their physical appearance or electrical behavior. Such networks are exemplified by a T or π network. The nodes of such networks occur in integral multiples of 2 (see Fig. 5.7.1h).

Every 4-terminal network of these two structurally symmetric types, cross-connected elements of which occur only as shown by a–A', A–a' in Fig. 5.7.1b, can be separated into two identical half sections by bisecting along a line midway between input and output, so to speak. The manner in which the external short-circuiting connections of Figs. 3.1.3 and 3.1.4 and of Figs. 5.7.1a and 5.7.1d and the external connections of Figs. 5.7.1g and 5.7.1j apply an impedance-measuring voltage, and the resulting voltage relations in such structurally symmetric networks lead to the following conclusions:

1. In the network of Figs. 5.7.1a and 5.7.1b, all node pairs located such as a and A' as well as A and a' are at the same potential. The connections between all such nodes as these may therefore be opened.

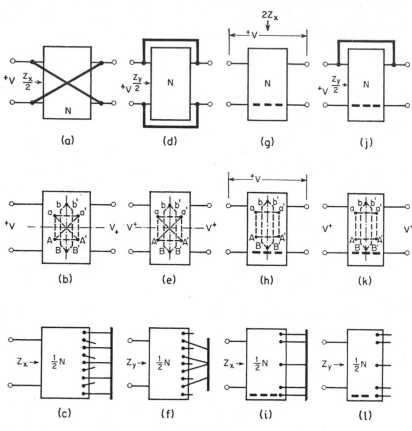

Fig. 5.7.1

All node pairs of this network such as a and a' (b and b') or A and A' (B and B') have such a voltage between them that the centers of the connectors a–a' (b–b') and A–A' (B–B') are at the same potential. These mid-points may therefore be connected without affecting the operation of the network.

2. In the network of Figs. 5.7.1d and 5.7.1e all node pairs such as a and a', A and A', b and b' etc. are at the same potential, and the connection between them may be opened. On the other hand, the cross-

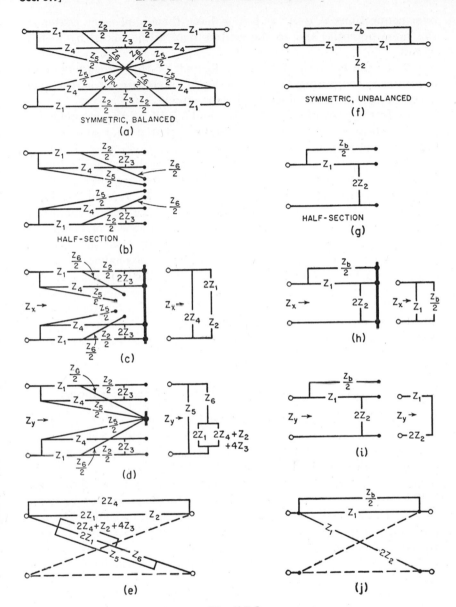

Fig. 5.7.2

over connections as a–A' and A–a' have their impedance centers at the same potential and so the centers may all be joined by a short circuit.

3. In the network of Figs. 5.7.1g and 5.7.1h, the centers of the impedances connecting the two network halves are all at the same potential and may be joined by a short circuit.

4. In the network of Figs. 5.7.1j and 5.7.1k, all the corresponding nodes such as a and a' are at the same potential, and so any direct connectors of such nodes may be opened.

Because of the voltage relations indicated in the foregoing, the two halves of structurally symmetric 4TN, under the external connections and voltage applications of Figs. 5.7.1a, 5.7.1d, 5.7.1g, and 5.7.1j may be completely isolated from each other by opening certain connectors and joining points on other connectors. The sequences of sketches of Fig. 5.7.1 indicate the equivalences which result from this isolating the two half sections and thereby placing these two halves in parallel as in Figs. 5.7.1a, 5.7.1d, and 5.7.1j, or in series as in Fig. 5.7.1g.

Two examples of the use of open and short-circuited half sections to establish a lattice equivalent are given by Fig. 5.7.2. These examples should serve to illustrate the use of the half section technique for obtaining the symmetric lattice equivalent of a structurally symmetric 4TN.

5.8 Low-pass ladder networks, some general considerations[1]

The ladder networks which are used for filtering are of a restricted class. Indeed, general practice restricts these ladder networks (for low pass) to certain tandem arrangements of the three basic structurally unsymmetric (half sections) 4TN of Figs. 5.8.1a, b, c. A detailed discussion of the properties of certain combinations of these basic half sections to form other useful *half sections* is given in Chapter 6. In the remaining discussion of this chapter certain combinations of these basic half sections, which produce *structurally symmetric* 4TN, are considered. The discussion at this point is further restricted to 4TN formed solely from a tandem combination of the basic half section of Fig. 5.8.1a alone or of Fig. 5.8.1b alone or of Fig. 5.8.1c alone, but never by a mixture of these networks. The manner of connecting these basic 4TN for this discussion (half sections) is indicated by the diagrams of Figs. 5.8.1e and f. Two groups of structurally symmetric (lattice) networks may thus be formed from each of the three basic,

[1] The basic ideas of Secs. 5.8 and 5.9 were developed by Dr. Tarik Özker in his Ph.D thesis of June 1951 at the University of Illinois.

structurally unsymmetric 4TN. Even with these restrictions, all 4TN combinations so formed are *not* low pass. The discussion here is restricted to the low-pass forms only.

Consider the set of half sections of Figs. 5.8.2a and d. Certain characteristics of the Z_y and Z_x impedances of the lattice equivalent to the full structurally symmetric ladder are evident at once. The lattice impedance Z_x is formed by short-circuiting the half sections and the lattice impedance Z_y is formed by the unaltered half section (see Sec. 5.7). Examination of these half sections (either open or short-circuited) shows that the 2TN are identical at each frequency for which any one

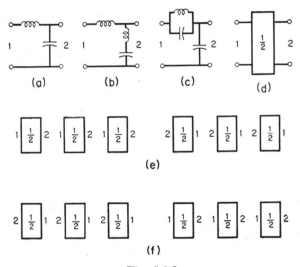

Fig. 5.8.1

of the parallel resonators resonates, simply because at such frequencies the networks are separated into two parts electrically, of which the input ones are identical. There is no information here as to the pole and zero pattern for Z_x and Z_y, but certainly $Z_x = Z_y$ and $H(x) = 1$ at each of the frequencies of resonance of the parallel resonators, with the possible exception of the first one at ω_1. Even in this case, however, the limit of the ratio of the continued fraction expansion for $Z_x(x)$ and $Z_y(x)$ as x approaches x_1 is found to be unity. Consequently, a pole of transfer loss is located at each of these frequencies. Furthermore, Z_x and Z_y, as formed from these half section ladders, cannot be equal at other than resonant frequencies of the parallel resonators, because at these other frequencies Z_x and Z_y differ by an impedance, which is always nonzero, across the nonzero terminals. Consequently, poles of transfer loss occur at the resonant frequencies of the parallel resonators, and at no other frequencies. Since the parallel resonators can be made to resonate at any desired frequencies, the poles of transfer loss can be located arbitrarily in the block band.

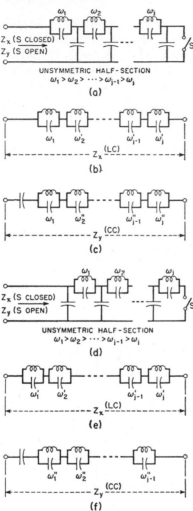

Fig. 5.8.2

Consider next the Foster forms of the lattice equivalent of the symmetric ladder (Fig. 5.8.2) obtained by the series and parallel resonator equivalents of Chapter 1. On the face of it, the poles and zeros of Z_x and Z_y have no certain relation to the poles of transfer loss. However, there is a definite relation between these critical frequencies, as the following argument shows. Since the impedances Z_x and Z_y formed from the half sections are never the same (equal) except at poles of transfer loss, and since a zero of both Z_x and Z_y or a pole of both Z_x and Z_y means that these impedances are the same (equal, and independent of the switch S of Fig. 5.8.2) it follows that *poles of transfer loss occur at all critical frequencies in the block region.* Note, however, that if the number of poles of transfer loss is greater (it cannot be less) than the number of block-band critical frequencies, poles of transfer loss must occur at other than block-band critical frequencies.

As an example of this last situation, a ladder half section, which exhibits three poles of transfer loss, is shown by Fig. 5.8.3, together with some of the low-pass reactance patterns which are available from this full ladder and its lattice equivalent for $\omega_1 > \omega_2 > \omega_3$, i.e., under the restrictions of this discussion. Note that the poles of transfer loss do not all occur at block-band control frequencies on

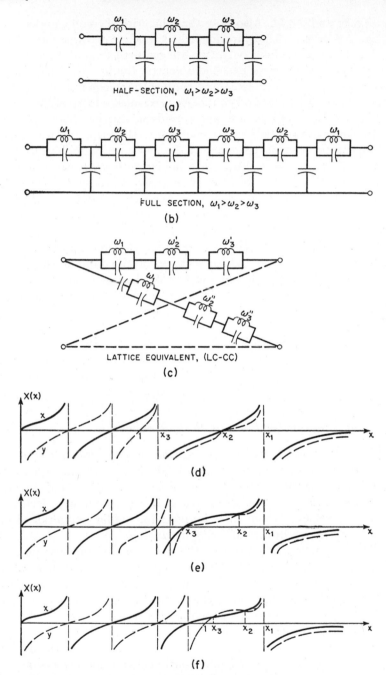

HALF-SECTION, $\omega_1 > \omega_2 > \omega_3$

(a)

FULL SECTION, $\omega_1 > \omega_2 > \omega_3$

(b)

LATTICE EQUIVALENT, (LC-CC)

(c)

(d)

(e)

(f)

Fig. 5.8.3

Figs. 5.8.3e and 5.8.3f. Also note that the critical frequency locations of Figs. 5.8.3e and 5.8.3f are inefficient in view of three and of four pass-band controls where only two are required to give three poles of transfer loss. These extra pass-band control frequencies serve no useful purpose then, since they cannot control the image impedance while located in the pass band and cannot be used most effectively to control the transfer loss, and so are not considered further here. The fact that the poles of transfer loss are confined to the region between cutoff and the highest control frequency of the block region follows from the fact that above ω_1 (or x_1) the whole ladder network is capacitive and is such that $|X_y| > |X_x|$ above x_1. Otherwise the poles of transfer loss x_2 and x_3 may be located at will between cutoff and x_1, subject to $x_2 > x_3$, and to coincidence of poles of transfer loss with whatever control frequencies exist in the region $1 < x < x_1$.

In general terms (merely illustrated incompletely in the foregoing discussion), for low-pass ladder sections of the kind illustrated by Figs. 5.8.1b, c, e, and f: (1) poles of transfer loss occur at the resonant frequencies of the resonators; (2) the block-band control frequencies (image impedance controls), less than or equal to the number of poles of transfer loss, all occur at poles of transfer loss; (3) a symmetric lattice which has reactance patterns of the form required for a particular type of ladder (parallel or series resonator type), and which has a pole of transfer loss at and only at each block-band critical frequency, always has a symmetric ladder equivalent.

5.9 Element values for low-pass ladder networks

Even after establishing the location of the control frequencies of a filter in terms of a lattice network which has a ladder equivalent, determination of the element values of the equivalent ladder from a set of simultaneous nonlinear equations is a formidable undertaking. A workable scheme which may be used for ladder networks of any complexity is given in the following discussion.

The partial fraction form of the equation for the driving-point impedance of a purely reactive 2TN (Chapter 1) is more or less natural if the network is to be realized or exhibited in terms of series or parallel resonators. On the other hand, the natural form of the equation for the driving-point impedance of such a 2TN in ladder form is the continued fraction. Indeed, the necessary and sufficient condition for a 4TN to have a ladder equivalent is that the equation for the driving-point impedance have a particular continued fraction expansion. For example, if the lattice is of the LC-CC class and if the ladder equivalent is to exist (Fig. 5.8.2) its continued fraction expansion must be of the form

$$Z_d(x) = -jx\left[\frac{A_1}{x^2 - x_{p1}^2} + \cfrac{1}{B_1 x^2 + \cfrac{1}{\cfrac{A_2}{x^2 - x_{p2}^2} + \cfrac{1}{B_2 x^2 + \ldots}}}\right] \quad (5.9.1)$$

or

$$Z_d(x) = -jx\left[\cfrac{1}{B_1 x^2 + \cfrac{1}{\cfrac{A_1}{x^2 - x_{p1}^2} + \cfrac{1}{B_2 x^2 + \cfrac{1}{\cfrac{A_2}{x^2 - x_{p2}^2} + \ldots}}}}\right] \quad (5.9.2)$$

depending, respectively, on whether a parallel resonator in series or a capacitor in shunt is at the input. The termination (last term) of these continued fraction expansions depends on the extent of the network. In any event, the expansions for $Z_x(x)$ and $Z_y(x)$ are identical except for the inclusion of one extra term in these impedance expressions.

One method of determining the element values of the ladder is largely a matter of establishing the proper continued fraction expansion. Once this expansion has been computed, the known locations of the poles of transfer loss (x_{pi}) permit evaluation of the ladder element values. The following example illustrates the technique more effectively than further word description could do.

Example 5.9.1

A low-pass lattice with poles of transfer loss at $x_{p1} = 5$ and $x_{p2} = 2$ is specified by (see Fig. 5.9.1a)

$$Z_x(x) = -jx\frac{x^2 - 4}{(x^2 - 0.54)(x^2 - 25)}$$

and

$$Z_y(x) = -jx\frac{(x^2 - 0.54)(x^2 - 4)}{x^2(x^2 - 1)(x^2 - 25)}$$

Determine the ladder network consisting of parallel resonators in series and capacitors in shunt.

Solution

Since $Z_y(x)$ is of higher degree than $Z_x(x)$, then $Z_y(x)$ contains all elements of $Z_x(x)$ plus at least one other. Furthermore, $Z_y(x)$ and $Z_x(x)$ have a common pole, so the ladder network has a parallel resonator in series at the input (see Fig. 5.9.1b) which resonates at $x_{p1}(x = 5)$.

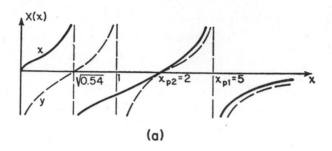

(a)

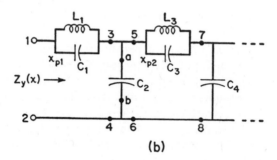

(b)

Fig. 5.9.1

The pole at x_{p1} may be extracted from $Z_y(x)$ by the method of partial fractions.[2] If this scheme is used, the residue of the pole at $x = 5$ is

$$A_1 = \frac{(x^2 - 0.54)(x^2 - 4)}{x^2(x^2 - 1)}\bigg|_{x=5} = 0.8561$$

This pole of residue A_1 should next be removed from $Z_y(x)$ as follows:

$$\frac{(x^2 - 0.54)(x^2 - 4)}{x^2(x^2 - 1)(x^2 - 25)} - \frac{0.8561}{x^2 - 25} = \frac{0.1439x^2 - 0.0864}{x^2(x^2 - 1)}$$

Therefore

$$Z_y(x) = -jx\frac{0.8561}{x^2 - 25} - jx\frac{0.1439x^2 - 0.0864}{x^2(x^2 - 1)}$$

[2] Reed and Reed, *Mathematical Methods in Electrical Engineering*, Harper & Brothers, New York, 1951, Chap. 5.

The last fraction of this last expression is the impedance looking into 3-4 of Fig. 5.9.1b, i.e.,

$$Z_{34}(x) = -jx \frac{0.1439x^2 - 0.0864}{x^2(x^2 - 1)}$$

Examination of Fig. 5.9.1b shows that at x_{p2}, since the L_3C_3 parallel resonator is open,

$$Z_{34}(x_{p2}) = -jx_{p2} \frac{1}{x_{p2}^2 \omega_0 C_2}$$

Equating these last two expressions gives

$$-jx \frac{1}{x^2 \omega_0 C_2}\bigg|_{x=2} = -jx \frac{0.1439x^2 - 0.0864}{x^2(x^2 - 1)}\bigg|_{x=2}$$

from which

$$\omega_0 C_2 = \frac{x^2 - 1}{0.1439x^2 - 0.0864}\bigg|_{x=2} = 6.13$$

Extracting the admittance of C_2 from the admittance Y_{34} gives the admittance $Y_{56}(x)$.

Thus, using $\omega_0 C_2$ as computed in the foregoing,

$$Y_{56}(x) = \frac{x^2(x^2 - 1)}{-jx(0.1439x^2 - 0.0864)} - \frac{x^2 \omega_0 C_2}{-jx}$$

$$= \frac{x^2(0.118x^2 - 0.471)}{-jx(0.1439x^2 - 0.0864)}$$

The reciprocal of this last result is

$$Z_{56}(x) = -j1.22x \frac{x^2 - 0.60}{x^2(x^2 - 4)}$$

The pole of this impedance should now be extracted by a second use of the method of partial fractions. At once

$$A_2 = \frac{x^2 - 0.60}{x^2}\bigg|_{x=2} = 0.850$$

The impedance $Z_{78}(x)$ is then

$$Z_{78}(x) = Z_{56}(x) - j1.22x \frac{0.850}{x^2 - 4}$$

$$= -j1.22x \frac{x^2 - 0.60}{x^2(x^2 - 4)} - j \frac{1.037x}{x^2 - 4} = \frac{1}{j5.46x}$$

This last computation completes the establishment of the continued fraction and indicates that the ladder network of Fig. 5.9.1b is the correct representation of $Z_y(x)$.

All the foregoing computations combined into the proper continued fraction give

$$Z_y(x) = \frac{-j0.8561x}{x^2 - 25} + \cfrac{1}{j6.13x + \cfrac{1}{\cfrac{-j1.037x}{x^2 - 4} + \cfrac{1}{j5.46x}}}$$

$$= Z_{13} + \cfrac{1}{Y_{ab} + \cfrac{1}{Z_{57} + \cfrac{1}{Y_{78}}}}$$

Determination of the element values of the ladder network follows at once from the fact that the admittance of a capacitor as a function of x is

$$Y_c(x) = j\omega_0 C x$$

and the impedance of a parallel resonator as a function of x is (the reactance formula of Fig. 1.1.1d transformed)

$$Z_p = \frac{-jx/\omega_0 C}{x^2 - 1/\omega_0 L \omega_0 C}$$

Comparison of the terms of the continued fraction expansion given in the foregoing for $Z_y(x)$ and these last two equations specify that

$$\omega_0 C_1 = \frac{1}{0.8561} = 1.17$$

$$\omega_0 C_2 = 6.13$$

$$\omega_0 C_3 = \frac{1}{1.037} = 0.964$$

$$\omega_0 C_4 = 5.46$$

$$\omega_0 L_1 = \frac{1}{25\omega_0 C_1} = \frac{0.8561}{25} = 0.0342$$

$$\omega_0 L_3 = \frac{1}{4\omega_0 C_3} = \frac{1.037}{4} = 0.259$$

The specification of a cutoff frequency then determines all the element values of the ladder network equivalent of $Z_y(x)$, and so the half section of the ladder equivalent. The network for $Z_x(x)$ is obtained by short-circuiting across 7-8 of $Z_y(x)$ of Fig. 5.9.1b.

If the lattice impedance functions $Z_x(x)$ and $Z_y(x)$ are to correspond to a half section with a leading capacitor such as that of Fig. 5.8.2d, the impedance into the ladder is, at the highest frequency pole of transfer loss, just that of the shunt capacitor at the input. Removal of this capacitor admittance first permits the use of the continued fraction expansion process of the preceding example.

A ladder equivalent involving series resonators in shunt and inductors in series may be handled precisely as in the foregoing except that the admittance functions $Y_x(x)$ and $Y_y(x)$ should be used.

One further brief comment should perhaps be made. Much work has been done in the past in deriving electric filters with the ladder as the starting structure. The constant-k, m-derived, and various multiple-m-derived filters all are such structures. Note, however, that the lattice technique given here and the technique given for establishing the ladder equivalents covers all the various derived networks plus many other possibilities. The notion of derived networks is, therefore, not considered in this book beyond naming some simple structures in correspondence with past designations.

Problems

5.1 (a) Verify the formulas (3.1.5) and (3.1.6) by use of the lattice-ladder equivalent of Fig. 3.1.4.

(b) Establish formulas for a symmetric lattice equivalent of a symmetric π by means of Fig. 3.1.4.

5.2 Establish formulas for the lattice equivalent of a symmetric bridged T by means of the equivalence of Fig. 3.1.4.

5.3 (a) Use the equivalence of Figs. 5.2.1a and 5.2.1g to establish the formulas for the elements of a symmetric T network which is equivalent to a lattice with impedances Z_x and Z_y.

(b) Repeat part (a) with Fig. 5.3.1 for a lattice-π combination.

5.4 (a) Show for a $X_{L00}X_{C01}$ lattice that $L_x > L_y$, $L_x = L_y$, and $L_x < L_y$ lead to three different situations in so far as a ladder equivalent exists. Sketch the $A_I(x)$, $B_I(x)$, $H(x)$, and $Z(x)$ curves for each of the structures. Note that $L_x = L_y$ gives the constant-k ladder and $L_x > L_y$ gives the m-derived.

(b) Repeat part (a) for the $X_{C00}X_{L10}$ lattice. Indicate the constant-k and the m-derived condition on the lattice.

5.5 Determine as many as possible (at least five) ladder equivalents of an $X_{L11}X_{C01}$ low-pass lattice. Give the conditions on the network elements and on the location of the poles of $A_I(x)$ for each case.

5.6 Repeat the preceding problem for the $X_{C11}X_{L10}$ low-pass lattice.

5.7 (a) Show that the driving-point impedances of the four 2TN of Figs. 5.7.1a, 5.7.1d, 5.7.1g, and 5.71j are as indicated.

(b) Show by considering the voltage relations on the interior of the balanced symmetric network of Figs. 5.7.1a and 5.7.1b that the driving-point impedance of the half section is as shown in Fig. 5.7.1c. The crossover connectors should be opened and the direct connectors short-circuited at their midpoints.

(c) Repeat part (b) for Fig. 5.7.1f.

(d) Repeat part (b) for Fig. 5.7.1i.

(e) Repeat part (b) for Fig. 5.7.1l.

5.8 Prove that the network transformations of Secs. 5.2 and 5.3 are valid by using the half section equivalences of Fig. 5.7.1.

5.9 Use the half section technique of Sec. 5.7 to show that the lattice of Fig. 5.4.1a is equivalent to the 4TN of Figs. 5.4.1e and 5.4.1g.

5.10 (a) Use the half section technique of Sec. 5.7 to show that the equivalences of Fig. 5.2.2 are valid.

(b) Repeat part (a) for Fig. 5.1.1.

5.11 Use the method of Sec. 5.7 to determine the two symmetric lattice from the half section of Fig. P.2.14.

5.12 Consider the two-ladder 4TN, formed by four of the basic sections of Fig. 5.81a connected as indicated by Fig. 5.8.1. Specify the pass and block characteristics.

5.13 Give in detail an argument to show that Z_x and Z_y cannot be equal at other than a resonant frequency of one of the parallel resonators of Fig. 5.8.2d. Show that they are equal at ω_1.

5.14 Show by means of the transformations of Chapter 1 (qualitatively) that the four networks shown for Z_x and Z_y on Fig. 5.8.2 are correct.

5.15 Consider the basic half section of Fig. 5.8.1b. Show for the two kinds of half sections formed from this basic half section, corresponding to Fig. 5.8.2, that $Z_x = Z_y$ at and only at the resonant frequencies of the shunt series resonators.

5.16 Establish the set of networks and reactance patterns corresponding to Fig. 5.8.3 for a half section as shown in Fig. 5.8.2d. Include three poles of transfer loss in the system.

5.17 Demonstrate that ladder equivalents of the form used here are derivable from the *LL-CL* and *LC-CC* lattice networks only.

5.18 Discuss in general terms, for three half sections of the form of Fig. 5.8.1b connected as in Fig. 5.8.1f, the full section as is done in Secs. 5.8 and 5.9.

5.19 Determine the ladder equivalent of the lattice of Example 5.9.1 in the form which arises from combinations of Fig. 5.8.1b.

CHAPTER SIX

Filter Terminating Half Sections

The troublesome and, in many designs, crippling effect of parasitic magnetic coupling and parasitic capacitive coupling which appears in extensive single-lattice networks frequently forces the realization of the physical network into the form of a cascade connection of simpler 4TN. The simpler 4TN which are cascaded are frequently reduced to the point of each unit producing only one pole of transfer loss. No problem arises in carrying out this simplification in so far as the transfer loss is concerned. Image impedance match, however, is a different matter. In order to avoid mismatch of image impedances at each junction of the cascaded 4TN, the image impedances of all the cascaded 4TN should be the same if symmetric networks are cascaded. On the other hand, unsymmetric ladder sections in the form of half sections are available which permit all the cascaded ladder sections, except two terminating ones, to be symmetric and to be reduced to the level of constant-k image impedance with or without a pole of transfer loss. The two unsymmetric half sections located at the ends of the filter then match the constant-k image impedance at the joining terminal pair and present, at the input and output of the filter, image impedances which are as elaborate as desired. Filters with different image impedances at the input and output may be formed in this manner by using different half sections.

The burden of elaborate image impedance requirement may thus be carried in the two terminating half sections only, thereby materially reducing the complexity of the network as a whole. The saving in number of network elements is appreciable and wherever a ladder network may be used the use of terminating half sections is worth while.

6.1 *Half-section transfer loss*

Since the transfer loss is not changed by an interchange of the two-terminal pairs of a 4TN, the tandem connection of two image impedance-matched half sections has a transfer loss of twice that of a half section; therefore, the transfer loss of a half section is *one-half* the transfer loss of the whole section constructed from two identical image impedance matched half sections.

The transfer loss characteristics of half sections are therefore not essentially different than for full sections.

6.2 Half section from $X_{L00}X_{C01}$ and $X_{L10}X_{C00}$ lattices (constant-k)

The low-pass half section of Fig. 6.2.1 leads to the symmetric lattice $X_{L00}X_{C01}$ if Z_x and Z_y are formed at the left-hand terminal pair by the method of Sec. 5.7. The symmetric lattice $X_{L10}X_{C00}$ arises from a similar treatment at the right pair of terminals.

The transfer loss of these half sections is half that of either lattice section, i.e., half the transfer loss of the $m = 1$ curve of Fig. 4.7.1.

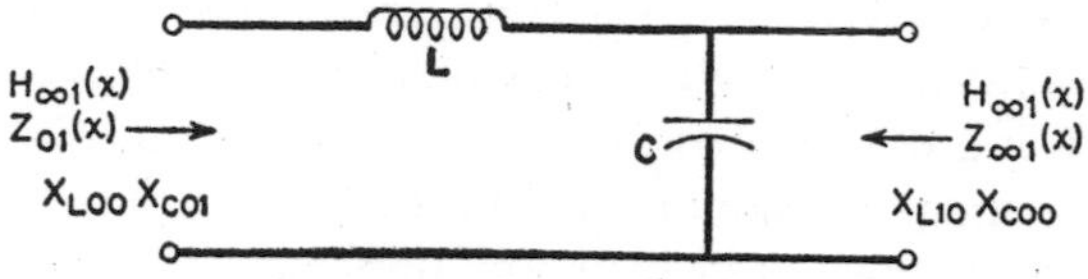

$$L = \frac{R_0}{\omega_0}, \quad C = \frac{1}{R_0\omega_0}$$

$$Z_{01}(x) = \frac{R_0}{R}\sqrt{1 - x^2}, \quad Z_{\infty 1}(x) = \frac{R_0}{R}\frac{1}{\sqrt{1 - x^2}}, \quad H_{\infty 1}(x) = \frac{x}{\sqrt{x^2 - 1}}$$

Fig. 6.2.1

The image impedance functions of the two lattice structures which may be formed from this half section are different. The image impedance functions of either end of the half section are, of course, the same as for the lattice formed at that end. These impedance functions are given in Fig. 5.5.1. Note that $L_x = L_y$ for Fig. 5.5.1c and $C_x = C_y$ for Fig. 5.5.1g. Evidently, the left terminal pair of the half section has the image impedance of Fig. 5.5.1b, i.e., Z_{01} (zero at cutoff and one crossing of the unity line). The right terminal pair has the image impedance function of Fig. 5.5.1f, i.e., $Z_{\infty 1}$ [a pole at cutoff and one unit value of $Z(x)$].

6.3 Half section from $X_{L10}X_{C11}$ and $X_{L10}X_{C00}$ lattices

The half section of Fig. 6.3.1 may be used to form two lattices, the $X_{L10}X_{C00}$ from the right terminal pair and that $X_{L10}X_{C11}$ from the left terminal pair. This fact specifies at once the image impedance characteristics of this half section. The impedance function Z_{02} is shown on Fig. 5.6.1f and $Z_{\infty 1}$ on Fig. 5.5.1f. For the network of

Fig. 5.6.1c, $C_x = C_y$ and $L_x = L_y$. Note that realization of the two possible unit values of $Z_{02}(x)$ restricts the location of x_p (Sec. 4.4).

Since the lattice $X_{L10}X_{C00}$, or the m-derived section of Fig. 5.6.1h, as derived from the cascading of two of the half sections of Fig. 6.3.1 always has one pole of transfer loss, the half section has a transfer loss of the same general form (one pole) but of half the magnitude (Fig. 4.7.1 from $m < 1$). The same conclusion follows from forming the $X_{L10}X_{C00}$ lattice or the peak section of Fig. 5.5.1j.

As an auxiliary idea of importance note that the two half sections of Figs. 6.2.1 and 6.3.1 may be cascaded by joining them at the $Z_{\infty 1}$

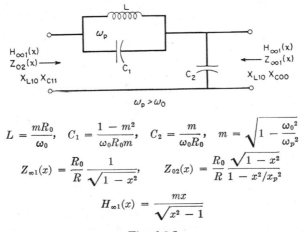

$$L = \frac{mR_0}{\omega_0}, \quad C_1 = \frac{1 - m^2}{\omega_0 R_0 m}, \quad C_2 = \frac{m}{\omega_0 R_0}, \quad m = \sqrt{1 - \frac{\omega_0^2}{\omega_p^2}}$$

$$Z_{\infty 1}(x) = \frac{R_0}{R} \frac{1}{\sqrt{1 - x^2}}, \qquad Z_{02}(x) = \frac{R_0}{R} \frac{\sqrt{1 - x^2}}{1 - x^2/x_p^2}$$

$$H_{\infty 1}(x) = \frac{mx}{\sqrt{x^2 - 1}}$$

Fig. 6.3.1

ends. The resulting unsymmetric half section presents a still different combination of impedance functions Z_{01} and Z_{02} and has a transfer function which is the sum of half the transfer loss of a constant-k section and half that of a peak section.

6.4 Half section from $X_{L00}X_{C01}$ and $X_{L11}X_{C01}$ lattices

The half section of Fig. 6.4.1 may be used to form the $X_{L00}X_{C01}$ lattice from the left-hand pair of terminals and the $X_{L11}X_{C01}$ lattice from the right-hand pair of terminals. The impedance functions of this half section are as shown on the figure. The location of x_p is restricted if $Z_{02}(x)$ is to be realized.

The transfer loss of the half section being considered here is the same as that of the half section of Fig. 6.3.1, namely, one-half the transfer loss of a peak section, or m-derived section (Fig. 4.7.1 for $m < 1$).

Evidently the half sections of Figs. 6.2.1 and 6.4.1 may be cascaded at the Z_{01} ends to form a section with the further impedance function combination of $Z_{\infty 1}$ and $Z_{\infty 2}$ at opposite ends. Such a network

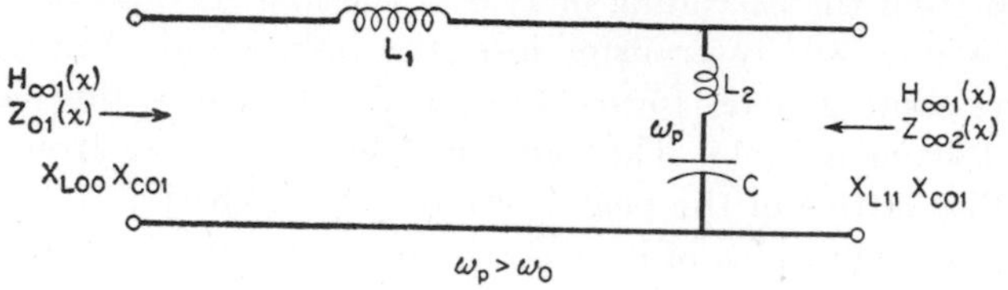

$$L_1 = \frac{mR_0}{\omega_0}, \quad L_2 = \frac{(1 - m^2)R_0}{m\omega_0} \quad C = \frac{m}{\omega_0 R_0}, \quad m = \sqrt{1 - \frac{\omega_0^2}{\omega_p^2}}$$

$$Z_{01}(x) = \frac{R_0}{R}\sqrt{1 - x^2}, \qquad Z_{\infty 2}(x) = \frac{R_0}{R}\frac{1 - x^2/x_p^2}{\sqrt{1 - x^2}}$$

$$H_{\infty 1}(x) = \frac{mx}{\sqrt{x^2 - 1}}$$

Fig. 6.4.1

combination has a transfer loss of one-half the sum of the transfer loss of a peak and a constant-k section.

6.5 Half section from $X_{L21}X_{C11}$ and $X_{L21}X_{C22}$ lattices

The half section represented by Fig. 6.5.1, if considered in terms of the open- and short-circuit scheme of Sec. 5.7, specifies either of the two symmetric lattices $X_{L21}X_{C11}$ or $X_{L21}X_{C22}$. This half section is a tandem combination of two of the simpler half sections of Fig. 6.3.1, but the connection is not one of image impedance match. As the following discussion demonstrates, this mismatch is effective in upgrading the image impedance into $Z_{\infty 3}$ at one end of the half section, and leaving the transfer loss unchanged as the sum of the transfer losses of the two component sections.

Consider first the transfer function. At once, from the discussion of Sec. 5.8, the half section of Fig. 6.5.1 has two poles of transfer loss, ω_{p1} and ω_{p3}. Furthermore, since the maximum-pole type of transfer functions, in terms of x, are specified by the poles of $A_I(x)$ and *not the form of network*, the two-pole $A_I(x)$ of the half section of Fig. 6.5.1 is just the sum of the transfer loss of two sections of the kind represented by Fig. 6.3.1.

Turn next to a consideration of the image impedances of the half section of Fig. 6.5.1. Viewed from the right, Z_x and Z_y are both capacitive at ω_{p3} and ω_{p1}. On the basis of the sketches suggested in

Problem 6.5, only one reactance pattern shows Z_x and Z_y both capacitive at ω_{p3} and ω_{p1}. This reactance pattern for which a pole of Z_x is cutoff has no control frequencies in the block region (Fig. 6.5.2a). The image impedance then at terminals 3–4 of Fig. 6.5.1 is of the $Z_{\infty 1}$ form.

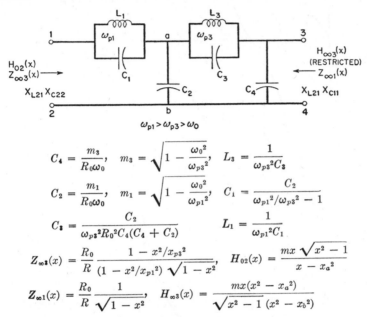

$$C_4 = \frac{m_3}{R_0 \omega_0}, \quad m_3 = \sqrt{1 - \frac{\omega_0^2}{\omega_{p3}^2}}, \quad L_3 = \frac{1}{\omega_{p3}^2 C_3}$$

$$C_2 = \frac{m_1}{R_0 \omega_0}, \quad m_1 = \sqrt{1 - \frac{\omega_0^2}{\omega_{p1}^2}}, \quad C_1 = \frac{C_2}{\omega_{p1}^2 / \omega_{p3}^2 - 1}$$

$$C_3 = \frac{C_2}{\omega_{p3}^2 R_0^2 C_4 (C_4 + C_2)} \qquad L_1 = \frac{1}{\omega_{p1}^2 C_1}$$

$$Z_{\infty 3}(x) = \frac{R_0}{R} \frac{1 - x^2/x_{p3}^2}{(1 - x^2/x_{p1}^2) \sqrt{1 - x^2}}, \quad H_{02}(x) = \frac{mx \sqrt{x^2 - 1}}{x - x_a^2}$$

$$Z_{\infty 1}(x) = \frac{R_0}{R} \frac{1}{\sqrt{1 - x^2}}, \quad H_{\infty 3}(x) = \frac{mx(x^2 - x_a^2)}{\sqrt{x^2 - 1} \, (x^2 - x_b^2)}$$

Fig. 6.5.1

Viewed from the left-hand end, the half section of Fig. 6.5.1 forms a symmetric lattice: (1) with two poles of transfer loss (at least one pass-band control); (2) with one of these poles at x_{p1}, a pole of both $X_x(x)$ and $X_y(x)$; and (3) with $|X_x(x)| < |X_y(x)|$ for $x > x_{p1} > x_{p3} > 1$ since for $x > x_{p1}$, $X_x(x)$ and $X_y(x)$ are both capacitive and $C_y < C_x$. The reactance patterns of Fig. 6.5.2b are thus indicated. The impedance function may thus be of the $Z_{\infty 3}(x)$ variety.

Determination of the six element values of the half section of Fig. 6.5.1 of necessity requires six independent relations which relate the network and reactance patterns of Fig. 6.5.2. Two of these relations are at once

$$\omega_{p3}^2 = \frac{1}{L_3 C_3} \tag{6.5.1}$$

$$\omega_{p1}^2 = \frac{1}{L_1 C_1} \tag{6.5.2}$$

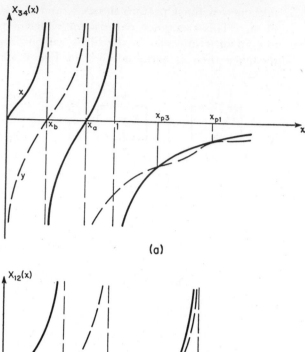

(a)

(b)

Fig. 6.5.2

A third relation arises from the fact that at ω_{p3} the L_3C_3 resonator opens, and (see Fig. 6.5.2) $Z_x(\omega_{p3})$ and $Z_y(\omega_{p3})$ of the $X_{L21}X_{C22}$ lattice both vanish, so that

$$Z_x(\omega_{p3}) = Z_y(\omega_{p3}) = 0$$

$$= \frac{1}{j\omega_{p3}C_2} + \frac{\omega_{p3}}{jC_1(\omega_{p3}{}^2 - \omega_{p1}{}^2)} \qquad (6.5.3)$$

A fourth relation arises from the requirement that cutoff occurs at a pole of $Z_y(\omega)$ (see Fig. 6.5.2). This requirement again specifies that the impedance to the right of the half section of Fig. 6.5.1 must have a pole at ω_0, otherwise $Z_y(\omega)$ would not have a pole at this frequency. Mathematically, this last requirement is specified by equating the admittance to the right of a–b of Fig. 6.5.1 to zero, i.e.,

$$0 = j\omega_0 C_2 + \frac{1}{1/j\omega_0 C_4 + \omega_0/jC_3(\omega_0{}^2 - \omega_{p3}{}^2)} \qquad (6.5.4)$$

A fifth relation arises from the condition that at ω_{p1} looking to the left from terminals 3–4 of Fig. 6.5.1 gives the image impedance at that frequency, because

$$Z_x(\omega_{p1}) = Z_y(\omega_{p1})$$

so
$$Z_I(\omega_{p1}) = \sqrt{Z_x(\omega_{p1})Z_y(\omega_{p1})} = Z_x(\omega_{p1})$$

Mathematically therefore

$$\frac{1}{Z_{\infty1}(\omega_{p1})} = \frac{\sqrt{1 - \omega_{p1}{}^2/\omega_0{}^2}}{R_0}$$

$$= j\omega_{p1}C_4 + \frac{1}{1/j\omega_{p1}C_2 + \omega_{p1}/jC_3(\omega_{p1}{}^2 - \omega_{p3}{}^2)} \qquad (6.5.5)$$

A sixth and final required relation comes from the fact that $Z_{\infty1}(\omega)$ is seen from 3–4 at ω_{p3}. Therefore

$$Z_{\infty1}(\omega_{p3}) = \frac{R_0}{R} \frac{1}{\sqrt{1 - \omega_{p3}{}^2/\omega_0{}^2}} = \frac{1}{j\omega_{p3}C_4R} \qquad (6.5.6)$$

The solution of the set of six equations given in the foregoing leads to the set of element value formulas given in Fig. 6.5.1. Specification of ω_{p1}, ω_{p3}, R_0, and ω_0 determines these element values and so the network.

6.6 Half section from $X_{L11}X_{C12}$ and $X_{L22}X_{C12}$ lattices

The half section of Fig. 6.6.1, if considered in terms of the open- and short-circuit scheme of Sec. 5.7, specifies the two symmetric lattices $X_{L11}X_{C12}$ and $X_{L22}X_{C12}$. The image impedance and transfer loss characteristics are deduced in the following.

The ladder and so the lattice equivalent exhibits two poles of transfer loss at the frequencies of resonance of the series resonators of Fig. 6.6.1, since $Z_x = Z_y$, at these frequencies. This transfer loss is one-half that of the full section, and is one-half the sum of the transfer loss of two peak sections.

The impedance function at the terminal pair 3–4 is $Z_{01}(x)$, one unit value of $Z(x)$ and a zero at cutoff, as the following brief argument shows. At ω_{p3} both Z_x and Z_y are inductive, and at ω_{p1} both Z_x and Z_y are inductive. A sketch of the possible low-pass reactance patterns of an $X_{L11}X_{C12}$ lattice shows only one pattern where Z_x and Z_y fit these requirements. This reactance pattern has two pass-band controls, no

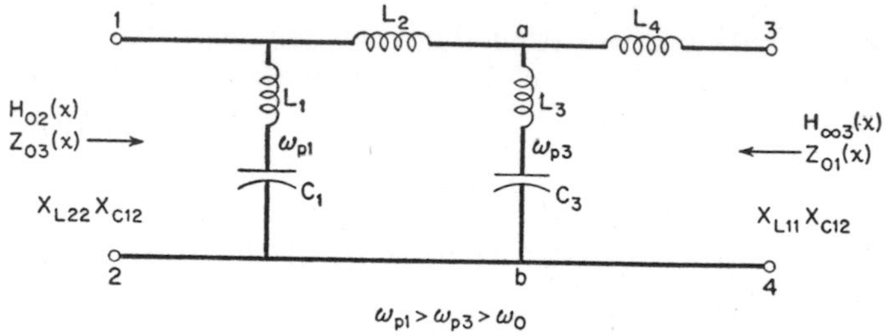

$$\omega_{p1} > \omega_{p3} > \omega_0$$

$$L_4 = \frac{m_3 R_0}{\omega_0}, \quad m_3 = \sqrt{1 - \frac{\omega_0^2}{\omega_{p3}^2}}, \quad C_3 = \frac{1}{\omega_{p3}^2 L_3}$$

$$L_2 = \frac{m_1 R_0}{\omega_0}, \quad m_1 = \sqrt{1 - \frac{\omega_0^2}{\omega_{p1}^2}}, \quad L_1 = \frac{L_2}{\omega_{p1}^2/\omega_{p3}^2 - 1}$$

$$L_3 = \frac{R_0^2 L_2}{\omega_{p3}^2 L_4(L_4 + L_2)} \qquad\qquad C_1 = \frac{1}{\omega_{p1}^2 L_1}$$

$$Z_{03}(x) = \frac{R_0}{R} \frac{(1 - x^2/x_{p1}^2)\sqrt{1 - x^2}}{1 - x^2/x_{p3}^2}, \quad H_{02}(x) = \frac{mx\sqrt{x^2 - 1}}{x^2 - x_a^2}$$

$$Z_{01}(x) = \frac{R_0}{R}\sqrt{1 - x^2} \qquad\qquad H_{\infty 3}(x) = \frac{mx(x^2 - x_a^2)}{\sqrt{x^2 - 1}\,(x^2 - x_b^2)}$$

Fig. 6.6.1

block-region controls, with cutoff at a zero of Z_y. The impedance function at 3–4 of Fig. 6.6.1 is, as a result, of the $Z_{01}(x)$ form. Also the ratio function is of the $H_{\infty 3}(x)$ form.

Viewed from the left-hand pair of terminals 1–2, the lattice formed from the half section of Fig. 6.6.1 has two pole-zero combinations, which lead to a low-pass structure. One of these patterns of interest here is shown on Fig. 6.6.2. The impedance function available from a lattice exhibiting such reactance patterns has three unit values of $Z(x)$ because of two block-region controls. This impedance function is of the Z_{03} form from the reactance patterns of Fig. 6.6.2. The element value formulas are determined next.

Immediately, from Fig. 6.6.1, two equations arise from the formulas for the resonant frequencies ω_{p1} and ω_{p3}:

$$\omega_{p1}{}^2 = \frac{1}{L_1 C_1} \tag{6.6.1}$$

$$\omega_{p3}{}^2 = \frac{1}{L_3 C_3} \tag{6.6.2}$$

A second relation arises from the fact that at the terminals 3–4 the image impedance is seen at ω_{p3}. Hence

$$Z_{01}(\omega_{p3}) = \frac{R_0}{R} \sqrt{1 - \frac{\omega_{p3}{}^2}{\omega_0{}^2}} = j\,\frac{\omega_{p3} L_4}{R} \tag{6.6.3}$$

A fourth relation arises from the fact that at cutoff, $Z_z(\omega)$ of terminals 1–2 vanishes (Fig. 6.6.2). Hence after removal of L_1 and

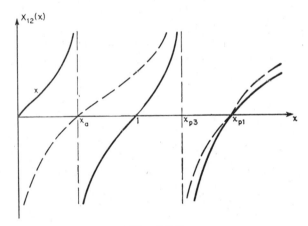

Fig. 6.6.2

C_1 and short-circuiting terminals 3–4, the impedance at terminals 1–2 vanishes, so

$$Z_x(\omega_0) = 0 = j\omega_0 L_2 + \cfrac{1}{\cfrac{1}{j\omega_0 L_4} + \cfrac{\omega_0}{jL_3(\omega_0{}^2 - \omega_{p3}{}^2)}} \tag{6.6.4}$$

A fifth relation comes from the fact that poles of Z_x and Z_y (zeros of Y_x and Y_y) occur at ω_{p3} (Fig. 6.6.2). The admittance Y_x or Y_y into terminals 1–2 of Fig. 6.6.1 at ω_{p3} consists of L_2 in parallel with the series resonator $L_1 C_1$. Therefore

$$0 = \frac{1}{j\omega_{p3} L_2} + \frac{\omega_{p3}}{jL_1(\omega_{p3}{}^2 - \omega_{p1}{}^2)} \tag{6.6.5}$$

The sixth and final relation arises from the fact that at ω_{p1} image impedance is seen at terminals 3–4. Consequently,

$$R_0 \sqrt{1 - \frac{\omega_{p1}^2}{\omega_0^2}} = j\omega_{p1}L_4 + \cfrac{1}{\cfrac{1}{j\omega_{p1}L_2} + \cfrac{\omega_{p1}}{jL_3(\omega_{p1}^2 - \omega_{p3}^2)}} \qquad (6.6.6)$$

The foregoing six equations define the element values as given by the formulas of Fig. 6.6.1.

6.7 Half section from $X_{L32}X_{C33}$ and $X_{L32}X_{C22}$ lattices

The half section represented by Fig. 6.7.1a leads to lattice sections $X_{L32}X_{C33}$ and $X_{L32}X_{C22}$ depending on which end of the half section is considered. This half section has three poles of transfer loss

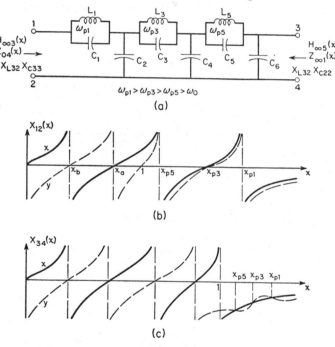

Fig. 6.7.1

and so must have a minimum of two pass-band controls. Viewed from the terminals 1–2, an $X_{L32}X_{C33}$ pattern exists (Fig. 6.7.1b) which has two pass-band controls and three block-region controls. Such a low-pass structure could present the impedance function $Z_{04}(x)$, and an $H_{\infty3}(x)$.

Viewed from the terminals 3–4, three low-pass reactance patterns are possible for the lattice $X_{L32}X_{C22}$ obtainable from the half section of Fig. 6.7.1a. The reactance pattern of Fig. 6.7.1c is the one which this lattice presents for the following reasons. Each of the three parallel resonators is capacitive above its resonant frequency and open at its resonant frequency. The impedance into terminals 3–4, therefore, is capacitive at each of the resonant frequencies ω_{p1}, ω_{p3}, ω_{p5}, is finite and of course nonvanishing. The reactance pattern of Fig. 6.7.1c is the only one which fits this requirement, namely, Z_x and Z_y both capacitive at ω_{p1}, ω_{p3} and ω_{p5}. The impedance function at terminals 3–4 is therefore as shown $Z_{\infty 1}$, and the ratio function is $H_{\infty 5}(x)$.

Formulas for the element values for the half section of Fig. 6.7.1 are not given. It should be possible to determine such formulas as in the two foregoing sections, but the algebra involved may be a bit awkward. Alternatively, after the lattice has been established in the mathematical form of Z_x and Z_y, the method of Sec. 5.9 can be used to determine the element values.

6.8 Half section from $X_{L22}X_{C23}$ and $X_{L33}X_{C23}$ lattices

The half section of Fig. 6.8.1a specifies the two lattices $X_{L22}X_{C23}$ and $X_{L33}X_{C23}$ as indicated on the diagram. This half section has three poles of transfer loss located at ω_{p5}, ω_{p3} and ω_{p1}. A sketch of the

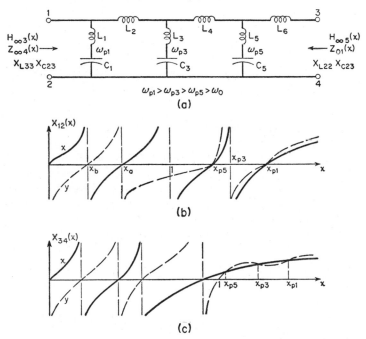

Fig. 6.8.1

reactance patterns for the $X_{L33}X_{C23}$ lattice shows that one pattern is possible which has two pass-band and three block-band controls with a pole of $Z_x(x)$ at cutoff (Fig. 6.8.1b); hence this structure may be established to have the impedance function $Z_{\infty 4}(x)$ at the 1–2 terminals and $H_{\infty 3}(x)$.

Viewed from the terminals 3–4, the impedances Z_x and Z_y of the lattice equivalent of the half-section of Fig. 6.8.1a are both inductive at all three frequencies ω_{p5}, ω_{p3}, and ω_{p1} (finite and nonvanishing). The only reactance pattern which fits this condition is the one given by Fig. 6.8.1c. Hence the impedance function at the terminals 3–4 is as shown, $Z_{01}(x)$, and the ratio function is $H_{\infty 5}(x)$.

Element value formulas are not given here for the half section of Fig. 6.8.1a. A modification of the method of Sec. 5.9 to fit this particular structure can be used to determine these element values for any specified Z_x and Z_y which have ladder equivalent half sections of this particular kind.

6.9 Interconnection of half sections

The half sections discussed in this chapter may be cascaded on the basis of image impedance match to present any pair combination of the various image impedances. The pole count of the transfer loss follows at once from the sum of the poles of transfer loss of the half sections cascaded. The transfer loss function can be determined by adding one-half the transfer loss of a set of sections with poles of transfer loss located as for the combination of half sections.

6.10 Multiple h and m derivations

The traditional approach to the design of ladder type filters has been to start with a ladder section and modify this section in a particular manner. The m- and multiple-m-derived filters[1] in particular are so formed. A simple T or π ladder section (constant-k) is subjected to an m derivation which specifies another T or π, respectively. The half sections of the m-derived structures are of the form given in Figs. 6.3.1 and 6.4.1. A full section, formed from the half section of Fig. 6.2.1, is the initial or prototype structure. The m-derived half section presents a more elaborate image impedance, i.e., it allows one more unit value of $Z(x)$ than the prototype half section. Also a pole of transfer loss appears in the m-derived characteristic, whereas none existed in the transfer loss of the prototype.

[1] Zobel, O. J., "Extensions to the Theory and Design of Electric Wave-Filters," *Bell System Tech. J.*, April 1931, p. 284.

Successive m derivations lead to image impedance and transfer loss characteristics of higher numbers of unit values of $Z(x)$ and $H(x)$. The m derivations, however, lead to structures of more and more complex shunt and series arms, which complicate parasitic compensation so seriously that the m derivation structures of all but the first have been abandoned.

An alternative derivative method[2] known as the h-derived method leads to simpler forms of the series and shunt arms of the ladder, while at the same time it leads to more of these arms. In particular, the half sections of this chapter are the ones which may also be reached by the h derivation.

Problems

6.1 Connect two half sections, one of the type shown in Fig. 6.2.1 and the second as shown in Fig. 6.3.1, so that the image impedances are matched at the junction. Plot the total transfer loss and both image impedances for $R_0 = 100$, $\omega_0 = 500,000$, $m = 0.5$. Show that the transfer loss is one-half that of the sum of the transfer loss of a peak section and a constant-k section.

6.2 Repeat the preceding problem for two half sections of the type shown in Figs. 6.2.1 and 6.4.1.

6.3 Show that the half section of Fig. 6.5.1 leads to the lattices $X_{L21}X_{C11}$ and $X_{L21}X_{C22}$.

6.4 Establish the reactance patterns of Z_x and Z_y of the symmetric lattice which is determined at the terminals 1-2 of the half section of Fig. 6.5.1. This lattice must have a minimum of one pass-band control frequency and two block-band control frequencies in order for the network to have two poles of transfer loss and three unit values of $Z(x)$. From these reactance patterns write the formula for $H(x)$. Note that this function has two undetermined elements, namely, the pass-band control and a multiplying constant. Specification of the location of the two unit values of $H(x)$, poles of $A_I(x)$, determines these two elements.

Consider next the tandem arrangement of the two peak sections (Fig. 5.5.1j) which have transfer-loss poles at the same frequencies as the foregoing lattice. Determine the reactance patterns for the lattice equivalent to these tandem sections by using the equivalents of Fig. P.3.2. Show that the transfer loss of the two peak sections in tandem is therefore the same as twice the transfer loss of the network of Fig. 6.5.1.

6.5 Sketch all the reactance patterns for Z_x and Z_y of the symmetric lattice formed from the half section of Fig. 6.5.1 as viewed from the right. Determine from these sketches and known properties of the half section which of these reactance patterns applies to the lattice equivalent.

[2] Bode, H. W., "A General Theory of Electric Wave Filters," *J. Math. Phys.*, 13, 275–362 (1934).

6.6 Sketch all the reactance patterns possible for the symmetric lattice which may be formed from viewing the half section of Fig. 6.5.1 at the left-hand terminals. Indicate the best impedance function possible for each reactance pattern.

6.7 Solve the set of six equations of Sec. 6.5 to obtain the formulas for the element values which are given on Fig. 6.5.1.

6.8 Sketch all the possible reactance patterns for Z_x and Z_y of the lattice formed from terminals 3–4 of the half section of Fig. 6.6.1. Show which one corresponds to the full ladder section.

6.9 Establish as many reactance patterns as possible for the lattice formed at the left-hand terminals of the half section of Fig. 6.6.1. (a) Indicate the impedance function characteristics possible. (b) Establish element value formulas for the network which has an impedance function $Z(x)$ with two unit values.

6.10 Use the six equations of Sec. 6.6. to establish the element value formulas as given by Fig. 6.6.1.

6.11 Establish a set of nine equations which might be used for determining element value formulas for the half section of Fig. 6.7.1a.

6.12 Show that the impedance and ratio functions for the two ends of a ladder half section of the type shown by Fig. 6.7.1a are as shown.

6.13 Sketch the reactance patterns at the 1–2 end of the half section of Fig. 6.8.1a. Show from these sketches that $Z_{\infty 4}$ at 1–2 terminals and three poles of transfer loss are possible for this structure.

6.14 The seven half sections discussed through Sec. 6.8 permit by tandem combinations the formation of a ladder section which exhibits at its two ends any pair of the impedance functions $Z_{\infty 1}$, $Z_{\infty 2}$, $Z_{\infty 3}$, $Z_{\infty 4}$, Z_{01}, Z_{02}, Z_{03}, and Z_{04}. Establish the network combinations which may be used for such image impedance matching.

6.15 Establish the half section of a triple m-derivation, starting from a prototype T and π as formed from Fig. 6.2.1. Merely determine the form of the half section. Note the increase in complexity of shunt and series arms of the half section. The method to be used must be sought in the professional literature.

6.16 Establish sketches of the half section of a triple h derivation starting from the basic structure of Fig. 6.2.1. Compare with the half sections of this chapter. The method to be used must be sought in professional literature.

6.17 Show, for the half section of Fig. 6.5.1, that the transfer loss is the sum of the transfer losses of two half sections of the type of Fig. 6.3.1. Do so by showing that the transfer loss derived from $H_{02}(x)$ is the same as the sum of the transfer loss derived from $H_{\infty 1}(x)$.

CHAPTER SEVEN

Insertion Loss and Insertion Phase

The input-output current relations, as well as input-output terminal-voltage relations, of a symmetric 4TN with image impedance terminations are completely specified by the transfer function $P_I(\omega)$ (Sec. 2.8). If, as is usual in practice, a marked difference between image impedance and termination exists, the transfer function serves to specify only the first approximation to the behavior of a 4TN, and other methods are used for evaluating this behavior of a 4TN in any particular operating circuit.

A comparison of the input current and voltage with the output current and voltage under operating conditions could be used. Mathematically such a comparison is not too difficult. On the other hand, measurement of amplitude and phase of current and voltage over wide frequency ranges is relatively difficult. The use of transfer impedance $(Z_t = V_{in}/I_{out})$ is more or less impractical for the same reason. A process has been evolved, however, which is in general use. This insertion function process is widely used because it is easy to measure, because it is independent of the particular network under consideration, and because the mathematical formulation splits readily into a form which permits consideration of impedance mismatch and transfer function more or less independently of each other.

7.1 Insertion function definition and measurement

By definition the insertion function is

$$P_s = A_s + jB_s = \ln \frac{I'_R}{I_R} = \ln \left| \frac{I'_R}{I_R} \right| + j(\phi'_R - \phi_R) \quad (7.1.1)$$

where I'_R is the receiver current with source and receiver directly connected, I_R is the receiver current with the 4TN interposed between source and receiver, A_s is the *insertion loss* in nepers, and B_s is the *insertion phase* in radians or degrees. Ordinarily the insertion *loss* is expressed in decibels rather than nepers (db number = 8.686 × neper number), where

$$A_s = 20 \log \left| \frac{I'_R}{I_R} \right| \qquad (7.1.2)$$

is the *insertion loss* in decibels. The insertion phase

$$B_s = \phi'_R - \phi_R \qquad (7.1.3)$$

may be expressed in radians or degrees as desired. The degree unit is perhaps more common. Exactly this same result arises from the voltage ratio V'_R/V_R since $V'_R = Z_R I'_R$ and $V_R = Z_R I_R$.

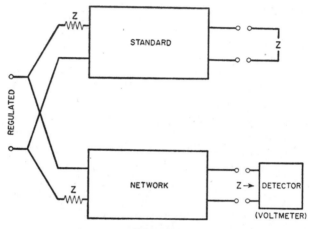

Fig. 7.1.1

The magnitude of the insertion function, i.e., $\sqrt{A_s{}^2 + B_s{}^2}$, has no meaning, in direct correspondence with the fact that $\sqrt{A_I{}^2 + B_I{}^2}$ also has no meaning.

The insertion loss is measured by means of the arrangement of Fig. 7.1.1. A standard attenuator and the network to be tested are connected in parallel at the input. With impedances matched as shown, the detector and impedance Z are interchanged as the standard is adjusted until the detector deflection is the same for its two positions. The insertion loss may then be read directly from the calibrated standard.

7.2 Insertion function: mathematical details

The insertion function may be expressed for a general passive 4TN by means of the formulas derived in Chapter 2. Thus from Eq. (2.8.7),

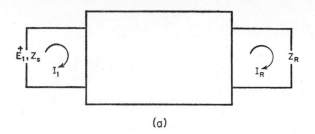

(a)

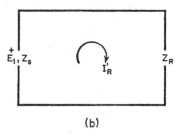

(b)

Fig. 7.2.1

the output current I_R of the general 4TN (Fig. 7.2.1a) is

$$I_R = E_1 \frac{2[\sqrt{Z_{I1}}/(Z_S + Z_{I1})][\sqrt{Z_{I2}}/(Z_R + Z_{I2})]\epsilon^{-P_I(x)}}{1 - K_S K_R \epsilon^{-2P_I(x)}} \qquad (7.2.1)$$

The current of Z_R when directly connected to the source is (Fig. 7.2.1b)

$$I'_R = \frac{E_1}{Z_S + Z_R} \qquad (7.2.2)$$

Therefore, multiplying numerator and denominator by $2\sqrt{Z_S Z_R}$ in anticipation of subsequent developments,

$$\frac{I'_R}{I_R} = \frac{\epsilon^{P_I(x)}(1 - K_S K_R \epsilon^{-2P_I(x)})2\sqrt{Z_S Z_R}}{2(Z_S + Z_R)[\sqrt{Z_{I1}}/(Z_S + Z_{I1})][\sqrt{Z_{I2}}/(Z_R + Z_{I2})]2\sqrt{Z_S Z_R}} \qquad (7.2.3)$$

This ratio can be separated into five convenient factors in the form

$$\frac{I'_R}{I_R} = \frac{2\sqrt{Z_S Z_R}}{Z_S + Z_R} \frac{Z_S + Z_{I1}}{2\sqrt{Z_S Z_{I1}}} \frac{Z_R + Z_{I2}}{2\sqrt{Z_R Z_{I2}}} \epsilon^{P_I(x)}(1 - K_S K_R \epsilon^{-2P_I(x)}) \qquad (7.2.4)$$

In accordance with the definition of Eq. (7.1.1), therefore, the insertion function is

$$P_s(x) = A_s(x) + jB_s(x) = \ln \frac{I'_R}{I_R}$$

$$= \ln \frac{2\sqrt{Z_S Z_R}}{Z_S + Z_R} + \ln \frac{Z_S + Z_{I1}}{2\sqrt{Z_S Z_{I1}}} + \ln \frac{Z_R + Z_{I2}}{2\sqrt{Z_R Z_{I2}}}$$

$$+ P_I(x) + \ln\left[1 - K_S K_R \epsilon^{-2P_I(x)}\right] \quad (7.2.5)$$

Ease of measurement is not the sole advantage of this insertion function. An additional virtue is that, for many operating conditions, some of the terms vanish to simplify the expression. The remainder of this chapter is devoted to the detailed consideration of these various terms which when *added* give the insertion function.

Incidentally it is of interest to note that the insertion function is readily expressible in terms of the transfer impedance Z_t, where (Fig. 7.2.1a)

$$Z_t = \frac{E_1}{I_R} \qquad (7.2.6)$$

or in terms of a voltage transfer function,

$$T_v = \frac{E_1}{V_R} = \frac{E_1}{I_R Z_R} \qquad (7.2.7)$$

At once, from these last two equations and Eq. (7.2.2),

$$\frac{I'_R}{I_R} = \frac{Z_t}{Z_S + Z_R} = \frac{Z_R T_v}{Z_S + Z_R} \qquad (7.2.8)$$

and the insertion function is

$$P_s = A_s + jB_s = \ln Z_t + \ln \frac{1}{Z_S + Z_R}$$

$$= \ln T_v + \ln \frac{Z_R}{Z_S + Z_R} \qquad (7.2.9)$$

7.3 Impedance mismatch, general

The first three terms on the right of Eq. (7.2.5) vanish separately if $Z_S = Z_R$, $Z_S = Z_{I1}$, or $Z_R = Z_{I2}$. The nonvanishing of these terms is dependent, therefore, on the differing or mismatch of impedances. Consequently it would not seem to be inaccurate to use *impedance mismatch terms* for their designation. However, common usage at the present time is to label these terms as transformer function:

$$\ln \frac{2\sqrt{Z_S Z_R}}{Z_S + Z_R} \qquad (7.3.1)$$

reflection function (input):

$$\ln \frac{Z_S + Z_{I1}}{2\sqrt{Z_S Z_{I1}}} \qquad (7.3.2)$$

reflection function (output):

$$\ln \frac{Z_R + Z_{I2}}{2\sqrt{Z_R Z_{I2}}} \qquad (7.3.3)$$

The reason for the designation transformer function is shown on Fig. 7.3.1. The ideal transformer with complex ratio of transformation

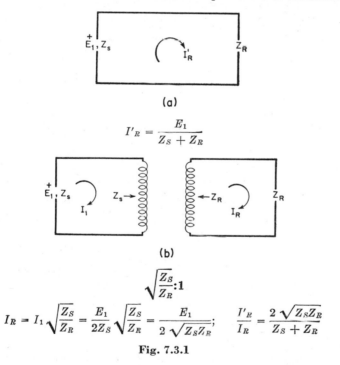

$$I_R = I_1 \sqrt{\frac{Z_S}{Z_R}} = \frac{E_1}{2Z_S}\sqrt{\frac{Z_S}{Z_R}} = \frac{E_1}{2\sqrt{Z_S Z_R}}; \qquad \frac{I'_R}{I_R} = \frac{2\sqrt{Z_S Z_R}}{Z_S + Z_R}$$

Fig. 7.3.1

has an insertion function identical with the so-called transformer term of Eq. (7.3.1).

The reflection function terms have received their designation from analogous terms which appear in the study of transmission lines. In any event they vanish or do not vanish as the terminations do or do not match their respective image impedances. The most important mathematical properties of these impedance mismatch functions are deduced next.

Note first, since

$$\ln \frac{Z_a + Z_b}{2\sqrt{Z_a Z_b}} = \ln \frac{\sqrt{Z_a/Z_b} + \sqrt{Z_b/Z_a}}{2} \qquad (7.3.4)$$

the two impedance mismatch (reflection) functions are identical as functions of either Z_a/Z_b or Z_b/Z_a. Note further, since

$$\ln x = -\ln 1/x \qquad (7.3.5)$$

a study of the function of Eq. (7.3.4) covers all three of the impedance mismatch functions by use of an extra minus sign for the "transformer" term. Attention is therefore directed toward a study of Eq. (7.3.4).

In terms of a slightly generalized $Z(x)$, namely,

$$Z(x) = |Z(x)|\epsilon^{j\phi} = \frac{Z_a(x)}{Z_b(x)} \qquad (7.3.6)$$

where $Z_a(x)/Z_b(x)$ may represent $Z_{I1}(x)/Z_S(x)$, $Z_{I2}(x)/Z_R(x)$, or $Z_S(x)/Z_R(x)$, the mismatch insertion function (reflection or transformer) is

$$P_{sm}(x) = \pm 20 \log \frac{\sqrt{Z_a(x)/Z_b(x) + Z_b(x)/Z_a(x)}}{2}$$

$$= \pm 20 \log \frac{\sqrt{Z(x)} + 1/\sqrt{Z(x)}}{2}$$

$$= \pm 20 \log \frac{1 + Z(x)}{2\sqrt{Z(x)}} = \pm 20 \log \frac{1 + 1/Z(x)}{2\sqrt{1/Z(x)}} \qquad (7.3.7)$$

7.4 Impedance mismatch losses

In the first place, because of the minus sign of Eq. (7.3.5), a value of $Z(x)$ of Eq. (7.3.6), which produces a reflection loss, produces a transformer *gain* with a phase of opposite sign. With this fact in mind, consider the implications of the curves of Fig. 7.4.1:

1. $\phi = 0$ corresponds to purely resistive Z_a and Z_b, i.e., Z_S and Z_R of ordinary practice and Z_{I1} and Z_{I2} of the pass band. The reflection

loss or transformer gain ranges from zero to indefinitely large as the appropriate purely resistive impedances ranges from equality to a ratio which is indefinitely large. If the terminating impedances (resistive) are independent of frequency as in the most common case of terminations, the transformer term represents a constant gain. Since Z_I is a function of frequency, the reflection term specifies a

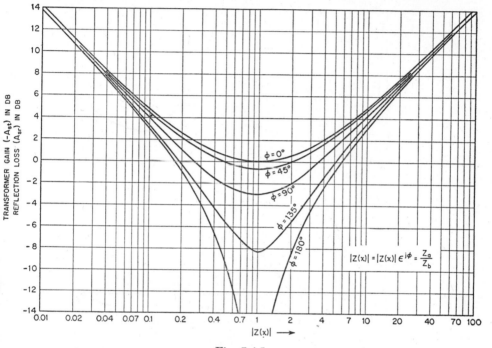

Fig. 7.4.1

variable loss in the pass band, small or large depending on how well Z_I approximates a straight line.

2. $\phi = \pm 90°$ corresponds to a purely reactive Z_b and a purely resistive Z_a, i.e., to the *block* region mismatch functions. The curve for $\phi = 90°$ on Fig. 7.4.1 indicates that as a reactive Z_b (or Z_a) ranges over $0 \le x_b \le \infty$, the reflection loss $A_{\sigma r}$ ranges from ∞ to -3 to ∞. The curves of Fig. 7.4.2 show a typical frequency variation of an image reactance and attendant reflection loss for the block region. Note the *gain* of 3 db, at

$$|Z(x)| = |Z_I(x)/R| = 1$$

between each critical frequency of the image impedance, and the pole of reflection *loss* at each critical frequency. Note further that these poles of reflection loss may or may not coincide with poles of transfer loss $A_I(x)$, i.e., balanced bridge. In fact the poles of reflection loss occur at frequencies at which $Z_I(x)$ has a pole or zero which in turn is the frequency at which $Z_x(x)$ and $Z_y(x)$ have a simultaneous zero or pole, i.e., an opened or short-circuited lattice (bridge). If $Z_x(x)$

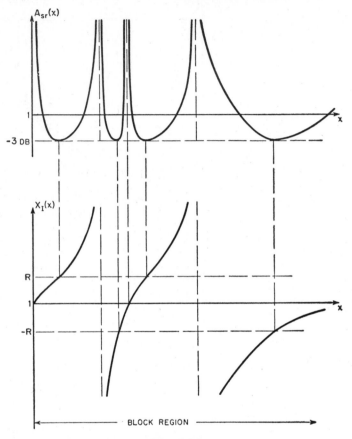

Fig. 7.4.2

and $Z_y(x)$ have such a simultaneous zero or pole, the source and receiver are electrically separated. Such a separation of driver and receiver may or may not appear as a pole of transfer function, but always does appear as a pole of reflection loss.

The set of curves of Fig. 7.4.3 may be used as a means of quickly estimating the reflection loss in the block region of a low-pass filter with one image impedance control.

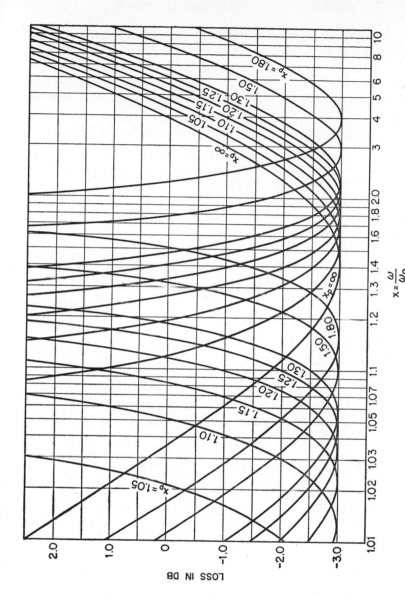

Fig. 7.4.3. Reflection (mismatch) loss in decibels for a pure resistance matched against a pure reactance—block region of LP filter with one $Z(x)$ control.

173

The mismatch loss as presented in the foregoing is, of course, the loss at one end of the network. As indicated by Eq. (7.2.5), the total reflection loss is the sum of the reflection loss at output and input.

The reflection loss for $Z_T = R + j0$ and $Z_I = 0 + jX_I$, i.e., for $\phi = \pm 90°$, as discussed in the foregoing, covers many of the situations

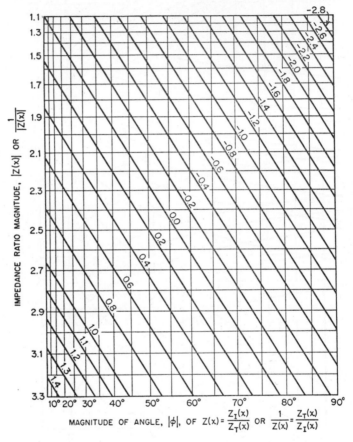

Fig. 7.4.4. Block region reflection loss in decibels (diagonals).

arising in practice. However, a more general requirement arises often enough to justify some more general considerations. One useful method of general treatment, from a design standpoint, is by way of charts.

Charts of reflection loss have been developed on the basis of Eq. (7.3.7). Two such charts are given by Figs. 7.4.4 and 7.4.5. The magnitude of the angle ϕ of $Z(x)$ is used to enter the chart. Also $Z(x)$ or $1/Z(x)$ is used to enter the charts, depending on which one has a magnitude greater than unity. Note that dissipative as well as nondissipative conditions are represented in these charts.

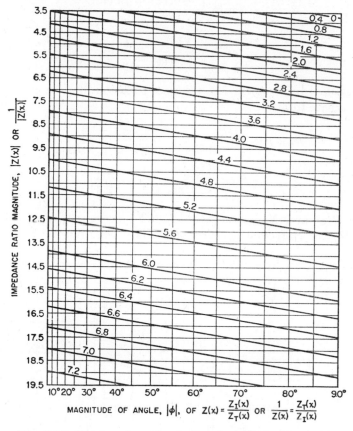

Fig. 7.4.5. Block region reflection loss in decibels (diagonals).

7.5 Reflection phase

A formula for the mismatch phase, which is convenient for many puspones, may be established as follows. If "im" means "take the imaginary part of" and $Z_T(x)$ represents a general terminating imped-ance, from Eq. (7.3.7), then

$$B_{sr}(x) = \text{im} \ln \frac{Z_T(x) + Z_I(x)}{2\sqrt{Z_T(x)Z_I(x)}} = \text{im} \ln \frac{1 + Z(x)}{2\sqrt{Z(x)}}$$

$$= \text{im} \ln \frac{1 + 1/Z(x)}{2\sqrt{1/Z(x)}} \tag{7.5.1}$$

If $Z(x)$ is expressed in terms of rectangular components, $R(x) + jX(x)$,

$$
\begin{aligned}
B_{sr}(x) &= \operatorname{im} \ln \frac{1 + R(x) + jX(x)}{2\sqrt{|Z(x)|}e^{j\phi/2}} \\
&= \tan^{-1}\frac{X(x)}{1 + R(x)} - \frac{1}{2}\tan^{-1}\frac{X(x)}{R(x)}
\end{aligned}
\tag{7.5.2}
$$

As suggested by Problem 7.6, this last equation may be expressed in the alternate form

$$
\begin{aligned}
B_{sr}(x) &= \tan^{-1}\frac{X(x)[|Z(x)| - 1]}{[|Z(x)| + 1][|Z(x)| + R(x)]} \\
&= \tan^{-1}\left[\frac{|Z(x)| - 1}{|Z(x)| + 1}\tan\frac{\phi}{2}\right]
\end{aligned}
\tag{7.5.3}
$$

where $R(x)$ and $X(x)$ are the real and imaginary parts of $Z(x) = Z_I(x)/Z_T(x)$. Note that the sign of $B_{sr}(x)$ is the same as that of $X(x)$

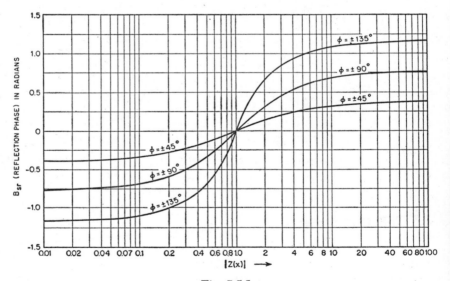

Fig. 7.5.1

if $|Z(x)| > 1$ and opposite if $|Z(x)| < 1$. Also note that the reflection phase vanishes if $|Z(x)| = 1$.

Charts of reflection phase are given by Figs. 7.5.1 and 7.5.2. A chart such as that of Fig. 7.5.1 is restricted only by the number of curves plotted. Instructions for the use of Fig. 7.5.2 are given in the

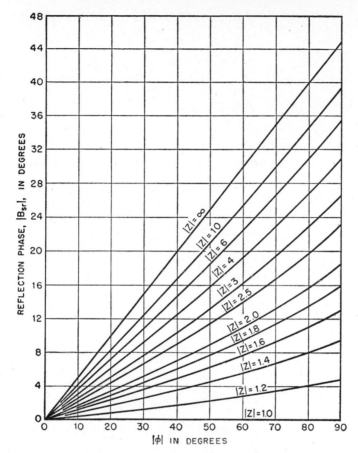

Fig. 7.5.2. The value B_{sr} takes on the sign of ϕ if $|Z(x)| > 1$. If $|Z(x)| < 1$, the $|Z|$ values are to be used as values of $1/|Z|$; B_{sr} takes the sign opposite ϕ.

$$B_{sr} = \operatorname{im} \ln \frac{1 + Z(x)}{2\sqrt{Z(x)}} = \frac{1 + 1/Z(x)}{2\sqrt{1/Z(x)}}$$

$$Z(x) = \frac{Z_I(x)}{Z_T} = \left|\frac{Z_I(x)}{Z_T}\right| \epsilon^{j\phi}$$

caption. Note that this chart is not restricted to nondissipative impedances but may be applied in general only if $\phi \leq 90°$.

A special case of the reflection phase characteristic of particular interest in filter design is that of a purely resistive termination of the 4TN, $Z_T(x) = R(x) + j0$, and purely reactive image impedance, $Z_I(x) = 0 + jX_I(x)$. The reflection phase is, under such restrictions,

$$B_{sr}(x) = \text{im ln} \frac{Z_T(x) + Z_I(x)}{2\sqrt{Z_T(x)Z_I(x)}} = \text{im ln} \frac{R(x) + jX_I(x)}{2\sqrt{R(x)jX_I(x)}}$$

$$= \text{im ln} \frac{\sqrt{R^2(x) + X_I^2(x)}}{2\sqrt{R(x)|X_I(x)|}} \epsilon^{j(\tan^{-1}X_I/R_T \pm 45°)}$$

$$= \tan^{-1} \frac{X_I(x)}{R(x)} \pm 45° \qquad (7.5.4)$$

The sign associated with the 45° is opposite that of $X_I(x)$. This last equation can be transformed into an alternate form. From the first

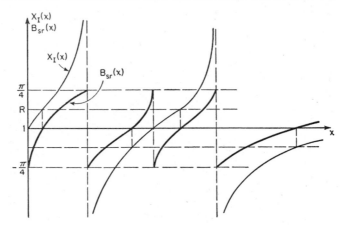

Fig. 7.5.3

of the trigonometric relations of Problem 7.6 and this last relation,

$$B_{sr}(x) = \tan^{-1} \frac{X_I(x)/R(x) \pm 1}{1 \pm X_I(x)/R(x)} \qquad (7.5.5)$$

if $Z_T(x) = R(x) + j0$ and $Z_I(x) = 0 + jX_I(x)$. The reflection phase evidently varies over $\pi/2$ radians for each zero to infinity or infinity to zero variation of $X_I(x)$. The fact that $\tan^{-1} X_I(x)/R(x)$ is a first or fourth quadrant angle, since $R(x) > 0$, is helpful in deducing the curve of $B_{sr}(x)$. The curves of Fig. 7.5.3 illustrate the character of the block-band reflection phase as a function of frequency under the special case of this last equation.

7.6 Transfer function

The transfer function $P_I(x)$, which appears as one of the elements of the insertion function of Eq. (7.2.5), is discussed in detail in the preceding chapter. In filter design the transfer function is usually the dominant term of the insertion function. Design techniques are based on the transfer function as a first approximation which is corrected by the transformer, reflection, and interaction functions.

Usually the transfer loss is expressed in decibels, so that

$$P_I(x) = A_I(x) \text{ nepers} + jB_I(x) \text{ degrees}$$
$$= 8.686A_I(X) \text{ decibels} + jB_I(x) \text{ degrees} \quad (7.6.1)$$

7.7 Interaction function of the block region

The foregoing discussions of this and the preceding chapter cover material which is fully adequate for determination of the insertion function over the whole frequency range for all linear, reciprocal 4TN and all terminations. Special cases of particular usefulness are also considered. In the remainder of this chapter further *special* situations are considered.

The interaction function, the last term on the right of Eq. (7.2.5) is, in nepers and degrees,

$$A_{si}(x) + jB_{si}(x) = \ln\left[1 - \left(\frac{Z_S - Z_{I1}}{Z_S + Z_{I1}}\right)\left(\frac{Z_R - Z_{I2}}{Z_R + Z_{I2}}\right)\epsilon^{-2P_I(x)}\right] \quad (7.7.1)$$

As a general rule this interaction function is negligible in the block region. However, certain designs require correction on the basis of interaction, and unless experience indicates the contrary, interaction should be considered.

7.8 Interaction and reflection loss of the pass band

Attention is directed in this section specifically to the pass band. In this region $A_I(x) = 0$ by definition, so the insertion function consists of the transfer phase, transformer term, reflection and interaction terms.

The transformer term and the transfer phase are considered in detail in the preceeding. The pass-band reflection and interaction effects are considered in this section in terms of a combined total. The most important practical case is for equal terminations and the image impedance purely resistive, i.e., for $Z_S = Z_R = Z_T = R + j0$ and $Z_I(x) = R_I(x) + j0$. Under these conditions the *total* insertion loss of the pass band in decibels is the sum of three logarithms, or the logarithm of the product of the three terms, two reflection and one interaction, which produces, from the second, third, and fifth terms of

Eq. (7.2.5) the formula

$$A_{sp}(x) = 20 \log \left| \frac{(R + R_I)^2}{4RR_I} \left[1 - \frac{(R - R_I)^2}{(R + R_I)} \epsilon^{-j2B_I(x)} \right] \right| \quad (7.8.1)$$

In terms of the already used $Z(x) = R_I(x)/R$, this equation becomes

$$A_{sp}(x) = 20 \log \left| \frac{[1 + Z(x)]^2}{4Z(x)} \left[1 - \frac{[1 - Z(x)]^2}{[1 + Z(x)]^2} \epsilon^{-j2B_I(x)} \right] \right| \quad (7.8.2)$$

The curve of $A_{sp}(x)$ shown in Fig. 7.8.1 illustrates in a general way the pass-band insertion loss of the last equation for equal resistive terminations. Note that this insertion loss may be characterized in a rough fashion by

$A_{sp}(x)$ vanishes at $B_I(x) = k\pi/2$, $k = 0, 2, 4, 6, \ldots$. See abscissa points g, h, i, j, k of Fig. 7.8.1.

$A_{sp}(x)$ vanishes at $Z(x) = 1$. See abscissa points l, m, n, o of Fig. 7.8.1.

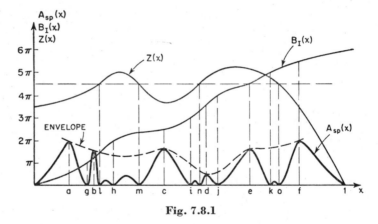

Fig. 7.8.1

$A_{sp}(x)$ has maxima approximately at $B_I(x) = k\pi/2$, $k = 1, 3, 5,$ $\ldots$. See abscissa points a, b, c, d, e, f of Fig. 7.8.1. On the basis of the location of these zeros and maxima, the pass-band loss can be sketched with sufficient accuracy for most design purposes. Often the envelope of maxima corresponding to values which are odd multiples of $\pi/2$ is sufficient for estimating the pass-band insertion loss. The maxima of the ripples can be expected to be within this envelope plotted on a nondissipative basis, since the effect of dissipation is to reduce the amplitude of the maxima. The effect of the extra zeros introduced at the $B_I(x) = k\pi/2$ (k even) frequencies can at most be one of lowering the loss between the maxima at $B_I(x) = k\pi/2$ (k odd). Since the envelope of maxima is sufficient for most purposes and is easy to compute, it is considered further.

On the basis of a variation of $Z(x)$, which is slow with respect to the effect of the exponential of Eq. (7.8.2), the maxima of the pass-band insertion loss occur when this exponential is negative, i.e., when

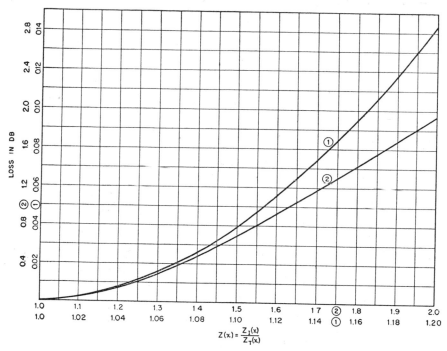

Fig. 7.8.2. Reflection and interaction loss envelope (pass band), where $Z_I(x)$ and $Z_T(x)$ are resistive.

$$\text{Loss} = 20 \log \left| \frac{1}{2} Z(x) + \frac{1}{Z(x)} \right| \quad \text{(db)}$$

$B_I(x) = k\pi/2$, k odd. The equation for these maxima is

$$A_{sp\,max} = 20 \log \left| \frac{[1 + Z(x)]^2}{4Z(x)} \left\{ 1 + \frac{[1 - Z(x)]^2}{[1 + Z(x)]^2} \right\} \right| \quad (7.8.3)$$

$$= 20 \log \left[\frac{1}{2} \left| \frac{1}{Z(x)} + Z(x) \right| \right] \quad (7.8.4)$$

This relation is shown graphically by Fig. 7.8.2. From a known frequency, location of the odd $\pi/2$ values of $B_I(x)$, and a known $Z(x)$ relation, the envelope of maxima of pass-band insertion loss may be sketched from the curves of Fig. 7.8.2.

and collecting terms,

$$B'_{sp}(x) = \text{im } \ln \frac{(Z_1 + Z_2) \cos B_I(x) + j(1 + Z_1 Z_2) \sin B_I(x)}{2 \sqrt{Z_1 Z_2} \; \epsilon^{jB_I(x)}} \qquad (7.9.5)$$

or in terms of the relations of Eqs. (7.8.11) and (7.8.13),

$$B'_{sp}(x) = \text{im } \ln$$

$$\frac{\frac{1}{2}\{[Z_m(x) + 1/Z_m(x)] \cos B_I(x) + j[Z_M(x) + 1/Z_M(x)] \sin B_I(x)\}}{\epsilon^{jB_I(x)}}$$

$$(7.9.6)$$

Directly from this last equation,

$$B'_{sp}(x) = \tan^{-1}\left[\frac{Z_M(x) + 1/Z_M(x)}{Z_m(x) + 1/Z_m(x)} \tan B_I(x) \right] - B_I(x) \qquad (7.9.7)$$

Note that this expression does not include the transfer phase. Exclusive of the transformer phase, the pass-band phase is, on adding $B_I(x)$,

$$B_{sp}(x) = \tan^{-1}\frac{Z_M(x) + 1/Z_M(x)}{Z_m(x) + 1/Z_m(x)} \tan B_I(x) \qquad (7.9.8)$$

Problems

7.1 Consider the formula

$$A_s = 20 \log \frac{I'_R}{I_R} \quad \text{db}$$

As a means of gaining some idea of the reduction in magnitude of the numbers involved as well as some idea of the significance of the decibel numbers, tabulate

$$A_s = 20 \log 10^n = 20n \quad \text{db}$$

for integral values of $n = 1, 2, 3, 4, \ldots, 10$. In a third column of this table place the corresponding $|I'_R/I_R|$ number.

To obtain an $|I_R|$ of 1 amp with a 100 db loss, the current $|I'_R|$ should be what?

7.2 Make a tabulation of the series resistance and shunt resistance of T pads which give insertion losses of 0.5, 1.0, 1.5, 2, 10, 15, and 20 db. The terminations are each 1 ohm. Show how to convert these resistances of the T pad for terminations of $R \neq 1$.

7.3 Establish the properties of the reflection *loss* under pure reactance terminations for $x > 1$.

7.4 Plot the block region reflection loss

$$Z(x) = \frac{Z_I(x)}{R} = \pm j \frac{1.7(x^2 - x_2{}^2)}{\sqrt{x^2 - 1}\,(x^2 - x_1{}^2)}$$

if $R = 100$, $x_2 = 3$, $x_1 = 4$.

7.5 Use the charts of Figs. 7.4.3, 7.4.4, and 7.4.5 to plot the block region reflection loss for

$$Z_R(x) = 100 + j50x$$

with $Z_I(x)$ as in Problem 7.4.

7.6 Use the standard trigonometric relations

$$\tan(a \pm b) = \frac{\tan a \pm \tan b}{1 \mp \tan a \tan b}, \qquad \tan \frac{\phi}{2} = \frac{\sin \phi}{1 + \cos \phi}$$

to show that Eq. (7.5.3) is an alternative form of Eq. (7.5.2).

7.7 Plot, as a function of x, the reflection phase of the block region for the impedance function of Problem 7.4.

7.8 Plot the reflection phase under the conditions of Problem 7.5. Use Fig. 7.5.2.

7.9 Plot the pass-band insertion loss for the $Z(x)$ of Problem 7.5. Assume a linear phase $B_I(x)$ in the pass band over a total range of 4π.

7.10 Use Fig. 7.8.2, $Z(x)$ of Problem 7.4 and linear phase $B_I(x)$, over a 0 to 6π range in the pass band to sketch the envelope of maxima of the pass-band insertion loss.

CHAPTER EIGHT

Effect of Dissipation

If the techniques presented in this book are to be used to design an electric filter (nondissipative basis), there can be no question that dissipation in the actual network must be small. Otherwise poles of transfer loss, sharpness of cut-off, and impedance match are not exhibited by the physical network effected from the nondissipative design. Since, however, there is inevitably some dissipation in any network, a precise design must not only lead to a highly reactive network, but must also predict the effect of the inevitable even though small dissipation. This chapter is devoted to a brief consideration of methods of incorporating such dissipative effects into the design of filters.

8.1 *Small dissipative effects in general: Mayer's theorem*

The dissipative effect of an inductor can be represented in terms of a resistor in series with an inductor (nondissipative). The impedance of such a unit is

$$Z_L(\omega) = R + j\omega L = j\left(\omega - j\frac{R}{L}\right)L = j(\omega - jd_L)L = j\omega'L \quad (8.1.1)$$

where
$$d_L = R/L \quad (8.1.2)$$
$$\omega' = \omega - jd_L \quad (8.1.3)$$

A dissipative capacitor can be represented as a resistor in parallel with a capacitor (nondissipative), the impedance of which is

$$Z_C(\omega) = \frac{1}{G + j\omega C} = \frac{1}{j(\omega - jG/C)C}$$

$$= \frac{1}{j(\omega - jd_C)} = \frac{1}{j\omega'C} \quad (8.1.4)$$

where
$$d_C = G/C \quad (8.1.5)$$
$$\omega' = \omega - jd_C \quad (8.1.6)$$

Both theoretical considerations and experience[1] have indicated that, in the pass band where filters have an image impedance which is approximately a pure resistance, and in the block region where a filter acts as an electrically long structure, dissipation may be considered as: (1) in the inductors alone, (2) in the capacitors alone, or (3) equally divided between the inductors and capacitors. Mathematically, therefore, on the basis of (3), the effect of dissipation is entered into the nondissipative functions by replacing ω by ω', where

$$\omega' = \omega - j\,\frac{d_L + d_C}{2} \tag{8.1.7}$$

If, as is customarily the situation, d_C vanishes, adjustment to fit the requirement of this last equation leads to

$$\omega' = \omega - j\,\frac{d_L}{2} = \omega - j\,\frac{\omega}{Q} \tag{8.1.8}$$

where

$$Q = 2\,\frac{\omega L}{R} = 2Q_L \tag{8.1.9}$$

i.e., *twice* the Q of the coils.

An approach to the problem of including dissipative effects into filter design, which may be used for computation but is much more useful for the general conclusions which may be drawn from the mathematical results, arises from the well-known Taylor series. In terms of an analytic function of a complex variable, $\Phi(\lambda)$, where λ is considered as complex, the Taylor series for $\Phi(\lambda)$ in the vicinity of Φ_0 is

$$\Phi(\lambda) = \Phi_0 + \Delta\lambda\,\frac{d\Phi_0}{d\lambda} + \frac{(\Delta\lambda)^2}{2!}\,\frac{d^2\Phi_0}{d\lambda^2} + \cdots \tag{8.1.10}$$

For the particular case under consideration, all dissipation in coils, the increment due to dissipation is

$$\Delta\lambda = \left(\lambda - j\,\frac{d_L}{2}\right) - \lambda = -j\,\frac{d_L}{2} = -j\,\frac{\omega}{2Q_L} = -j\,\frac{\omega}{Q} \tag{8.1.11}$$

Therefore the Taylor series is

$$\Phi(\lambda) = \Phi_0 + \left(-j\,\frac{\omega}{Q}\right)\frac{d\Phi_0}{d\lambda} + \frac{1}{2!}\left(-j\,\frac{\omega}{Q}\right)^2\frac{d^2\Phi_0}{d\lambda^2} + \cdots \tag{8.1.12}$$

[1] Bode, H. W., *Network Analysis and Feedback Amplifier Design*, D. Van Nostrand Company, Inc., New York, 1945, p. 216.

Suppose next that the analytic function $\Phi(\lambda)$ is expressed in terms of real and imaginary components of the type of interest here.

$$\Phi(\lambda) = A_d(\omega) + jB_d(\omega) = A(\omega) + jB(\omega) - j\frac{\omega}{Q}\left[\frac{dA(\omega)}{d\lambda} + j\frac{dB(\omega)}{d\lambda}\right]$$

$$- \frac{\omega^2}{2!Q^2}\left[\frac{d^2A(\omega)}{d\lambda^2} + j\frac{d^2B(\omega)}{d\lambda^2}\right] + j\frac{\omega^3}{3!Q^3}$$

$$\left[\frac{d^3A(\omega)}{d\lambda^3} + j\frac{d^3B(\omega)}{d\lambda^3}\right] - \cdots \quad (8.1.13)$$

But since $\Phi(\lambda)$ is analytic, the derivatives are the same in all directions; hence, in particular, derivatives along the ω axis may be used to replace derivatives with respect to λ. Therefore, after making this substitution and then equating reals and imaginaries,

$$A_d(\omega) = A(\omega) + \frac{\omega}{Q}\frac{dB(\omega)}{d\omega} - \frac{1}{2!}\frac{\omega^2}{Q^2}\frac{d^2A(\omega)}{d\omega^2} - \frac{1}{3!}\frac{\omega^3}{Q^3}\frac{d^3B(\omega)}{d\omega^3} + \cdots$$

$$(8.1.14)$$

$$B_d(\omega) = B(\omega) - \frac{\omega}{Q}\frac{dA(\omega)}{d\omega} - \frac{1}{2!}\frac{\omega^2}{Q^2}\frac{d^2B(\omega)}{d\omega^2} + \frac{1}{3!}\frac{\omega^3}{Q^3}\frac{d^3A(\omega)}{d\omega^3} + \cdots$$

$$(8.1.15)$$

Note particularly that $A(\omega)$ and $B(\omega)$ are the functions before the change in variable is made, i.e., before dissipation is added, hence the functions for purely reactive networks.

For the majority of practical cases, moderate variation in the network functions and high Q values, these last equations become

$$A_d(\omega) = A(\omega) + \frac{\omega}{Q}\frac{dB(\omega)}{d\omega} \quad (8.1.16)$$

$$B_d(\omega) = B(\omega) - \frac{\omega}{Q}\frac{dA(\omega)}{d\omega} \quad (8.1.17)$$

This pair of equations is particularly valuable for interpretive purposes.

Suppose, for example, that $A_d(\omega)$ and $B_d(\omega)$ of these last two equations represent the dissipative transfer loss and transfer phase. The correction on the nondissipative functions which small dissipative introduces is proportional to the derivatives, not of the function itself, but of its mate. Over frequency ranges for which the phase is linear, or nearly so, small dissipation has practically no effect on the nondissipative transfer loss except to add a flat loss with no distortion.

In addition to the use to which Eqs. (8.1.16) and (8.1.17) may be put for qualitative purposes, it is possible and sometimes useful to use these equations for actual computation during the preliminary stages of a design.

The fact that the functions must be analytic in any region for which these last two equations may be used indicates they should not be used on the transfer function near cutoff or near poles.

8.2 Computation of the effects of dissipation

An obvious and frequently used method of anticipating the effect of dissipation on a filter design is to use straight computation. The functions $H(x)$ and $Z(x)$ and so $A_I(x)$, $B_I(x)$, and $Z_I(x)$ can be computed on a dissipative basis from the defining equations given in foregoing chapters. The insertion loss and so the behavior of the filter can then be fully determined.

The time and effort required for computation of the dissipative behavior of a network which has elaborate properties is such that some forethought should be expended in planning the computation. One of the methods frequently used is to form the final network by cascading a set of simple networks which give the electrical properties sought. These simple networks individually offer no serious computational difficulties, and so the total network presents no computational difficulty except that of the time consumed. The elaborate design of the next chapter gives fully the significance of designing in terms of a cascaded combination of simple 4TN to produce an elaborate insertion loss pattern. A brief consideration is given next to a type of mathematical manipulation which is frequently useful.

On the basis that the dissipation of a network is such that the Q_L of all inductors is the same, and the Q_C of all capacitors is the same but not necessarily the same as for the inductors, i.e., Q_L and Q_C may or may not be equal, useful general formulas for driving-point impedances of such semiuniformly dissipative networks may be derived as follows. Consider first the relations

$$Z_L(\omega) = R_L + j\omega L = L\left[j\omega\left(1 - j\frac{R_L}{\omega L}\right)\right]$$

$$= L\left[j\omega\left(1 - j\frac{1}{Q_L}\right)\right] = Lg_L(\omega) \qquad (8.2.1)$$

where

$$g_L(\omega) = j\omega\left(1 - j\frac{1}{Q_L}\right), \qquad Q_L = \frac{\omega L}{R_L} \qquad (8.2.2)$$

and

$$Z_C(\omega) = R_C + \frac{1}{j\omega C} = \frac{1}{C}\left[\frac{1}{j\omega}\left(1 + j\frac{R_C}{1/\omega C}\right)\right]$$

$$= \frac{1}{C}\left[\frac{1}{j\omega}\left(1 + j\frac{1}{Q_C}\right)\right] = \frac{1}{C}g_C(\omega) \qquad (8.2.3)$$

where

$$g_C(\omega) = \frac{1}{j\omega}\left(1 + j\frac{1}{Q_C}\right), \qquad Q_C = \frac{1}{R_C\omega C} = \frac{G_C}{\omega C} \qquad (8.2.4)$$

See Problem 8.5 for a suggestion for an alternative treatment.

In terms of these relations, the equations for any network driven from a pair of terminals, Eq. (1.2.1) in a more detailed form, may be written

$$
\begin{bmatrix} V_1 \\ 0 \\ \cdot \\ \cdot \\ \cdot \\ 0 \end{bmatrix} =
\begin{bmatrix}
L_{11}g_L(\omega) + \frac{1}{C_{11}}g_C(\omega) & L_{12}g_L(\omega) + \frac{1}{C_{12}}g_C(\omega) & \cdots & L_{1n}g_L(\omega) + \frac{1}{C_{1n}}g_C(\omega) \\
L_{21}g_L(\omega) + \frac{1}{C_{21}}g_C(\omega) & L_{22}g_L(\omega) + \frac{1}{C_{22}}g_C(\omega) & \cdots & L_{2n}g_L(\omega) + \frac{1}{C_{2n}}g_C(\omega) \\
\cdot & \cdot & & \cdot \\
\cdot & \cdot & & \cdot \\
\cdot & \cdot & & \cdot \\
L_{n1}g_L(\omega) + \frac{1}{C_{n1}}g_C(\omega) & L_{n2}g_L(\omega) + \frac{1}{C_{n2}}g_C(\omega) & \cdots & L_{nn}g_L(\omega) + \frac{1}{C_{nn}}g_C(\omega)
\end{bmatrix}
\begin{bmatrix} I_1 \\ I_2 \\ \cdot \\ \cdot \\ \cdot \\ I_n \end{bmatrix}
$$

$$(8.2.5)$$

If the symbolisms

$$h_1 = \sqrt{\frac{g_L(\omega)}{g_C(\omega)}} = j\omega\sqrt{\frac{1 - j/Q_L}{1 + j/Q_C}} = j\omega q \qquad (8.2.6)$$

where

$$q_1 = \sqrt{\frac{1 - j/Q_L}{1 + j/Q_C}} \qquad (8.2.7)$$

and

$$h_2 = \sqrt{g_L(\omega)g_C(\omega)} = \sqrt{(1 - j/Q_L)(1 + j/Q_C)} \qquad (8.2.8)$$

are used, the system of Eqs. (8.2.5) may be written

$$
\begin{bmatrix} \dfrac{V_1}{h_2} \\ 0 \\ \cdot \\ \cdot \\ \cdot \\ 0 \end{bmatrix}
=
\begin{bmatrix}
L_{11}h_1 + \dfrac{1}{h_1 C_{11}} & L_{12}h_1 + \dfrac{1}{h_1 C_{12}} & \cdots & L_{1n}h_1 + \dfrac{1}{h_1 C_{1n}} \\
L_{21}h_1 + \dfrac{1}{h_1 C_{21}} & L_{22}h_1 + \dfrac{1}{h_1 C_{22}} & \cdots & L_{2n}h_1 + \dfrac{1}{h_1 C_{2n}} \\
\cdot & \cdot & \cdot & \cdot \\
\cdot & \cdot & \cdot & \cdot \\
\cdot & \cdot & \cdot & \cdot \\
L_{n1}h_1 + \dfrac{1}{h_1 C_{n1}} & L_{n2}h_1 + \dfrac{1}{h_1 C_{n2}} & \cdots & L_{nn}h_1 + \dfrac{1}{h_1 C_{nn}}
\end{bmatrix}
\begin{bmatrix} I_1 \\ I_2 \\ \cdot \\ \cdot \\ \cdot \\ I_n \end{bmatrix}
$$

$$(8.2.9)$$

But the form of this set of equations is exactly that of the equations for a nondissipative network with $j\omega$ replaced by h_1 and with the driving voltage V_1 replaced by V_1/h_2. The formulas of Chapter 1 for the driving-point impedance of reactive 2TN may accordingly be readily modified to fit the semiuniform dissipative case; the impedance in each case should be multiplied by h_2, all roots are unchanged, and each ω should be replaced by ωq. The results of such substitutions are as follows:

Equation (1.5.14) becomes

$$Z_d(\omega) = j\omega L_\infty \left(1 + j\frac{1}{Q_C}\right) \frac{(\omega^2 q^2 - \omega_2{}^2)(\omega^2 q^2 - \omega_4{}^2)(\omega^2 q^2 - \omega_6{}^2)}{\omega^2(\omega^2 q^2 - \omega_3{}^2)(\omega^2 q^2 - \omega_5{}^2)}$$

$$(8.2.10)$$

Equation (1.5.19) becomes

$$Z_d(\omega) = -j\omega \frac{1}{C_\infty}\left(1 + j\frac{1}{Q_C}\right) \frac{(\omega^2 q^2 - \omega_2{}^2)(\omega^2 q^2 - \omega_4{}^2)}{\omega^2(\omega^2 q^2 - \omega_3{}^2)(\omega^2 q^2 - \omega_5{}^2)} \qquad (8.2.11)$$

Equation (1.5.24) becomes

$$Z_d(\omega) = j\omega L_\infty \left(1 - j\frac{1}{Q_L}\right) \frac{(\omega^2 q^2 - \omega_2{}^2)(\omega^2 q^2 - \omega_4{}^2)}{(\omega^2 q^2 - \omega_1{}^2)(\omega^2 q^2 - \omega_3{}^2)} \qquad (8.2.12)$$

Equation (1.5.29) becomes

$$Z_d(\omega) = -j\omega \frac{1}{C_\infty}\left(1 - j\frac{1}{Q_L}\right)\frac{(\omega^2 q^2 - \omega_2{}^2)(\omega^2 q^2 - \omega_4{}^2)}{(\omega^2 q^2 - \omega_1{}^2)(\omega^2 q^2 - \omega_3{}^2)(\omega^2 q^2 - \omega_5{}^2)}$$

$$(8.2.13)$$

The modification of these last equations corresponding to a common practical situation of no resistance associated with capacitors follows at once from the vanishing of $1/Q_C$. Note that the constants ω_2, ω_3, etc. are the poles and zeros of the purely reactive network.

Example 8.2.1

Suppose one of the simplest lattices which can be used for a low pass filter is examined. A series arm of a coil and a lattice arm of a series resonator is such a network. The two impedances of this lattice are (from Eq. 8.2.1)

$$Z_x(x) = j\omega_0 L_x x\left(1 - j\frac{1}{Q_{Lx}}\right) = L_x g_{Lx}(x) \qquad (8.2.14)$$

$$Z_y(x) = j\omega_0 L_y x\left(1 - j\frac{1}{Q_{Ly}}\right) + \frac{1}{j\omega_0 C_y x}\left(1 + j\frac{1}{Q_{Cy}}\right)$$

$$= L_y g_{Ly}(x) + \frac{1}{C_y}g_{Cy}(x) \qquad (8.2.15)$$

The ratio function $H(x)$ is then

$$H(x) = \sqrt{\frac{L_x}{L_y}}\sqrt{\frac{g_{Lx}(x)}{g_{Ly}(x) + g_{Cy}(x)/L_y C_y}} \qquad (8.2.16)$$

and, since
$$\omega_0{}^2 = 1/L_y C_y, \qquad m = \sqrt{L_x/L_y} \qquad (8.2.17)$$

$$H(x) = m\sqrt{\frac{1 - j/Q_{Lx}}{(1 - j/Q_{Ly}) - (1 + j/Q_{Cy})/x^2}} \qquad (8.2.18)$$

Or further, for $Q_{Ly} = Q_{Lx} = Q_{Cy} = Q$, i.e., uniform dissipation, the ratio function is

$$H(x) = \frac{m}{\sqrt{1 - 1/x^2 q^2}} \qquad (8.2.19)$$

where
$$q = \sqrt{\frac{1 - j/Q}{1 + j/Q}} \qquad (8.2.20)$$

Finally, if there is no dissipation associated with C_y,

$$H(x) = \frac{m}{\sqrt{1 - 1/x^2(1 - j12)}} \qquad (8.2.21)$$

This last formula is sufficiently accurate for the majority of networks and may be used to compute the transfer loss for the dissipative network.

An assumption which is entirely satisfactory for practical design is that Q is *independent of frequency*. The computational difficulties are much eased by this assumption.

8.3 *The use of charts: block region*

The transfer loss in the block region ($x > 1$), except near cutoff, is, for practical purposes, the same for dissipation of high Q or for purely reactive networks. Consequently, the establishment of the transfer loss of the block region is given in detail in Chapters 3 and 4.

The reflection loss of the block region is given in the charts of Figs. 7.4.4 and 7.4.5. Use of these charts requires the complex number image impedance and terminating impedance. These two impedances must be calculated. For most practical purposes the block-band reflection loss may be computed on a pure reactance basis. Dissipative effects of high-Q coils are usually negligible in affecting the reflection loss. The charts of Figs. 7.4.3, 7.4.4, and 7.4.5 may be used to compute this loss.

The reflection loss at each end of the filter plus the transfer loss ordinarily gives the total insertion loss of the block region.

8.4 *The use of charts: pass band*

In the pass band the insertion loss is affected markedly by dissipation. Direct computation may be used, of course, to determine the pass-band loss. Where it is possible to effect the design in terms of a cascaded set of sections of one pole or no pole of transfer loss, the computed results of Tabulation 8.4.1 may be used for $x < 1$. The results given in this tabulation are for a single pole of transfer loss per section. Note that the peak value of transfer loss is actually not indefinitely large but is as given opposite x_r in the tabulation.

Further consideration of the components of insertion loss of the pass band are given in Secs. 7.8 and 7.9. Use should be made of the material of Chapter 4 to the extent that design precision requires.

The design given in detail in the next chapter serves to simplify the discussion of this chapter.

TAB 8.4.1. TRANSFER LOSS (DB) PER SECTION OF DISSIPATIVE LOW-PASS FILTERS

	$x_p =$ 1.01	1.02	1.03	1.04	1.05	1.06	1.08	1.10	1.14
x									
Q = 10									
0.80	.434	.573	.721	.816	.825	.938	1.016	1.025	1.086
0.85	.651	.877	1.025	1.086	1.216	1.303	1.346	1.425	1.477
0.90	1.129	1.477	1.694	1.867	1.954	2.041	2.102	2.172	2.215
0.92	1.468	1.893	2.172	2.337	2.449	2.493	2.588	2.736	2.632
0.94	1.980	2.562	2.858	3.057	3.179	3.231	3.318	3.353	3.283
0.96	2.788	3.622	3.935	4.143	4.265	4.291	4.369	4.273	4.169
0.98	4.004	5.125	5.602	5.863	5.967	5.993	5.837	5.750	5.402
0.99	4.725	6.028	6.645	6.905	7.062	7.044	6.992	6.671	6.297
1.00	5.377	6.984	7.791	8.069	8.035	8.260	8.052	7.765	7.218
x_r	5.924	8.530	10.77	12.25	13.724	15.079	17.285	19.040	21.949
Q = 20									
0.80	.217	.304	.382	.382	.417	.434	.495	.521	.547
0.85	.356	.443	.339	.565	.669	.669	.686	.730	.756
0.90	.599	.825	.886	.929	.999	1.042	1.086	1.129	1.129
0.92	.816	1.068	1.112	1.259	1.303	1.329	1.390	1.459	1.390
0.94	1.199	1.477	1.624	1.720	1.763	1.798	1.824	1.807	1.737
0.96	1.894	2.258	2.415	2.502	2.519	2.554	2.493	2.432	2.345
0.98	3.474	4.065	4.169	4.195	4.074	4.039	3.822	3.665	3.388
0.99	4.951	5.655	5.724	5.594	5.490	5.264	4.951	4.630	4.239
1.00	6.706	7.861	8.033	7.678	7.383	7.062	6.488	6.054	5.385
x_r	8.347	12.047	14.853	16.938	18.718	20.238	22.174	24.651	27.682
Q = 30									
0.80	.113	.200	.261	.278	.304	.347	.347	.356	.365
0.85	.235	.261	.382	.391	.460	.469	.478	.496	.504
0.90	.408	.521	.599	.634	.695	.712	.738	.738	.756
0.92	.556	.721	.808	.843	.886	.912	1.060	.990	.938
0.94	.834	1.025	1.112	1.155	1.199	1.216	1.233	1.216	1.103
0.96	1.312	1.616	1.711	1.772	1.772	1.781	1.737	1.676	1.590
0.98	2.780	3.153	3.136	3.127	3.066	2.953	2.779	2.649	2.432
0.99	4.934	4.838	4.708	4.473	4.326	4.126	3.839	3.561	3.214
1.00	7.435	7.817	7.444	6.931	6.497	6.080	5.524	5.081	4.517
x_r	10.284	14.705	17.806	20.108	22.062	23.626	25.971	28.073	31.139
Q = 40									
0.80	.104	.148	.191	.200	.235	.243	.252	.261	.269
0.85	.156	.208	.261	.278	.304	.330	.347	.373	.382
0.90	.304	.417	.452	.478	.521	.530	.565	.565	.565
0.92	.443	.530	.608	.643	.660	.678	.712	.730	.695
0.94	.608	.773	.843	1.025	1.164	.955	.938	.929	.912
0.96	1.051	1.251	1.312	1.346	1.364	1.390	1.303	1.259	1.216
0.98	2.276	2.510	2.484	2.476	2.389	2.302	2.172	2.041	1.894
0.99	4.039	4.117	4.082	3.605	3.518	3.344	3.057	2.823	2.606
1.00	7.687	7.505	6.862	6.927	5.820	5.411	4.994	4.517	3.996
x_r	11.835	16.816	20.065	22.497	24.451	26.058	28.577	30.575	33.641
Q = 50									
0.80	.104	.130	.156	.174	.182	.191	.200	.208	.217
0.85	.156	.174	.191	.226	.243	.261	.295	.304	.313
0.90	.208	.313	.365	.391	.417	.434	.434	.452	.452
0.92	.330	.426	.478	.504	.530	.539	.565	.565	.582
0.94	.495	.599	.660	.712	.730	.738	.747	.747	.738
0.96	.851	.990	1.07	1.09	1.09	1.09	1.07	1.04	1.01
0.98	1.89	2.07	2.09	2.03	1.95	1.88	1.82	1.67	1.53
0.99	3.52	3.68	3.39	3.17	2.99	2.87	2.61	2.43	2.23
1.00	7.50	7.17	6.36	5.78	5.30	4.99	4.46	4.13	3.61
x_r	13.50	18.60	21.98	24.41	26.49	28.14	30.49	32.49	35.70
Q = 100									
0.80	.043	.052	.069	.078	.078	.087	.096	.096	.104
0.85	.069	.087	.113	.122	.122	.122	.130	.130	.139
0.90	.113	.156	.174	.191	.200	.200	.208	.217	.226
0.92	.165	.200	.217	.235	.252	.261	.269	.269	.278
0.94	.243	.295	.330	.347	.356	.356	.365	.365	.356
0.96	.434	.504	.539	.556	.556	.556	.547	.539	.495
0.98	1.02	1.09	1.07	1.04	.999	.973	.938	.869	.799
0.99	2.04	1.95	1.79	1.71	1.59	1.52	1.41	1.29	1.20
1.00	7.05	5.63	4.86	4.41	4.03	3.66	3.25	2.95	2.55
x_r	18.50	24.32	27.80	30.31	32.14	33.88	36.48	38.39	42.13
Q = 150									
0.80	.034	.043	.043	.052	.061	.061	.069	.069	.069
0.85	.052	.061	.069	.069	.078	.087	.096	.104	.104
0.90	.087	.104	.122	.122	.130	.139	.139	.139	.139
0.92	.113	.139	.156	.122	.174	.174	.174	.182	.182
0.94	.122	.200	.217	.226	.235	.235	.235	.243	.235
0.96	.287	.330	.347	.356	.356	.356	.347	.339	.313
0.98	.669	.738	.712	.695	.634	.617	.608	.585	.512
0.99	1.48	1.35	1.26	1.14	1.11	1.06	.973	.869	.764
1.00	6.25	4.73	4.08	3.56	3.27	3.00	2.65	2.39	2.04
x_r	21.80	27.80	32.07	33.70	35.79	37.35	39.96	42.13	45.17
Q = 200									
0.80	.026	.034	.034	.034	.043	.043	.043	.052	.052
0.85	.043	.043	.052	.061	.061	.061	.069	.069	.078
0.90	.061	.078	.087	.087	.087	.096	.096	.096	.104
0.92	.087	.104	.113	.122	.122	.122	.130	.130	.139
0.94	.122	.148	.156	.165	.165	.174	.174	.182	.182
0.96	.217	.243	.261	.269	.269	.269	.260	.261	.252
0.98	.521	.539	.539	.521	.504	.486	.469	.443	.408
0.99	1.06	1.03	.955	.903	.851	.790	.730	.660	.591
x_r	22.93	29.62	33.35	35.96	38.04	39.70	42.47	44.47	47.60
1.00	5.62	4.21	3.56	3.13	2.81	2.55	2.21	1.99	1.72

TAB. 8.4.1. TRANSFER LOSS (DB) PER SECTION OF DISSIPATIVE LOW-PASS FILTERS

$x_p =$	1.20	1.25	1.30	1.35	1.40	1.50	2.00	2.50	3.00	∞
x										
0.80	1.155	1.173	1.216	1.207	1.207	1.207	1.190	1.181	1.155	1.129
0.85	1.494	1.520	1.537	1.563	1.563	1.520	1.477	1.459	1.433	1.407
0.90	2.215	2.215	2.172	2.128	2.085	2.041	1.867	1.844	1.781	1.755
0.92	2.623	2.519	2.476	2.476	2.397	2.302	2.128	2.085	2.067	1.911
0.94	3.144	3.040	2.988	2.953	2.866	2.719	2.380	2.363	2.345	2.258
0.96	3.909	3.778	3.561	3.561	3.474	3.266	2.997	2.797	2.780	2.606
0.98	5.081	4.777	4.604	4.430	4.213	3.996	3.561	3.483	3.370	3.127
0.99	5.759	5.429	5.212	4.994	4.708	4.473	3.996	3.761	3.735	3.518
1.00	6.558	6.167	5.950	5.602	5.385	5.125	4.386	4.195	4.082	3.909
x_r	25.146	27.187	28.890	30.488	31.704	33.962	41.563	46.470	50.118	—
0.80	.573	.591	.608	.608	.608	.608	.608	.599	.573	.452
0.85	.781	.781	.781	.781	.781	.781	.747	.730	.695	.651
0.90	1.129	1.129	1.129	1.094	1.068	1.042	.990	.973	.912	.886
0.92	1.346	1.320	1.303	1.268	1.233	1.199	1.112	1.068	1.060	1.042
0.94	1.694	1.650	1.563	1.520	1.477	1.433	1.303	1.251	1.233	1.181
0.96	2.102	2.041	1.911	1.911	1.885	1.798	1.1616	1.511	1.503	1.477
0.98	3.066	2.972	2.710	2.693	2.588	2.389	2.145	2.006	1.963	1.865
0.99	3.796	3.561	3.344	3.275	3.127	2.910	2.588	2.389	2.371	2.302
1.00	4.821	4.430	4.169	4.065	3.883	3.605	3.136	2.979	2.884	2.771
x_r	30.948	33.094	34.874	36.394	37.741	40.042	47.599	52.463	56.112	—
0.80	.391	.417	.400	.400	.400	.391	.391	.391	.391	.391
0.85	.504	.521	.521	.530	.547	.625	.495	.486	.469	.460
0.90	.756	.773	.843	.738	.712	.695	.678	.660	.617	.565
0.92	.912	.869	.825	.825	.825	.825	.738	.721	.712	.678
0.94	1.086	1.042	1.042	1.008	.886	.973	.886	.843	.825	.782
0.96	1.485	1.407	1.303	1.303	1.303	1.242	1.103	1.034	1.024	.955
0.98	2.189	2.041	1.937	1.920	1.841	1.720	1.485	1.459	1.425	1.286
0.99	2.840	2.641	2.519	2.328	2.302	2.154	1.911	1.824	1.755	1.650
1.00	3.996	3.648	3.474	3.361	2.997	2.953	2.571	2.432	2.380	2.215
x_r	34.466	38.611	38.375	39.869	41.215	43.517	51.074	55.938	59.586	—
0.80	.278	.287	.295	.304	.304	.304	.304	.304	.287	.287
0.85	.391	.391	.391	.400	.391	.391	.365	.365	.347	.347
0.90	.565	.565	.565	.547	.539	.530	.486	.478	.460	.452
0.92	.695	.651	.651	.634	.608	.591	.565	.539	.521	.504
0.94	.851	.825	.782	.782	.782	.758	.651	.617	.608	.591
0.96	1.112	1.060	1.025	1.008	.990	.947	.825	.782	.773	.738
0.98	1.694	1.563	1.520	1.477	1.407	1.303	1.138	1.094	1.068	.955
0.99	2.328	2.145	2.041	1.928	1.885	1.737	1.511	1.390	1.346	1.259
1.00	3.474	3.257	3.014	2.910	2.753	2.588	2.241	2.102	2.050	1.850
x_r	36.950	39.087	40.824	42.000	44.172	46.036	53.593	58.457	62.105	—
0.80	.226	.235	.235	.243	.243	.243	.235	.235	.235	.235
0.85	.321	.321	.313	.313	.313	.313	.295	.295	.295	.287
0.90	.460	.452	.460	.443	.434	.426	.382	.373	.365	.347
0.92	.547	.539	.539	.512	.504	.478	.443	.426	.417	.408
0.94	.678	.669	.634	.617	.617	.582	.539	.504	.504	.495
0.96	.912	.869	.825	.808	.790	.730	.660	.617	.608	.599
0.98	1.37	1.31	1.22	1.18	1.14	1.09	.955	.895	.834	.773
0.99	1.93	1.85	1.72	1.58	1.54	1.44	1.24	1.18	1.11	1.09
1.00	3.09	2.89	2.70	2.57	2.48	2.33	2.01	1.89	1.82	1.65
x_r	38.83	40.30	42.82	44.21	45.60	47.95	55.59	60.45	64.10	—
0.80	.104	.113	.122	.113	.113	.113	.113	.113	.113	.113
0.85	.148	.148	.148	.148	.148	.148	.139	.139	.139	.130
0.90	.226	.217	.217	.208	.208	.200	.182	.174	.165	.148
0.92	.269	.261	.261	.252	.243	.235	.208	.191	.182	.174
0.94	.339	.321	.313	.304	.295	.278	.243	.235	.235	.226
0.96	.452	.434	.408	.400	.382	.356	.330	.313	.304	.295
0.98	.704	.660	.617	.591	.582	.573	.504	.460	.443	.434
0.99	1.01	.990	.921	.860	.825	.764	.678	.643	.634	.617
1.00	2.21	2.03	1.91	1.78	1.72	1.63	1.41	1.30	1.28	1.25
x_r	44.73	47.08	48.73	50.29	51.68	53.86	61.58	66.45	70.71	—
0.80	.078	.078	.078	.078	.078	.078	.078	.078	.078	.078
0.85	.104	.104	.104	.104	.096	.096	.096	.087	.087	.087
0.90	.139	.139	.139	.130	.130	.122	.104	.104	.096	.096
0.92	.182	.174	.165	.156	.156	.148	.122	.122	.122	.122
0.94	.226	.217	.200	.191	.191	.174	.148	.148	.148	.148
0.96	.295	.278	.260	.251	.243	.235	.217	.208	.200	.200
0.98	.469	.443	.417	.408	.400	.373	.339	.313	.295	.295
0.99	.686	.660	.625	.591	.565	.539	.486	.443	.417	.408
1.00	1.78	1.66	1.55	1.48	1.42	1.36	1.16	1.06	1.04	.990
x_r	48.47	50.64	52.29	53.77	55.07	57.50	65.15	70.01	73.66	—
0.80	.061	.061	.061	.061	.061	.061	.061	.061	.061	.061
0.85	.078	.078	.078	.078	.087	.078	.069	.069	.069	.061
0.90	.113	.104	.104	.096	.096	.096	.087	.078	.078	.078
0.92	.130	.122	.122	.113	.113	.104	.096	.096	.096	.087
0.94	.165	.156	.139	.130	.122	.113	.113	.113	.113	.104
0.96	.217	.200	.182	.174	.174	.165	.156	.156	.156	.148
0.98	.365	.330	.313	.295	.295	.278	.243	.235	.235	.226
0.99	.530	.486	.469	.443	.434	.408	.356	.339	.321	.313
x_r	50.81	52.98	54.72	56.37	57.76	60.02	67.58	72.44	76.09	—
1.00	1.55	1.42	1.34	1.27	1.22	1.16	.99	.91	.89	.87

Problems

8.1 Consider a low-pass, constant-k, T-section filter, where $\omega_0 = 100{,}000$, $R_0 = 100$. Plot curves of transfer loss and phase, dissipative and nondissipative, for $Q_L = 50$. Use the complete formulas and the approximation of Eqs. (8.1.15) and (8.1.16). Show the effect of dissipation and note whether Eqs. (8.1.15) and (8.1.16) are effective in specifying this result.

8.2 Repeat the preceding problem for an m-derived network with $x_p = 1.02$.

8.3 Consider the LP lattice $X_{L00}X_{C01}$ for which $L_x = 500$ μh, $L_y = 1.5$ mh, $C_y = 0.05$ μf. Use the formulas of Sec. 8.2 to establish the equations for Z_x and Z_y. Assume $Q_L = 100$ and $Q_C = \infty$.

Calculate R_x and R_y from Q_L at the resonant frequency of Z_y. The constant K for each impedance may be evaluated by setting the Z_x and Z_y equa-equations equal to the impedance at the frequency for which R_x and R_y were determined.

Determine and plot $A_I(\omega)$ and $B_I(\omega)$ for this dissipative structure.

8.4 Repeat the preceding problem for the low-pass lattice $X_{L10}X_{C00}$. Take $L_x = 1.5$ mh, $C_x = 0.05$ μf and $L_y = 500$ μh.

8.5 If instead of RC series element an R element is paralleled with a C element, show that Eq. (8.2.5) applies exactly as given for $Z_L(\omega)$, $g_L(\omega)$, Q_L as given in Sec. 8.2 and for

$$Z_C(\omega) = \frac{1}{C}\left(\frac{1}{j\omega}\frac{1}{1 - j/Q_c}\right) = \frac{1}{C}g_C(\omega)$$

$$g_C(\omega) = \frac{1}{j\omega}\frac{1}{1 - j/Q_c}, \qquad Q_c = \frac{\omega C}{G_c}$$

$$h_1 = \sqrt{g_L(\omega)/g_C(\omega)} = j\omega\sqrt{(1 - j/Q_L)(1 - j/Q_c)} = j\omega q$$

$$h_2 = \sqrt{g_L(\omega)g_C(\omega)} = \sqrt{(1 - j/Q_L)/(1 - j/Q_c)}$$

Show the form that Eqs. (8.2.10), (8.2.11), (8.2.12), and (8.2.13) take under this change.

CHAPTER NINE

Design of a Low-Pass Filter

The material presented in the foregoing discussions of this book is almost wholly and directly pertinent to the design of low-pass filters. Of necessity these discussions have been of a more or less piecemeal character. The present chapter in a sense ties all the pieces together by way of a specific design.

9.1 Filter requirements

A structurally symmetric, unbalanced filter is to be designed to operate into and out of 75 ohms resistance. The image impedance

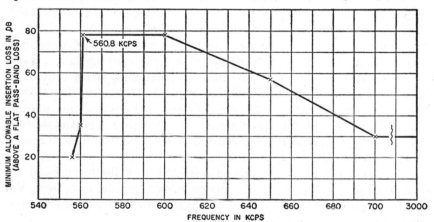

Fig. 9.1.1

must be better than an m-derived impedance, but not greatly better, i.e., a $Z(x)$ function which crosses the unity line three times is adequate if the deviation of the $Z(x)$ from unity is uniform over the pass band. The pass band is to cover the frequency range $0 \leq f \leq 551.7$ kc, i.e., the last useful frequency of the pass band is 551.7 kc.

The insertion loss, above the pass band, must not be less than given by the set of straight line segments of Fig. 9.1.1 over the frequency range $556 \leq f \leq 3000$ kc. Also the insertion loss should be as near flat as possible over the pass band, $0 \leq f \leq 551.7$ kc. The actual value of this pass band flat loss should be as low as possible.

Over the frequency range $551.7 \leq f \leq 556$ kc, or over a band of 4.3 kc, no requirements are placed on the filter behavior. This no requirement band serves to ease the design problem or perhaps more accurately, there always exists such a frequency range about cutoff over which no control of the filter characteristics is ordinarily possible.

The remainder of this chapter is a detailed discussion of the design of an unbalanced 4TN which meets the foregoing requirements.

9.2 Location of cut-off

The network requirements given in the preceding section in no way specify the location of cutoff beyond indicating that it should be somewhere in the frequency range: $551.7 \leq f \leq 556$ kc. The insertion loss rise of 78 db in a frequency band of $560.8 - 551.7 = 9.1$ kc indicates a sharp rise in loss, and therefore that the cutoff should be as near 560.8 as feasible. Placing cutoff too close to 560.8, however, is certain to lead to ultimate difficulties in realizing the required inductors and capacitors of the filter because of extremes in size, although the pass band deviation of $Z_I(x)$ is thereby reduced.

There is no known precise criterion for locating cutoff in spite of the dominant position of this frequency in the image impedance, transfer loss design techniques. Experience in designing filters ultimately removes the choice of cutoff from the region of pure guess into that of "engineering estimate." Still the location of cutoff is not precise. Midway between the last useful frequency of the pass band and the first useful frequency of the block band is a conservative first estimate. The difficulty with such a criterion is that the last useful frequency of the pass band and the first useful frequency of the block band are not always in evidence. In the design under consideration here, the last useful frequency of the pass band is in evidence (551.7 kc) but the first useful block-band frequency is not.

Suppose then that for the purposes of this design the cutoff is chosen at 555 kc, a little down frequency from the mid-point between the last useful pass-band frequency (551.6 kc) and the high-loss point (560.8 kc).

9.3 Location of image impedance controls

A minimum of two block-region control frequencies is required to realize the three crossings of $Z(x)$ and the unity line. Since at the start of the design, at least, there is no evident virtue in requiring more than this minimum of two impedance controls, the design is so started.

In accordance with the discussions of Chapter 6, a half section is available which presents the image impedance desired at one pair of terminals and constant-k image impedance at the other pair of terminals (Figs. 6.5.1 and 6.6.1). Two such terminating half sections are to be used on this filter. Location of the two poles of transfer loss can be effected by using the method of Sec. 4.14, since the image impedance should deviate as near uniformly as possible from 75 ohms over the total pass band (0 to 551.7 kc). These two poles of transfer loss should be located first and the corresponding transfer loss plotted, since this much of the transfer loss is fixed by the image impedance requirements and is not subject to change except in the allowance for dissipation.

Precisely as in Example 4.14.1, the two impedance controls are located as follows:

$$x_{uz} = \frac{\omega_u}{\omega_0} = \frac{f_u}{f_0} = \frac{551.7}{555} = 0.994054$$

$$\theta = \sin^{-1} k_z = 83.7488°$$

and from Eq. (4.14.8) the two impedance controls are located at

$$\frac{f_1}{f_0} = x_1 = \frac{1}{\text{sn}\,(2K/3)}, \quad \frac{f_2}{f_0} = x_2 = \frac{1}{\text{sn}\,(K/3)}$$

By interpolation from Tabulation 4.14.1, corresponding to the value of θ already computed,

$$\text{sn}\,\frac{2K}{3} = 0.986472, \qquad \text{sn}\,\frac{K}{3} = 0.836310$$

Then the control frequencies are located by

$$x_1 = x_{p1} = \frac{1}{0.986472} = 1.0137135$$

$$x_2 = x_{p2} = \frac{1}{0.836310} = 1.1957288$$

from which

$$f_1 = f_0 x_1 = \frac{555}{\text{sn}\,(2K/3)} = \frac{555}{0.986472} = 562.611 \text{ kc}$$

$$f_2 = f_0 x_2 = \frac{555}{\text{sn}\,(K/3)} = \frac{555}{0.836310} = 663.629 \text{ kc}$$

The values of the parameter m from these control frequencies are

$$m_1 = \sqrt{1 - \omega_0^2/\omega_1^2} = \sqrt{1 - (0.986472)^2} = 0.1639298$$
$$m_2 = \sqrt{1 - \omega_0^2/\omega_2^2} = \sqrt{1 - (0.836310)^2} = 0.5482568$$

The locations of the crossings of the unity line and $Z(x)$ are of no particular interest for the design, and so they are not computed.

The combined transfer loss of the two terminating half sections is that of two full peak sections, or m-derived sections, in cascade, with poles of transfer loss at the already computed frequencies of 562.6 kc and 663.6 kc.

The curves of Fig. 9.3.1 show the transfer loss curves for each of the two full peak sections and for the two full peak sections in cascade,

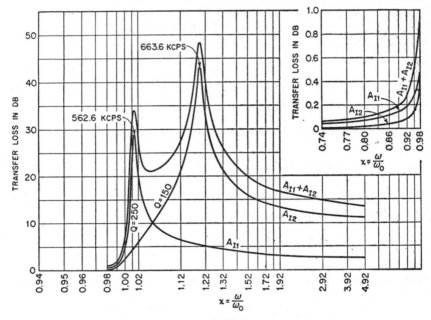

Fig. 9.3.1

which in turn is the transfer loss of the two terminating sections for the filter. The curve with peak nearest cutoff was calculated from Eqs. (8.2.21) and (3.2.10) for $Q = 250$ since dissipation is particularly effective in the vicinity of cutoff. A coil Q of 250 was chosen as being as high as economy balanced against rather severe requirements of transfer loss rise near cutoff would permit. The transfer loss curve with peak at 663.6 kc was calculated in the vicinity of cutoff (Eq. 8.2.21), taken from Tabulation 8.4.1 for the remainder of the pass band and from Tabulation 4.7.1 over the remainder of the frequency range. A $Q = 150$ was used for this computation. The remoteness of the peak of transfer loss from cutoff makes a lower-Q coil satisfactory.

9.4 Number of poles of transfer loss

There is no effective method available for determining the total number of poles of transfer loss required to meet other than a flat loss

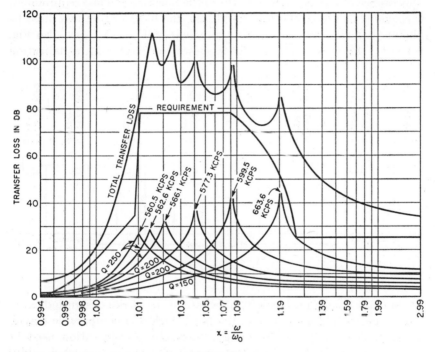

Fig. 9.4.1

specification. Rough sketching on the basis of purely reactive transfer loss curves, Tabulation 4.7.1 or Fig. 4.7.2, is perhaps the best method of obtaining a first estimate of the number and location of the poles of transfer loss. In so far as possible, anticipation of the dissipative lowering of peaks and raising of the loss near cutoff should be included in the estimate. Once this first rough estimate of the situation has been reached, computation and/or use of charts must be resorted to in order to introduce the effect of dissipation.

On the basis of such a pattern of estimation and computation, the transfer loss curves of Fig. 9.4.1 (individual and total) were established.

The realization of this transfer loss curve requires a ladder network consisting of the two terminating half sections connected in cascade with four peak sections. Such a network is represented by Fig. 9.4.2. Whether this network will produce the desired insertion loss is not yet evident. The reflection loss and interaction loss are still to be added. The transformer loss vanishes since the two terminal impedances are alike.

Another factor which calls for some consideration is the fact of the appearance of a pass-band loss. Since the block-region loss requirement is specified as above the pass-band loss, the block-region loss must be higher than the insertion loss requirement of Fig. 9.1.1 (see also Fig. 9.4.1) by the pass-band loss. As is shown in Chapter 11, equalization

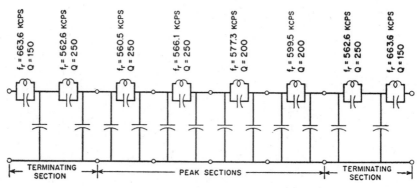

Fig. 9.4.2

of the pass band to a flat loss, at whatever level the design indicates, also serves to add a flat loss in the block region of comparable magnitude. At this stage in the design, therefore, consideration need be given only to whether the reflection and interaction loss when added to the transfer loss still leaves a little slack, so to speak.

As a consequence of requiring that the filter be realized as a ladder network, poles of reflection loss occur at the poles of transfer loss for the terminating half sections, i.e., at the image impedance control frequencies, 562.6 kc and 663.6 kc, and a 6 db gain occurs at some frequency between them. On the basis of subtracting 6 db from the low points of the transfer loss (Fig. 9.4.1), it seems likely that the reflection loss may not prevent the transfer loss already established from serving.

As suggested as an exercise for the reader by Problem 9.2, the interaction loss is negligible on the basis of a computational investigation.

9.5 Reflection loss

As a first estimate, fully adequate for the present design, the reflection loss on a purely reactive basis may be computed.

The image impedance formula for this reactive network, $Z_{\infty 3}(x)$ as in Fig. 6.5.1, is

$$Z_{\infty 3}(x) = \frac{R_0}{R} \frac{1 - x^2/x_1{}^2}{(1 - x^2/x_2{}^2) \sqrt{1 - x^2}} \tag{9.5.1}$$

The reciprocal of this equation, exclusive of the constant multiplier R_0/R, is shown plotted on Fig. 9.5.1. The reciprocal of $Z_{\infty 3}(x)$ is used

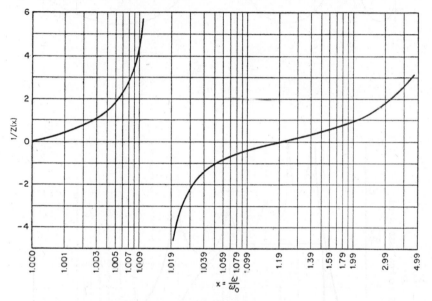

Fig. 9.5.1

in order to keep the curve between cutoff and x_1 more conveniently located on the graph (smaller numbers). Multiplication of values on this graph by R/R_0 (see Problem 9.4 for evaluation of R_0) gives $1/Z_{\infty 3}(x)$, which may be used to enter the charts of Figs. 7.4.4 and 7.4.5, or the real part of Eq. (7.3.7) may be used to compute the reflection loss component of insertion loss of the block region. The result of such computation is shown on Fig. 9.5.2.

Addition of this reflection loss to the total transfer loss of Fig. 9.4.1 gives the total insertion loss for the filter under consideration. The result of this addition is shown in Fig. 9.5.3, along with the requirement curve. Evidently, the insertion loss shown by this curve does meet

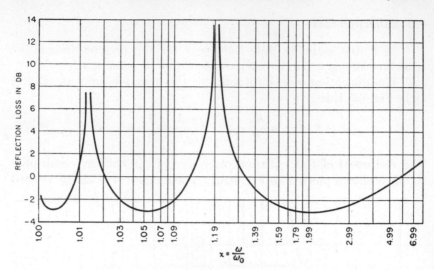

Fig. 9.5.2

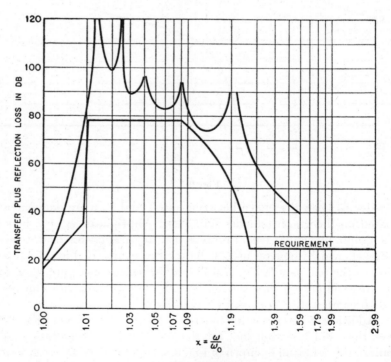

Fig. 9.5.3

the requirement given, and on the basis of so doing, may be considered as determining the filter sought.

9.6 Determination of element values

Determination of the element values of the network is a matter of routine computation from formulas given by Fig. 5.5.1j for all the interior peak sections. The terminating half sections should have element values as computed from the formulas given for such half section on Fig. 6.5.1. Computation of these elements is not carried out

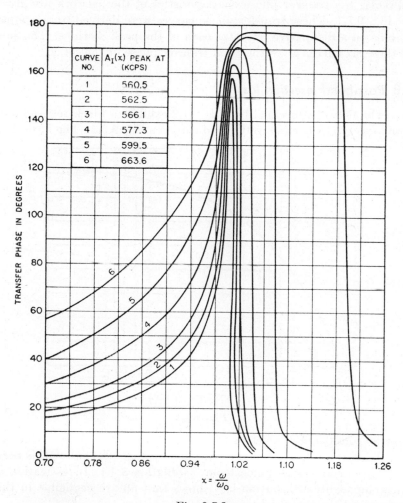

CURVE NO.	$A_T(x)$ PEAK AT (KCPS)
1	560.5
2	562.5
3	566.1
4	577.3
5	599.5
6	663.6

$$x = \frac{\omega}{\omega_0}$$

Fig. 9.7.1

here, since nothing would thereby be added to the value of the present discussion.

Once these element values are computed, the network is completely determined, since the Q values of the coils are already specified as given in the curves of Fig. 9.4.1 or in Fig. 9.4.2.

9.7 Transfer phase

The transfer phase of the filter designed in the foregoing is not in any way a contributing factor in the design. As an item of interest, however, the transfer phase characteristics of the network are given on Fig. 9.7.1. These transfer phase curves were derived from computations on a dissipative basis for each of the peak sections. The sum of these six curves gives the total transfer phase of the filter.

9.8 Pass-band insertion loss

The network specified by Fig. 9.4.2 exhibits a block-region insertion loss extremely close to that indicated on Fig. 9.5.3. The filter then

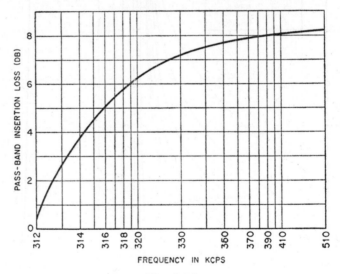

Fig. 9.8.1

may be considered as meeting the initial requirements except that the pass-band loss is far from flat. The curve of Fig. 9.8.1 shows this pass-band insertion loss as taken from Tabulation 8.4.1. Investigation of the components of insertion loss shows that all are negligible in this case except the transfer loss.

The technique for designing an additional network (equalizer), to be connected in cascade with the network represented by Fig. 9.4.2 so that the pass-band insertion loss is flat, is given in Chapter 11 (see also Problem 11.12).

Problems

9.1 Plot transfer loss curves for purely reactive peak sections which have poles of transfer loss at the 6 pole frequencies of Fig. 9.4.1. Add the six curves and compare the result with Fig. 9.4.1 and thereby note the effect of dissipation.

9.2 Calculate interaction loss at a few points, both pass and block region, for the location of transfer-loss poles as given in Fig. 9.4.1 and show thereby that this loss is entirely negligible for the design of this chapter.

9.3 Calculate the design resistance R_0 for the condition of deviation of $Z(x)$ from R as discussed in Sec. 4.14 and Example 4.16.1.

9.4 Compute the element values for the complete filter as specified by Fig. 9.4.2.

9.5 Design a low-pass filter which has an insertion loss of 78 db at 68 kc and the lowest possible loss at 64 kc. The impedance at and in the vicinity of 64 kc must be resistive and slowly varying. The terminal impedances are 75 ohms resistance.

9.6 Calculate and plot the pass-band insertion loss of the network represented by Fig. 9.4.2 for $0 \leq x \leq 1.05$. Compare with Figs. 9.3.1 and 9.8.1.

CHAPTER TEN

Frequency Transformations

The material presented in the preceding parts of this book is almost entirely a consideration of the properties of low-pass structures. Early in the discussion it is indicated that there is little loss of generality in such a restriction. Indeed considerable simplification in the treatment of this rather complex problem is thereby made possible. That the low-pass techniques developed in the foregoing are actually usable to effect the design of high-pass, symmetrical band-pass, and symmetrical band-block filters is demonstrated in this chapter.

10.1 *Frequency transformation: basic concepts*

An understanding of a particular interpretation of the common technique of changing variable in mathematical expressions is essential to an effective understanding of the frequency transformations of this chapter. Consider some function $f(x)$ and a second function $x = \Phi(x')$. The equality

$$f(x) = f[\Phi(x')] = F(x') \tag{10.1.1}$$

is valid, but precisely what does this equality mean? It certainly does not mean that the functions $f(x)$ and $F(x')$, when plotted on their respective abscissa scales (x and x'), need bear any pictorial resemblance to each other. The equality does indicate that at each x' value which specifies a corresponding x value from $x = \Phi(x')$ (there may be one or several), the ordinate value is the same (see Fig. 10.1.1). The effect of interpreting a transformation of variable in the foregoing manner is to view such transformations as contracting, expanding, relocating portions of, or reversing all or portions of the abscissa and its associated curve $f(x)$. The following discussions amply illustrate the meaning intended in this last statement.

An additional aspect of *frequency* transformations of use in filter design is the requirement that the transformation must lead to physical networks. For example, if ω and ω' both represent real frequencies and so $\omega > 0$ and $\omega' > 0$ are the useful ranges of these variables, and if a transformation $\omega = -2\omega'$ were used, the impedance of an inductor would change from $Z_L(\omega) = j\omega L$ to $Z_L(\omega') = -j\omega'2L = j\omega'(-2L)$. The inductor for variable ω' would then be nonphysical as $-2L$.

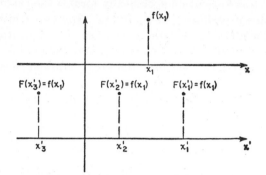

x_1', x_2', x_3' SPECIFY x_1 THROUGH A
CUBIC RELATION $x = \phi(x')$

Fig. 10.1.1

Such a transformation would not be useful if physical networks must be the end result.

10.2 Frequency transformation: expansion or contraction of frequency spectrum

Consider the frequency transformation

$$p = \frac{\omega_1}{\omega'_1} p' \qquad (10.2.1)$$

where $\qquad p = j\omega \quad \text{and} \quad p' = j\omega' \qquad (10.2.2)$

and ω_1 and ω'_1 are positive constants, so that

$$\omega = \frac{\omega_1}{\omega'_1} \omega' \qquad (10.2.3)$$

Such a transformation leads to

$$Z_L(\omega) = j\omega L = j\omega'\left(\frac{\omega'}{\omega'_1} L\right) = j\omega'L_L, \qquad L_L = \frac{\omega_1}{\omega'_1} L \quad (10.2.4)$$

$$Z_C(\omega) = \frac{1}{j\omega C} = \frac{1}{j\omega'(\omega'C/\omega'_1)} = \frac{1}{j\omega'C_C}, \qquad C_C = \frac{\omega_1}{\omega'_1} C \quad (10.2.5)$$

Since every impedance of a network would be affected in exactly the manner shown by these last equations, a network consisting of L' and C' elements would have the same frequency response at any ω' as the corresponding network of L and C elements at $\omega = (\omega_1/\omega'_1)\omega'$. Incidentally, this transformation specifically locates the same ordinate, or functional value if preferred, at ω_1 and ω'_1, any two arbitrarily chosen points on the ω and ω' abscissas, since from the transformation, when $\omega = \omega_1$, then $\omega' = \omega'_1$. Also the arrow-marked regions a, b, c, and d of Fig. 10.2.1a are transformed into the arrow-marked regions a', b', c', and d', respectively.

The foregoing transformation in terms of the variables $x = \omega/\omega_0$ and $x' = \omega'/\omega'_0$ is

$$x = \frac{x_1}{x'_1} x' \qquad (10.2.6)$$

which transforms the point x_1 into x'_1, or vice versa (see Fig. 10.2.1a).

A different interpretation of the frequency transformation is more useful for purposes of filter design. It is more convenient to consider both ω and ω' (x and x') as plotted on the same abscissa and to interpret the transformation as a shift and/or deformation of the curves, $f(x)$ and $F(x)$ of Fig. 10.2.1b for this shift or deformation on a linear abscissa. If the abscissa is logarithmic, as is common in studying network functions, and the transformation of Eq. (10.2.6) is used,

$$y = \log x, \qquad y' = \log x'$$

$$y = \log \frac{x'_1}{x_1} + \log x' = \log \frac{x_1}{x'_1} + y' \qquad (10.2.7)$$

The effect of the linear shift of Eqs. (10.2.3) and (10.2.6) is then to shift a curve unaltered in form along the abscissa, $\Phi(y)$ and $\psi(y')$ of Fig. 10.2.1b.

The linear transformation described in this section is useful to make corrective adjustments in a design characteristic which does not meet requirements at some particular frequency. For example, as suggested by Fig. 10.2.1c, a frequency characteristic $f(x)$ which does not meet the requirements at a can be shifted by the transformation $x = (x_1/x'_1)x'$ to meet the requirement as shown by $F(x')$.

One caution should perhaps be noted in connection with this linear transformation. While any one frequency point may be transformed into any other frequency point, the frequency spectrum is expanded or contracted by the transformation so that the frequency spacing is altered. For example, the frequency spacing between the last useful frequency of impedance and the first useful frequency of

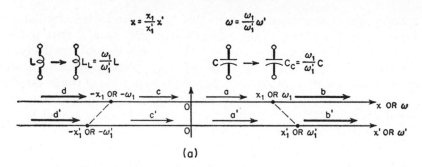

$$x = \frac{x_1}{x_1'}x' \qquad \omega = \frac{\omega_1}{\omega_1'}\omega'$$

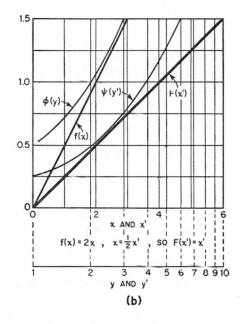

(b)

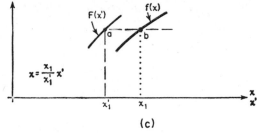

(c)

Fig. 10.2.1

transfer loss is expanded or contracted by the linear transformation. Design requirements may be tight enough that such a shift (either contraction or expansion) may not be permissible. Alternatively, if the frequency spacing between x_{uz} and x_{uA} is considered as fixed, the linear transformation expands or contracts the portion of the frequency functions between these frequencies. In any event, the effect of the linear transformation at critical points should be investigated before it is incorporated into a design.

10.3 Frequency transformation; low pass to high pass

The reciprocal transformation

$$p = j\omega = \frac{\omega_1\omega'_1}{j\omega'} = \frac{\omega_1\omega'_1}{p'} \tag{10.3.1}$$

which leads to

$$\omega = -\frac{\omega_1\omega'_1}{\omega'} \tag{10.3.2}$$

and, if $x = \omega/\omega_0$ and $x' = \omega'/\omega'_0$, to

$$x = \frac{-x_1x'_1}{x'} \tag{10.3.3}$$

is next shown to transform a physical low-pass reactive network and its mathematical characteristics into a high-pass reactive network and its mathematical characteristics. Consider the element value transformations first.

The following two equations should be self-explanatory.

$$Z_L(\omega) = pL = \frac{\omega_1\omega'_1}{p'} L = \frac{1}{p'/\omega_1\omega'_1L} = \frac{1}{p'C_L}$$
$$C_L = \frac{1}{\omega\,\omega'_1L} \tag{10.3.4}$$

$$Z_C(\omega) = \frac{1}{pC} = \frac{1}{\omega_1\omega'_1C/p'} = p'\frac{1}{\omega_1\omega'_1C} p'L_C$$
$$L_C = \frac{1}{\omega_1\omega'_1C} \tag{10.3.5}$$

This reciprocal transformation therefore transforms physical L and C elements into physical C' and L' elements, respectively. Furthermore, if $0 \leq x \leq x_1$,   then $-\infty < x' \leq -x'_1$

if $x_1 \leq x < \infty$,   then $-x'_1 \leq x' \leq 0$

if $-x_1 \leq x \leq 0$,   then $x'_1 \leq x' < \infty$

if $-\infty < x \leq -x_1$,   then $0 \leq x' \leq x'_1$

the regions shown on the x scale of Fig. 10.3.1a transform into other regions as indicated on the x' scale, i.e., the regions are relocated; a into a', b into b', etc. by the reciprocal transformations.

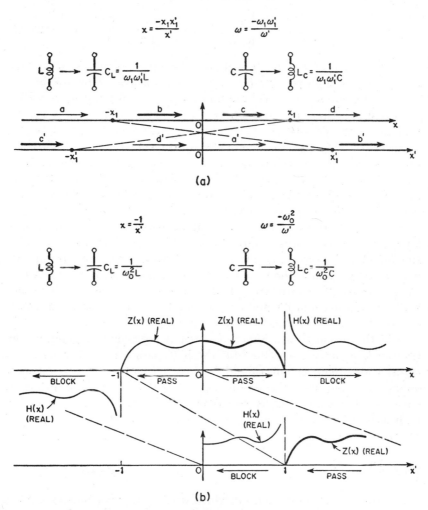

(a)

(b)

Fig. 10.3.1

A special case of this reciprocal transformation, for which cutoff ω_0 corresponds on both the x and x' scales to unity, is the most useful in practice. Only this special case is considered further, i.e., the case of $\omega_0 = \omega'_0 = \omega_1 = \omega'_1$. At once from Eqs. (10.3.3) and (10.3.2),

$$x = \frac{-1}{x'}, \qquad \omega = \frac{-\omega_0^2}{\omega'} \qquad\qquad (10.3.6)$$

The element values of the respective networks transform in accordance with (use the last three equations)

$$C_L = \frac{1}{\omega_0^2 L}, \qquad L_C = \frac{1}{\omega_0^2 C} \qquad\qquad (10.3.7)$$

The fact that the reciprocal transformation converts a low-pass system into a high-pass system can be demonstrated by use of Fig. 10.3.1b. Examination of Tabulations 3.5.1 and 3.6.1 shows that $H(x)$ is an odd function of x, and $Z(x)$ is an even function of x. A typical example of the pass-band $Z(x)$ and block-band $H(x)$ is shown plotted against x on Fig. 10.3.1b. These curves are also shown transferred to the x' scale by the reciprocal transformation such that cutoff is at unity on both scales (x and x'). The reciprocal transformation therefore interchanges the block and pass regions to form a high-pass filter from a low-pass design or network.

The application of the reciprocal transformation to changing a low-pass network or design into a high-pass network or design is much simpler than the foregoing discussion indicates. The high-pass mathematical patterns may be established from plotted low-pass curves by simply transferring ordinates at any chosen x to $x' = 1/x$. The network transformation, L's and C's to C's and L's, respectively, is easily effected by the two formulas of Eq. (10.3.7).

As the problem of a high-pass filter is presented in practice, the transfer-loss curve is specified for the high-pass filter. This high-pass transfer-loss requirement should be inverted in terms of reciprocal values of x and then the design carried out as a low-pass problem. Once the low-pass filter is completely designed, the corresponding high-pass network and curves are easily obtained on the basis of reciprocal values of x.

10.4 Frequency transformation: low pass to band pass

A frequency transformation which would relocate a low-pass, pass-band on an arbitrary region, $0 \leq x'_{01} \leq x' \leq x'_{02}$ would form a band-pass filter if all other factors were properly transformed at the same time. Such a transformation is given in general form by

$$p = k_1 p' + \frac{k_2}{p'} \tag{10.4.1}$$

which in terms of ω is, if $p = j\omega$, $p' = j\omega'$,

$$\omega = k_1 \omega' - \frac{k_2}{\omega'} \tag{10.4.2}$$

The first point to be established for this transformation is that it leads to a physical network.

Consider the impedance of any inductor first. Mathematically

$$Z_L(\omega) = j\omega L = j\left(k_1\omega' - \frac{k_2}{\omega'}\right)L = j\omega'(k_1 L) + \frac{1}{j\omega'/k_2 L}$$

$$= j\omega' L_L + \frac{1}{j\omega' C_L}, \quad L_L = k_1 L, \quad C_L = \frac{1}{k_2 L} \tag{10.4.3}$$

The impedance of each inductor of the low-pass structure is thereby transformed into the impedance of a physical series resonator. Consider next the impedance of each capacitor. Mathematically

$$Z_C(\omega) = \frac{1}{j\omega C} = \frac{1}{j(k_1\omega' - k_2/\omega_1)C} = \frac{1}{j\omega'(Ck_1) + Ck_2/j\omega'}$$

$$= \frac{1}{j\omega' C_C + 1/j\omega' L_C}, \quad C_C = k_1 C, \quad L_C = \frac{1}{k_2 C} \tag{10.4.4}$$

Consequently, the impedance of each capacitor of the low-pass structure becomes the impedance of a physical parallel resonator.

The transformations of Eqs. (10.4.1) and (10.4.2) thus satisfy the basic requirement of the frequency transformations of interest here, namely, they lead to a physical network from the starting point of a physical network, provided the constants k_1 and k_2 are both real and positive, $k_1 > 0$, $k_2 > 0$.

Consider next the evaluation of k_1 and k_2 so that the pass band between $-\omega_0$ and ω_0 is located between ω'_{01} and ω'_{02} as on Fig. 10.4.1a. The mathematical formulation of these conditions on the frequency transformation are

$$-\omega_0 = k_1\omega'_{01} - \frac{k_2}{\omega'_{01}}, \quad \omega_0 = k_1\omega'_{02} - \frac{k_2}{\omega'_{02}} \tag{10.4.5}$$

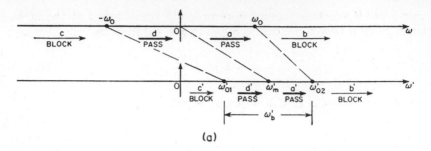

(a)

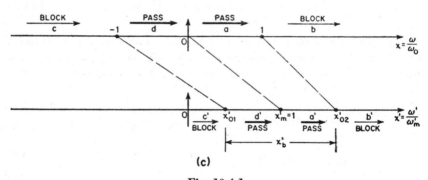

(b)

(c)

Fig. 10.4.1

Since these equations are linear in k_1 and k_2, they may be solved at once to give

$$k_1 = \frac{\omega_0}{\omega'_{02} - \omega'_{01}} = \frac{\omega_0}{\omega'_b} \tag{10.4.6}$$

$$k_2 = \omega_0 \frac{\omega'_{01}\omega'_{02}}{\omega'_{02} - \omega'_{01}} = \omega_0 \frac{\omega'_m{}^2}{\omega'_b} \tag{10.4.7}$$

where $\omega'_m = \sqrt{\omega'_{02}\omega'_{01}}$,   the mid-band ω (10.4.8)

and $\omega'_b = \omega'_{02} - \omega'_{01}$,   the band width   (10.4.9)

Note that these values for k_1 and k_2 are real and positive as required, since $\omega'_{02} > \omega'_{01}$, i.e., $\omega'_b > 0$.

On the basis of the foregoing values for k_1 and k_2, it can be shown that

if $0 \leq \omega' \leq \omega'_{01}$,   then $-\infty < \omega \leq -\omega_0$

if $\omega'_{01} \leq \omega' \leq \sqrt{\omega'_{01}\omega'_{02}} = \omega'_m$, then $-\omega_0 \leq \omega \leq 0$

if $\omega'_m = \sqrt{\omega'_{01}\omega'_{02}} \leq \omega' \leq \omega'_{02}$, then $0 \leq \omega \leq \omega_0$

if $\omega'_{02} \leq \omega' < \infty$,   then $\omega_0 \leq \omega < \infty$

which orients the pass and block regions as desired for a band-pass structure (see Fig. 10.4.1a).

On a frequency basis, the low-pass to band-pass transformation is now complete with (Eqs. 10.4.2, 10.4.6, 10.4.7) the transformation

$$\omega = \frac{\omega_0\omega'_m}{\omega'_b}\left(\frac{\omega'}{\omega'_m} - \frac{\omega'_m}{\omega'}\right) \tag{10.4.10}$$

from which $$\omega' = \frac{\omega'_b}{2\omega_0}\omega \pm \sqrt{\left(\frac{\omega'_b}{2\omega_0}\right)^2\omega^2 + \omega'^2_m} \tag{10.4.11}$$

The element values are (Eqs. 10.4.3, 10.4.4, 10.4.6, 10.4.7)

$$L_L = \frac{\omega_0}{\omega'_b}L \tag{10.4.12}$$

$$C_L = \frac{\omega'_b}{\omega_0\omega'^2_m}\frac{1}{L} \tag{10.4.13}$$

$$L_C = \frac{\omega'_b}{\omega_0\omega'^2_m}\frac{1}{C} \tag{10.4.14}$$

$$C_C = \frac{\omega_0}{\omega'_b}C \tag{10.4.15}$$

The frequencies corresponding to ω'_{01} and ω'_{02} are known, respectively, as the lower cutoff and upper cutoff. The band-pass filter passes between ω'_{01} and ω'_{02} and blocks at all other $\omega' > 0$. Each inductor of the low-pass filter is replaced by a series resonator and each capacitor by a parallel resonator.

In correspondence with the convenience of the variable x as used in the low-pass treatment of the foregoing, this same variable is useful in connection with a band-pass design by way of transformation from a low-pass design. A different definition of x' than heretofore used is convenient for the band-pass case. Thus, let

$$x = \frac{\omega}{\omega_0} \qquad (10.4.16)$$

$$x' = \frac{\omega'}{\sqrt{\omega'_{01}\omega'_{02}}} = \frac{\omega'}{\omega'_m} \qquad (10.4.17)$$

Corresponding to this last equation,

$$x'_{01} = \frac{\omega'_{01}}{\sqrt{\omega'_{01}\omega'_{02}}} = \frac{\omega'_{01}}{\omega'_m} \qquad (10.4.18)$$

$$x'_{02} = \frac{\omega'_{02}}{\sqrt{\omega'_{01}\omega'_{02}}} = \frac{\omega'_{02}}{\omega'_m} \qquad (10.4.19)$$

$$x'_b = x'_{02} - x'_{01} \qquad (10.4.20)$$

$$x'_m = \sqrt{x'_{01}x'_{02}} = \sqrt{\frac{\omega'_{01}}{\omega'_m}\frac{\omega'_{02}}{\omega'_m}} = 1 \qquad (10.4.21)$$

The definition of x' as given here was chosen to make this last relation hold.

Then Eq. (10.4.10) may be transformed into

$$x = \frac{1}{x'_b}\left(x' - \frac{1}{x'}\right) \qquad (10.4.22)$$

and Eq. (10.4.11) into

$$x' = \frac{x'_b}{2}x \pm \sqrt{\left(\frac{x'_b}{2}x\right)^2 + 1} \qquad (10.4.23)$$

The sketch of Fig. 10.4.1c shows the correspondence of points on the x and x' scales for the transformation given by these last two equations.

10.5 Frequency transformation: low pass to band elimination

The frequency transformation which forms a band-elimination filter must cover the positive frequency range by a block region with pass regions on each side. Such a transformation is given by

$$p = \frac{1}{k_1 p' + k_2/p'} \qquad (10.5.1)$$

which in terms of ω is

$$\omega = \frac{-1}{k_1\omega' - k_2/\omega'} \tag{10.5.2}$$

As for the other frequency transformations of this chapter, the first consideration is the determination of the restrictions on this transformation for it to produce a physical network from a physical network.

The impedance of each inductor of the low-pass network transforms as follows:

$$Z_L(\omega) = j\omega L = \cfrac{1}{j\omega'(k_1/L) + \cfrac{1}{j\omega'(L/k_2)}} = \frac{1}{j\omega' C_L + 1/j\omega' L_L} \tag{10.5.3}$$

from which
$$L_L = \frac{L}{k_2}, \quad C_L = \frac{k_1}{L} \tag{10.5.4}$$

The impedance of each inductor thus becomes the impedance of a parallel resonator.

The impedance of each capacitor becomes that of a series resonator as the following equations indicate.

$$Z_C(\omega) = \frac{1}{j\omega C} = j\omega'\left(\frac{k_1}{C}\right) + \frac{1}{j\omega'(C/k_2)} = j\omega' L_C + \frac{1}{j\omega' C_C} \tag{10.5.5}$$

if
$$L_C = \frac{k_1}{C}, \quad C_C = \frac{C}{k_2} \tag{10.5.6}$$

Note that k_1 and k_2 must be real and positive for the transformation of Eq. (10.5.2) to specify physical networks.

The required values of k_1 and k_2 may be established by requiring that ω_0 correspond to ω'_{01} and $-\omega_0$ to ω'_{02}. Thus

$$\omega_0 = \frac{-1}{k_1\omega'_{01} - k_2/\omega'_{01}} \tag{10.5.7}$$

$$-\omega_0 = \frac{-1}{k_1\omega'_{02} - k_2/\omega'_{02}} \tag{10.5.8}$$

The solution of this pair of equations, linear in k_1 and k_2, specifies

$$k_1 = \frac{1}{\omega_0(\omega'_{02} - \omega'_{01})} = \frac{1}{\omega_0\omega'_b} \tag{10.5.9}$$

$$k_2 = \frac{\omega'_{01}\omega'_{02}}{\omega_0(\omega'_{02} - \omega'_{01})} = \frac{\omega'^2_m}{\omega_0\omega'_b} \tag{10.5.10}$$

where ω'_m and ω'_b are as defined by Eqs. (10.4.8) and (10.4.9).

Both of these parameters, k_1 and k_2, are real and positive as required.

On the basis of the foregoing values for k_1 and k_2, it can be shown that

if $0 \leq \omega' \leq \omega'_{01}$ then $0 \leq \omega \leq \omega_0$

if $\omega'_{01} \leq \omega' \leq \sqrt{\omega'_{01}\omega'_{02}} = \omega'_m$ then $\omega_0 \leq \omega < \infty$

if $\omega'_m = \sqrt{\omega'_{01}\omega'_{02}} \leq \omega' \leq \omega'_{02}$ then $-\infty < \omega \leq -\omega_0$

if $\omega'_{02} \leq \omega' < \infty$ then $-\omega_0 \leq \omega \leq 0$

These inequalities demonstrate that the transformation under consideration leads to a band-block characteristic (see Fig. 10.5.1a).

The complete frequency transformation for low pass to band elimination is finally, therefore, from Eqs. (10.5.2), (10.5.9), and (10.5.10),

$$\omega = \frac{1}{(\omega'_m/\omega_0\omega'_b)(\omega'/\omega'_m - \omega'_m/\omega')} \qquad (10.5.11)$$

from which

$$\omega' = \frac{-\omega_0\omega'_b}{2}\frac{1}{\omega} \pm \sqrt{\left(\frac{\omega_0\omega'_b}{2}\frac{1}{\omega}\right)^2 + \omega'^2_m} \qquad (10.5.12)$$

The element values are (Eqs. 10.5.4, 10.5.6, 10.5.9, 10.5.10):

$$L_L = \frac{\omega_0\omega'_b}{\omega'^2_m} L \qquad (10.5.13)$$

$$C_L = \frac{1}{\omega_0\omega'_b}\frac{1}{L} \qquad (10.5.14)$$

$$L_C = \frac{1}{\omega_0\omega'_b}\frac{1}{C} \qquad (10.5.15)$$

$$C_C = \frac{\omega_0\omega'_b}{\omega'^2_m} C \qquad (10.5.16)$$

These element values are also given on Fig. 10.5.1b with their relation to the network transformation.

The variables x and x' are defined, for the band-elimination transformation exactly as for the band-pass transformation, see Eqs.

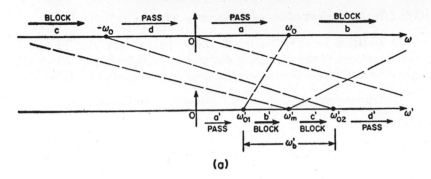

(a)

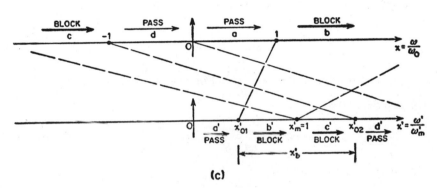

(b)

(c)

Fig. 10.5.1

(10.4.16) through (10.4.23). The two basic equations (Eqs. 10.5.11 and 10.5.12) become then,

$$x = \frac{-1}{(1/x'_b)(x' - 1/x')} \qquad (10.5.17)$$

$$x' = \frac{-x'_b}{2}\frac{1}{x} \pm \sqrt{\left(\frac{x'_b}{2}\frac{1}{x}\right)^2 + 1} \qquad (10.5.18)$$

The correspondence between the x and x' scales is shown by Fig. 10.5.1c.

10.6 *Effect on dissipation of frequency transformations*

In addition to affecting the L and C parameters, the frequency transformations of the foregoing discussions of this chapter affect the Q's (for fixed R under the transformation) as indicated in the following:

1. *Transformation* $p = \dfrac{\omega_1}{\omega'_1} p'$. Since L transforms into L_L, the Q's are

$$Q_{LL} = \frac{\omega L_L}{R}, \qquad Q_L = \frac{\omega L}{R} \tag{10.6.1}$$

and, using Eq. (10.2.4) and those last two relations,

$$Q_{LL} = \frac{\omega_1}{\omega'_1} Q_L \tag{10.6.2}$$

Similarly, since C transforms into C_C, the Q's are

$$Q_{CC} = \frac{1}{\omega C_C R}, \qquad Q_C = \frac{1}{\omega C R} \tag{10.6.3}$$

and, using Eq. (10.2.5) and these last two relations,

$$Q_{CC} = \frac{\omega'_1}{\omega_1} Q_C \tag{10.6.4}$$

2. *Transformation* $p = \dfrac{\omega_1 \omega'_1}{p'}$. For the transformation from L to C_L (see Sec. 10.3),

$$Q_{CL} = \frac{1}{\omega C_L R}, \qquad Q_L = \frac{\omega L}{R} \tag{10.6.5}$$

whence, using Eq. (10.3.7),

$$Q_{CL} = \frac{\omega_0^2}{\omega^2} Q_L = \frac{1}{x^2} Q_L \tag{10.6.6}$$

Also for the transformation from C to L_C,

$$Q_{LC} = \frac{\omega L_C}{R}, \qquad Q_C = \frac{1}{\omega C R} \tag{10.6.7}$$

whence, on using Eq. (10.3.7),

$$Q_{LC} = \frac{\omega^2}{\omega_0^2} Q_C = x^2 Q_C \tag{10.6.8}$$

3. *Transformation* $p = \dfrac{\omega_0 \omega'_m}{\omega'_b}\left(\dfrac{p'}{\omega'_m} + \dfrac{\omega'_m}{p'}\right)$. For the transformation from an inductor to a series resonator (Sec. 10.4),

$$Q_L = \frac{\omega L}{R}, \quad Q_{LL} = \frac{\omega L_L}{R}, \quad Q_{CL} = \frac{1}{\omega C_L R} \qquad (10.6.9)$$

Therefore, if Eq. (10.4.12) is used in addition to Eq. (10.6.9),

$$Q_{LL} = \frac{\omega_0}{\omega'_b} Q_L \qquad (10.6.10)$$

and if Eq. (10.4.13) is used as well as Eqs. (10.6.9),

$$Q_{CL} = \frac{\omega_0 \omega'^2_m}{\omega'_b \omega^2} Q_L \qquad (10.6.11)$$

For the transformation from a capacitor to a parallel resonator (Sec. 10.4),

$$Q_C = \frac{1}{\omega C R}, \quad Q_{LC} = \frac{\omega L_C}{R}, \quad Q_{CC} = \frac{1}{\omega C_C R} \qquad (10.6.12)$$

Therefore, from Eqs. (10.4.14) and these last equations,

$$Q_{LC} = \frac{\omega^2 \omega'_b}{\omega_0 \omega'^2_m} Q_C \qquad (10.6.13)$$

and from Eqs. (10.4.15) and (10.6.12),

$$Q_{CC} = \frac{\omega'_b}{\omega_0} Q_C \qquad (10.6.14)$$

4. *Transformation* $p = \dfrac{-1}{(\omega'_m / \omega_0 \omega'_b)(p'/\omega'_m + \omega'_m / p')}$ the transformation from an inductor to a parallel resonator (Sec. 10.5),

$$Q_L = \frac{\omega L}{R}, \quad Q_{LL} = \frac{\omega L_L}{R}, \quad Q_{CL} = \frac{1}{\omega C_L R} \qquad (10.6.15)$$

and so from Eqs. (10.6.15) and (10.5.13),

$$Q_{LL} = \frac{\omega_0 \omega'_b}{\omega'^2_m} Q_L \qquad (10.6.16)$$

and from Eqs. (10.6.15) and (10.5.14),

$$Q_{CL} = \frac{\omega_0 \omega'_b}{\omega^2} Q_L \qquad (10.6.17)$$

For the transformation from a capacitor to a series resonator (Sec. 10.5),

$$Q_C = \frac{1}{\omega CR}, \quad Q_{LC} = \frac{\omega L_C}{R}, \quad Q_{CC} = \frac{1}{\omega C_C R} \qquad (10.6.18)$$

whence with the aid of Eq. (10.5.15),

$$Q_{LC} = \frac{\omega^2}{\omega_0 \omega'_b} Q_C \qquad (10.6.19)$$

and from Eqs. (10.6.18) and (10.5.16),

$$Q_{CC} = \frac{{\omega'_m}^2}{\omega_0 \omega'_b} Q_C \qquad (10.6.20)$$

Problems

10.1 Plot the function

$$X(x) = \frac{x(x^2 - 1)}{x^2 - 9}$$

Replot this curve under the transformation $x = 2x'$. Do this last plotting by merely relocating ordinate values on the x scale. Check by actually computing a few points mathematically.

10.2 (a) Plot the function

$$H(x) = \frac{x_a^2 - x^2}{jx \sqrt{1 - x^2}}$$

Determine the k of $x = kx'$ such that $H(1)$ is shifted to $x' = 2$. If $\omega_0 = 1000$, what is the location of cutoff ω'_0, after the transformation if $x' = \omega/\omega_0$?

10.3 (a) Determine the high-pass, constant-k, T section for which $R_0 = 100$ ohms, $\omega_0 = 100,000$. Sketch the high-pass curves of $A_I(x)$, $B_I(x)$, $H(x)$, and $Z(x)$. (b) Repeat for a π section.

10.4 (a) Determine the T, m-derived, high-pass section for $\omega_0 = 5 \times 10^5$ $R_0 = 500$ ohms, $x_p = 0.92$. Sketch the high-pass curves of $A_I(x)$, $B_I(x)$, $Z(x)$, and $H(x)$. (b) Repeat (a) for a π section.

10.5 Establish the formulas and networks corresponding to Figs. 4.3.1, 4.4.1, 4.5.1, and 4.6.1 to fit a high-pass filter.

10.6 (a) Show that Eqs. (10.4.6) and (10.4.7) are correct as given.

(b) Show that the system of inequalities following Eq. (10.4.9) is correct.

(c) Show that the transformation of Eq. (10.4.17) gives the scale correspondences of Fig. 10.4.1c. Fill in the salient points of the negative half of the x'-scale.

10.7 (a) Determine the band-pass, constant-k, T section for which $R_0 = 500$ ohms, $\omega_{01} = 100,000$, $\omega_{02} = 200,000$. Sketch the band-pass curves of $A_I(x)$, $B_I(x)$, $H(x)$, and $Z(x)$. (b) Repeat for a π section.

10.8 (a) Determine the T, m-derived, band-pass section for $\omega_{01} = 500,000$, $\omega_{02} = 900,000$, $R_0 = 1000$ ohms, and the high-frequency pole of transfer loss is $\omega_{p2} = 950,000$. Sketch curves of $A_I(x)$, $B_I(x)$, $H(x)$, and $Z(x)$. (b) Repeat for a π section.

10.9 Establish the formulas and network diagrams corresponding to Figs. 4.3.1, 4.4.1, 4.5.1, and 4.6.1 for a band-pass filter.

10.10 A band-pass filter must have a symmetric transfer loss characteristic which above $x'_{02} = 1.02$ is not less than a curve joining the points in the adjacent table by straight lines.

X'	db
1.03	30
1.10	35
1.11	20
1.12	25
1.20	22

Let $R_0 = 100$ ohms, $\omega_{01} = 10^6$, $\omega_{02} = 1.2 \times 10^6$.

(a) Determine the single lattice which has the required transfer loss. Use no image impedance controls.

(b) Determine a ladder network which has the required transfer loss.

10.11 Prove the validity of the set of inequalities following Eq. (10.5.10).

10.12 Demonstrate that Fig. 10.5.1c is correct by establishing a set of inequalities in terms of x and x'. Note in this connection that $x'_{01}x'_{02} = 1$.

10.13 Repeat Problem 10.7 for a band-elimination filter.

10.14 Repeat Problem 10.8 for a band-elimination filter.

10.15 Repeat Problem 10.9 for a band-elimination filter.

10.16 Establish the relations corresponding to those of Sec. 10.6 for $Q_c = \omega C/G_c$.

CHAPTER ELEVEN

Constant-R, Insertion Loss Equalizers

Fundamentally there is no difference between a filter and an equalizer. Both networks are designed to insert a controlled insertion loss and/or insertion phase into a communication system. The aim with the networks classed as filters is, roughly, to design a network which has high discrimination over specified frequency ranges and the least possible over other frequency ranges. The equalizer, on the other hand, is ordinarily designed to present a controlled insertion loss, neither a maximum nor minimum, but simply an insertion loss of some particular form.

11.1 Constant-R networks, general

The network of particular use for many equalizing problems is known as a constant-R network. This network, in lattice form, is characterized as having an image impedance which is a positive constant for all frequencies, i.e., by definition

$$Z_x(x)Z_y(x) = R^2 = Z_I^2(x) \qquad (11.1.1)$$

from which at once

$$Z_y(x) = \frac{R^2}{Z_x(x)} \qquad (11.1.2)$$

The ratio function $H(x)$ is

$$H(x) = \sqrt{\frac{Z_x(x)}{Z_y(x)}} = \frac{Z_x(x)}{R} \qquad (11.1.3)$$

and the transfer function is

$$P_I(x) = A_I(x) + jB_I(x) = \ln\frac{1 + Z_x(x)/R}{1 - Z_x(x)/R} \qquad (11.1.4)$$

Incidentally, the transfer and insertion functions are identical for constant-R networks terminated in R; see Eq. (7.2.5).

From the last equation, the transfer loss vanishes if $Z_x(x)$ has a zero, has a pole, or becomes purely reactive. Because the transfer loss vanishes for $Z_x(x)$ purely reactive (all pass), control of transfer loss must be effected by inclusion of dissipative elements into the network. The following pattern for the inclusion of controlled dissipation has been found effective.

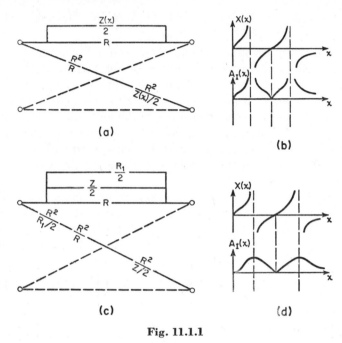

Fig. 11.1.1

Consider the constant-R lattice of Fig. 11.1.1a (see Sec. 1.7 for the determination of inverse networks). On substituting into Eq. (11.1.4) the $Z_x(x)$ value indicated by this figure, the product over the sum of R and $Z(x)/2$, the transfer function becomes

$$P_I(x) = \ln\left[1 + \frac{Z(x)}{R}\right] \qquad (11.1.5)$$

The transfer loss

$$A_I(x) = \ln\left|1 + \frac{Z(x)}{R}\right| \quad \text{nepers} \qquad (11.1.6)$$

vanishes with $Z(x)$ and becomes a pole with $Z(x)$, see Fig. 11.1.1b.

Further modification of the constant-R lattice into the form shown by Fig. 11.1.1c, i.e., controlled reduction of the resistance paralleling Z in the series arm, specifies the transfer loss as

$$A_I(x) = \ln \left| 1 + \frac{2[(R_1/2)(Z(x)/2)]}{R[R_1/2 + Z(x)/2]} \right| \qquad (11.1.7)$$

This last equation vanishes with and has the limit, as $Z(x)$ takes on a pole,

$$A_I(x_p) = \lim_{Z \to \infty} A_I(x) = \ln (1 + R_1/R) \quad \text{nepers} \qquad (11.1.8)$$

The poles of $A_I(x)$ are thus eliminated by adding in parallel the resistance $R_1/2$ to the series arm of the lattice of Fig. 11.1.1a and its inverse in series in the cross arm. The maximum value of $A_I(x)$ is thus completely under control from zero to any value, no matter how large, by placing the proper R_1 and its inverse in the network. The maximum values, all the same in magnitude, occur at the poles of a purely reactive $Z(x)$. The sketch of Fig. 11.1.1d when compared with Fig. 11.1.1b shows the effect on the transfer loss of changing the lattice of Fig. 11.1.1a to that of Fig. 11.1.1c.

For design purposes a specification of the maximum value of $A_1(x)$ is usually more convenient than is a specified value of R_1. The following equation derived from Eq. (11.1.8) gives an expression for R_1 in terms of the maximum transfer loss as [$A_1(x_p)$ expressed in decibels]

$$R_1 = R \left[\log^{-1} \frac{A_I(x_p)}{20} - 1 \right] \qquad (11.1.9)$$

11.2 One-ohm basis

A point of minor theoretical importance but of considerable use for computational purposes should be noted. Thus suppose $Z(x)$ of Eq. (11.1.5), represents any bridge impedance $Z_b(x)$, paralleling $R = 1$, and that Eq. (11.1.5) is used in designing an equalizer. Then since

$$P_I(x) = \ln [1 + Z_b(x)] = \ln \left[1 + \frac{RZ_b(x)}{R} \right] \qquad (11.2.1)$$

the network element values, all obtained on a one-ohm basis, can be altered without affecting the transfer function, by multiplying each R and L by R and dividing each C by R. The image impedance is altered, by such a change in element values, from 1 ohm to R ohms.

The discussion in the remainder of this chapter is on a one-ohm basis.

11.3 *Bridged-T form of equalizer*

The lattice network of Fig. 11.1.1c, if physical, always has a physical unbalanced equivalent in the form of a bridged T. This equivalence shown by Fig. 11.3.1 follows from the method of Sec. 5.2. The series removal of R from the two lattice arms followed by combining the two resulting shunt branches and the two series branches gives

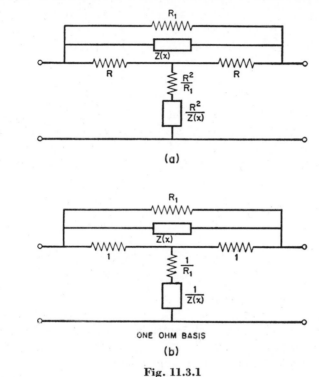

(a)

ONE OHM BASIS

(b)

Fig. 11.3.1

the bridged T shown. The bridged T on a one-ohm basis is shown by Fig. 11.3.1b.

11.4 *Transfer-loss equalizer with a purely reactive Z(x)*

Consideration is given first to equalizers for which the $Z(x)$ of Figs. 11.1.1 and 11.3.1 is purely reactive. Such a purely reactive $Z(x)$ permits formulation of an important first approximation to an equalizer design. Consider therefore that the number of poles and zeros of $Z(x)$ are known and are specifically located. As indicated in Chapter 1, only the multiplying constant in the expression for $Z(x)$ then remains undetermined. This constant may be evaluated by matching the transfer loss required to the transfer loss of the equalizer at some specified frequency x'. The procedure is as suggested in the following.

The admittance of a pure resistance R_1 paralleled with a purely reactive 2TN of impedance $Z(x) = jX(x)$, i.e., the admittance of the bridge of Fig. 11.3.1b, is

$$Y_b(x) = \frac{1}{R_1} + \frac{1}{jX(x)} = G_1 + j\frac{-1}{X(x)} = G_1 + jB(x) \quad (11.4.1)$$

On a one-ohm basis the transfer loss is

$$A_I(x) = 20\log|1 + Z_b(x)| = 20\log\left|1 + \frac{1}{G_1 + jB(x)}\right| \quad \text{db} \quad (11.4.2)$$

The value of G_1 is determined by a specified maximum transfer loss which occurs at the poles of $Z(x)$ and is given by the reciprocal of Eq. (11.1.9).

At a match point x' the transfer loss $A_I(x')$ may be taken directly from the required transfer loss curve. Then

$$\log^{-1}\frac{A_I(x')}{20} = \left|1 + \frac{1}{G_1 + jB(x')}\right| \quad (11.4.3)$$

and so

$$B(x') = \pm\sqrt{\frac{(G_1 + 1)^2 - G_1^2[\log^{-1} A_I(x')/20]^2}{[\log^{-1} A_I(x')/20]^2 - 1}} \quad (11.4.4)$$

which determines the susceptance at the match point x' from a known G_1 and $A_I(x')$ except for sign. This result, if used as indicated next, determines the positive constant multiplier of the susceptance function.

In accordance with the results of Chapter 1, the susceptance of any purely reactive 2TN may be expressed as

$$B(x) = \pm K\frac{N(x, x_z)}{D(x, x_p)} \quad (11.4.5)$$

where $N(x, x_z)$ and $D(x, x_p)$ represent polynomials in x in terms of their zeros x_z and x_p, K is a positive constant, and the sign is determined from the positive slope property of $B(x)$. If, as already postulated for this discussion, the zeros x_z and poles x_p are known, and if in addition $B(x')$ is known only K of this last expression is unspecified. A curve matching process can be used to determine G_1 and $A_I(x')$ and so $B(x')$ as follows: the value of $A_I(x_p)$ from the required equalizer transfer loss at any pole x_p of $Z(x)$ determines $G_1 = 1/R_1$ from Eq. (11.1.9); the value of $A_I(x')$ from the required equalizer transfer loss at some match point x', not a pole or a zero, completes the determination of $B(x')$. Then, from Eqs. (11.4.4) and (11.4.5),

$$K = B(x') \frac{D(x', x_p)}{N(x', x_z)} \tag{11.4.6}$$

The constant-R equalizer, the lattice of Fig. 11.1.1c, or the ladder of Fig. 11.3.1a, is thus completely determined in terms of (1) specified poles and zeros of $Z(x)$, (2) specified transfer loss at the poles of $Z(x)$ (all have the same loss), and (3) a transfer loss match at some other frequency x'. The following example should serve to add further meaning to the foregoing discussion.

Example 11.4.1

Determine R_1 and the purely reactive $Z(x)$ of Figs. 11.1.1c and 11.3.1 for an equalizer which is to equalize the pass-band insertion loss shown by curve 1 on Fig. 11.4.1 to a flat loss over the frequency range 311.9 kc $\leq f \leq$ 552.2 kc or if $x = f/420{,}000$, $0.743 \leq x \leq 1.315$.

Solution

As a first try, the level of the flat loss which the filter and equalizer in tandem is to present is taken as 15 db. This loss is to include the dissipative effects of the equalizer coils. As a first estimate of the effect of this dissipation assume 3 db is sufficient. Then the transfer loss of the equalizer with

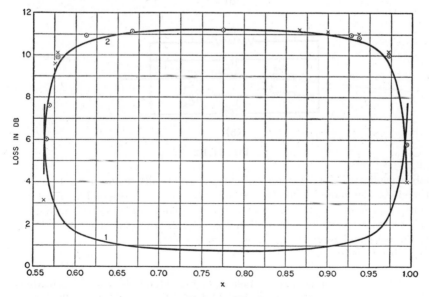

Fig. 11.4.1

nondissipative $Z(x)$ should have maxima of 12 db. Curve 2 of equalizer loss shown on Fig. 11.4.1 is the difference between 12 db and the lower curve, and is the transfer loss which the equalizer with nondissipative $Z(x)$ is to present.

A transfer loss curve, roughly of the form of the upper curve of Fig. 11.4.1 can be obtained from an equalizer which has one pole of $Z(x)$. However, the

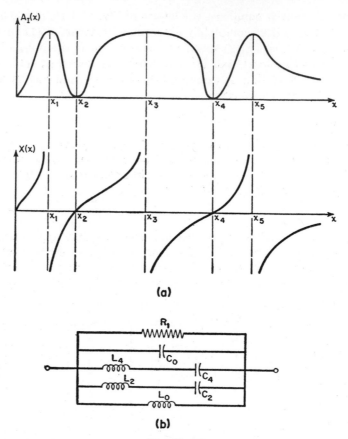

(a)

(b)

Fig. 11.4.2

adjustment available for curve matching is practically nonexistent. Consider, therefore, the more elaborate transfer loss curve, corresponding reactance curve, and R_1Z combination (bridge of a bridged-T network) which produces this reactance pattern as shown on Fig. 11.4.2. Adjustment of the location of the poles and zeros at x_1, x_5 and x_2, x_4, respectively, should offer sufficient flexibility to permit a design to be effected which matches the desired transfer loss with sufficient accuracy.

As a start, assume that the pole x_3 of Fig. 11.4.2a is at $x_p = 1.00$ where the maximum transfer loss from Fig. 11.4.1 is $A_I(x_p) = 11.2$ db. Then from

Eq. (11.1.9),

$$R_1 = \log^{-1} \frac{A_I(x_p)}{20} - 1 = \log^{-1} \frac{11.2}{20} - 1 = 2.63 \quad \text{ohms}$$

and

$$G_1 = \frac{1}{R_1} = 0.38 \quad \text{mho}$$

The choice of a match point for determining the K of Eq. (11.4.6) is entirely a matter of making a guess. Suppose that as a first estimate, therefore, $x' = 0.750$ ($f' = 315$ kc), at which frequency the transfer loss from Fig. 11.4.1 is $A_I(x') = 7.6$ db.

The substitution of these numerical values of G_1 and of $A_I(x')$ into Eq. (11.4.4) gives

$$|B(x')| = 0.475, \quad x' = 0.750 \qquad (f' = 315 \text{ kc})$$

The location of the poles and zeros of Z yet remains to be effected. The most effective method is simply to guess and then check by computation. As a first estimate of the location of the poles and zeros of Fig. 11.4.2a assume

$$f_1 = 220 \text{ kc}, \qquad x_1 = \frac{220}{420} = 0.524$$

$$f_2 = 310 \text{ kc}, \qquad x_2 = \frac{310}{420} = 0.738$$

$$f_3 = 420 \text{ kc}, \qquad x_3 = 1.000$$

$$f_4 = 555 \text{ kc}, \qquad x_4 = \frac{555}{420} = 1.321$$

$$f_5 = 700 \text{ kc}, \qquad x_5 = \frac{700}{420} = 1.667$$

The susceptance (the negative reciprocal of the reactance as specified by Fig. 11.4.2a) is, for $\omega_m = 2\pi 420{,}000$,

$$B(\omega) = \omega K \frac{(\omega^2 - \omega_1{}^2)(\omega^2 - \omega_3{}^2)(\omega^2 - \omega_5{}^2)}{\omega^2(\omega^2 - \omega_2{}^2)(\omega^2 - \omega_4{}^2)}$$

$$= K\omega_m \frac{(x^2 - x_1{}^2)(x^2 - x_3{}^2)(x^2 - x_5{}^2)}{x(x^2 - x_2{}^2)(x^2 - x_4{}^2)}$$

The positive constant K of this last expression can be computed from the already determined value of $B(x)'$ at the match point $x' = 0.750$, when $f' = 315$ kc. The result of setting $x = x' = 0.750$ and $B(x') = 0.475$ in this last equation is

$$K = 0.010139 \times 10^{-6}$$

Spot checking of the transfer loss, with the now completely determined $Z(x) = -j/B(x)$, by means of Eq. (11.4.2) gives the values marked with x on Fig. 11.4.1. Further trial and error manipulation of the location of the poles and zeros x_1, x_5 and x_2, x_4 leads to a set of transfer loss values as given in Fig. 11.4.1 by the circled dots. The corresponding control frequencies and new value of K are

$$f_1 = 220 \text{ kc}, \qquad f_4 = 558 \text{ kc}$$
$$f_2 = 308 \text{ kc}, \qquad f_5 = 700 \text{ kc}$$
$$f_3 = 420 \text{ kc}, \qquad K = 0.014376 \times 10^{-6}$$

These six numbers determine the $Z(x)$ for the network of Fig. 11.4.2b, and by the method of Chapter 1, the values of the three L's and three C's.

Note incidentally in varying the position of the poles and zeros that adjustment of x_1 and x_2 can be carried out for practical purposes independently of the adjustment of x_4 and x_5. Further trial and error relocation of the control frequencies may, of course, lead to even closer match between the required transfer loss and that presented by the equalizer. Whether further effort in this direction is worth while must remain a decision of the designer.

11.5 Padding of transfer loss equalizers

The discussion of this section deals with a method of altering a constant-R equalizer in such a manner as to add a flat loss of any specified amount to the transfer loss characteristic of the equalizer. One of the uses of this padding, discussed in the following sections of this chapter, is that of making allowance in the transfer loss characteristic of an equalizer for the inevitable dissipation in coils.

The method of carrying out this padding process is illustrated by Fig. 11.5.1. The unpadded equalizer is specified by Figs. 11.5.1a and d in lattice and bridged-T forms. The transfer loss of this equalizer is specified by (Eq. 11.1.6 on a one-ohm basis)

$$A_I(x) = \ln |1 + Z'(x)| \tag{11.5.1}$$

where $Z'(x)$ is the impedance of R_I in parallel with Z.

The application of this last equation to the pad of Figs. 11.5.1b and e gives

$$A_{Ip}(x) = \ln |1 + R_p| \tag{11.5.2}$$

as the transfer loss, a constant, for the pad.

The transfer loss of the cascaded connection of the equalizer and pad is the sum of the transfer loss of the two networks, i.e. (one-ohm basis),

$$A_{It}(x) = A_I(x) + A_{Ip}(x) = \ln |1 + Z'(x)| + \ln |1 + R_p|$$
$$= \ln |1 + Z'(x)| |1 + R_p| \tag{11.5.3}$$

Since the product of the absolute values of two functions is the same as the absolute value of the products, this last equation can be expressed as

$$A_{It}(x) = \ln \left| [1 + Z'(x)](1 + R_p) \right|$$

$$= \ln \left| \left[1 + \frac{R_1 Z(x)}{R_1 + Z(x)} \right] (1 + R_p) \right|$$

$$= \ln \left| 1 + \left[R_p + \frac{(1 + R_p)R_1(1 + R_p)Z(x)}{(1 + R_p)[R_1 + Z(x)]} \right] \right| \quad (11.5.4)$$

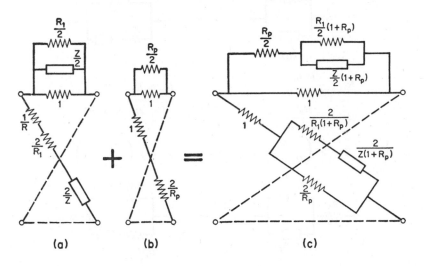

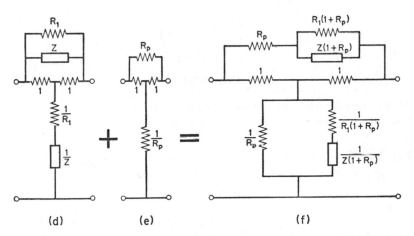

Fig. 11.5.1

But the term in brackets is exactly the impedance of the bridge of Fig. 11.5.1f, so this last equation specifies the transfer loss of the constant-R networks of Fig. 11.5.1c and f. The transfer loss of this last network is consequently exactly that of the networks of Fig. 11.5.1a and d plus a *constant* loss as specified by the pad of Figs. 11.5.1b or e.

An equivalence which is frequently useful is shown on Fig. 11.5.2. The details of working out the relation shown are merely a matter of

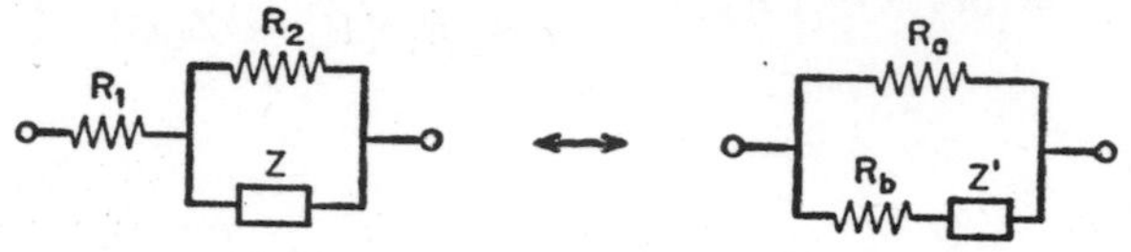

(a)   (b)

$$R_1 = \frac{R_a R_b}{R_a + R_b} \qquad\qquad R_a = R_1 + R_2$$

$$R_2 = \frac{R_a{}^2}{R_a + R_b} \qquad\qquad R_b = \frac{R_1(R_1 + R_2)}{R_2}$$

$$Z = Z'\left(\frac{R_a}{R_a + R_b}\right)^2 \qquad Z' = Z\left(\frac{R_1 + R_2}{R_2}\right)^2$$

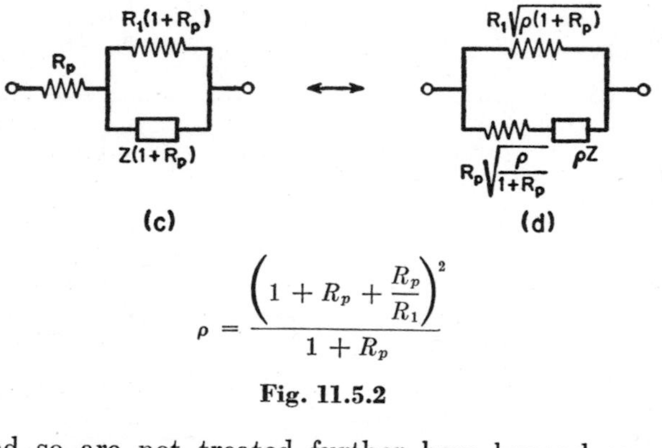

(c)   (d)

$$\rho = \frac{\left(1 + R_p + \dfrac{R_p}{R_1}\right)^2}{1 + R_p}$$

Fig. 11.5.2

algebra and so are not treated further here beyond suggesting in Problem 11.7 that the reader work out the details.

11.6 Modification of nondissipative equalizer design for use of physical elements

The combination of the diagrams of Figs. 11.5.1d, e, and f and Figs. 11.5.2c and d is shown, in terms of the equalizer bridge networks, in Figs. 11.6.1a, b, and c, for a $Z(x)$ consisting of a nondissipative series resonator. The bridge networks of Figs. 11.6.1a, b, and c indicate that replacement of R_1 and L of Fig. 11.6.1a by $R_b \neq R_1$ and a physical coil of finite Q has the sole effect of adding a flat loss to that of the nondissipative $Z(x)$ type equalizer illustrated by the bridge of Fig. 11.6.1a. Using this flat loss concept as a basis, a study of the behavior pattern of Fig. 11.6.1, when associated with certain approximations, can be used to design such a network as illustrated by Fig.

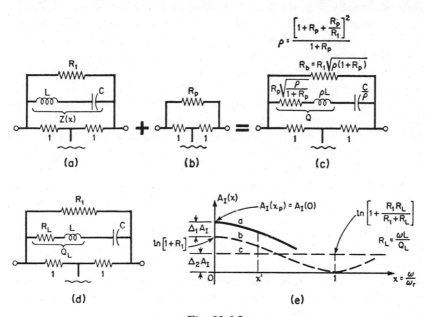

Fig. 11.6.1

11.6.1c and to indicate a pattern for designing more elaborate equalizers. The remainder of this section is devoted to the required study of the simple equalizer, and the next section to an extension of the ideas so established to more elaborate designs.

Two additional formulas for the diagrams of Figs. 11.6.1a and c are

$$Q = \frac{\omega(\rho L)}{R_p \sqrt{\rho/(1 + R_p)}} = \left(1 + \frac{1}{R_1} + \frac{1}{R_p}\right)\omega L \qquad (11.6.1)$$

and for $x = \omega/\omega_r$, where ω_r is the ω of resonance,

$$Z(x) = j\omega_r L x \left(1 - \frac{1}{x^2}\right) \qquad (11.6.2)$$

With these last two equations and others given in preceding parts of this book, the formulary of the diagrams of Fig. 11.6.1a, b, and c is complete. The problem of designing a dissipative network, i.e., Fig. 11.6.1c, which has a transfer loss matched to a given loss, can now be attacked.

Consider the a curve of Fig. 11.6.1e as the specified transfer loss which is to be matched by a bridged-T equalizer with bridge of the form shown by Fig. 11.6.1c. The first problem is that of estimating the flat loss which is equivalent to the dissipation of the coil. Experience soon indicates, particularly in connection with networks even slightly more complex than the one here being considered, that estimating the dissipation, and so indirectly the flat loss of the pad, by choosing a value of Q of Fig. 11.6.1c is not convenient. The initial estimate of the effect of dissipation is made in terms of the bridge of Fig. 11.6.1d. It should be recognized that use of this bridge is only an auxiliary device useful for starting the process of designing Fig. 11.6.1c. The transfer loss of Fig. 11.6.1d cannot, of course, equal that of Fig. 11.6.1a and b in tandem, because of the appearance of R_1 in both bridges. Once more then, experience has indicated that a *satisfactory initial estimate* of the flat loss corresponding to dissipation can be made in terms of Fig. 11.6.1d.

Consider then the bridge of Fig. 11.6.1d and the transfer loss curves of Fig. 11.6.1e. The a curve represents the transfer loss curve to be matched. The b curve is obtained by subtracting a flat $\Delta_1 A_I$, which the designer must estimate as a rough first but not final value of the flat loss corresponding to dissipation. The $\Delta_2 A_I$, and so the c curve, represent a flat loss which is not the estimated discrimination, i.e., $\Delta_1 A_I$ and $\Delta_2 A_I$ are not equal. The b-curve is determined over the range of concern once the initial effect of dissipation is chosen, whereas the c curve is not, beyond the fact that it is a straight line. The b and c curves are assumed to represent the transfer loss of the equalizer determined by the bridge of Fig. 11.6.1a.

From the established points on the b curve at $x = 0$ and $x = x'$ and an assumed value of ω_r, values of R_1, L, and C can be determined according to the method of Sec. 11.4. The bridge of Fig. 11.6.1a is thereby completely determined.

The bridge of Fig. 11.6.1d is once more used as a point at which a first estimate may be made. At resonance, the transfer loss from Fig. 11.6.1d is a minimum and is, as shown on Fig. 11.6.1e,

$$A_I(1) = \ln \left| 1 + \frac{R_1 R_L}{R_1 + R_L} \right| = \ln \left| 1 + \frac{R_1(\omega_r L/Q_L)}{R_1 + \omega_r L/Q_L} \right| \quad (11.6.3)$$

The pad of Fig. 11.6.1b is assumed to have this same transfer loss; hence

$$R_p = \frac{R_1 R_L}{R_1 + R_L} = \frac{R_1(\omega_r L/Q_L)}{R_1 + \omega_r L/Q_L} \qquad (11.6.4)$$

Since it is Q_L and not R_L which is desired in these formulas, the equation for Q of the final bridge network may be expressed in terms of Q_L rather than R_L by substituting $\omega L = Q_L R_L$, as obtained from Fig. 11.6.1d, into Eq. (11.6.1). The result is

$$Q = \frac{R_1(1 + R_p) + R_p}{R_1 - R_p} Q_L \qquad (11.6.5)$$

Note that for $R_1 > 0$ and $R_p > 0$, this last equation specifies that $Q > Q_L$. Also it is Q which applies to the final equalizer in Fig. 11.6.1c, not Q_L.

The preceding three equations determine the pad and so the final equalizer based on an estimate of Q_L. Thus, from this estimate of Q_L, since ω_r, L, and R_1 are already established: (1) Eq. (11.6.3) determines the pad loss (the minimum loss of the final equalizer); (2) Eq. (11.6.4) determines R_p, which determines ρ of Fig. 11.6.1c; and (3) Eq. (11.6.5) determines Q. All these various estimates must finally specify a Q which can be realized, and of course, all other network parameters of Fig. 11.6.1c.

11.7 Further design techniques

The remainder of the discussion on transfer loss equalizers is centered largely about the particular design initiated in Example 11.4.1. As a first step in extending the development of the preceding section, assume, as suggested by experience, that the same minimum loss occurs at each of the zeros of $Z(x)$, in Fig. 11.4.2, for high Q's and all Q's the same. Furthermore, assume, once more as experience justifies, that the effect of dissipation can be simulated by the cascading of a pad with the nondissipative equalizer. The nondissipative equalizer is specified by Example 11.4.1 based on a first estimate ($\Delta_1 A_I$ of Fig. 11.6.1e) of a flat 3 db as the effect of dissipation. The determination of the pad R_p yet remains, therefore.

On the assumption of all coil Q's, Q_L, the same and no dissipation associated with the capacitors, the dissipative-impedance formula of Eq. (8.2.13), for the bridge network of Fig. 11.4.2, modified as is Fig. 11.6.1d from Fig. 11.6.1a, is, for $d = 1/Q_L$,

$$Z(\omega) = -j\omega K(1 - jd)$$

$$\frac{[\omega^2(1 - jd) - \omega_2{}^2][\omega^2(1 - jd) - \omega_4{}^2]}{[\omega^2(1 - jd) - \omega_1{}^2][\omega^2(1 - jd) - \omega_3{}^2][\omega^2(1 - jd) - \omega_5{}^2]} \quad (11.7.1)$$

and for $x = \omega/\omega_m$,

$$Z(x) = -jK\frac{1 - jd}{\omega_m}$$

$$\frac{x[x^2(1 - jd) - x_2{}^2][x^2(1 - jd) - x_4{}^2]}{[x^2(1 - jd) - x_1{}^2][x^2(1 - jd) - x_3{}^2][x^2(1 - jd) - x_5{}^2]} \quad (11.7.2)$$

This equation can be altered into a more convenient form by making use of the relation

$$b_j(x) = \frac{x_j{}^2}{x^2} - 1 = \frac{f_j{}^2}{f^2} - 1 = \frac{\omega_j{}^2}{\omega^2} - 1 \quad (11.7.3)$$

Using this last variable change $Z(x)$ becomes

$$Z(x) = \frac{j\,K(1 - jd)}{\omega_m x}\frac{[b_2(x) + jd][b_4(x) + jd]}{[b_1(x) + jd][b_3(x) + jd][b_5(x) + jd]} \quad (11.7.4)$$

Experience indicates that, at a zero of $Z(x)$, d may be neglected except in the branch resonating. Also for high Q_L and so small d, $d \ll 1$. Therefore at a zero, say x_2, of Fig. 11.4.2a, the impedance function of Eq. (11.7.4) is approximately

$$Z(x_2) \approx j\frac{Kjd}{\omega_m x_2}\frac{b_4(x_2)}{b_1(x_2)b_3(x_2)b_5(x_2)} = \frac{-K}{\omega_m x_2 Q_L}\frac{b_4(x_2)}{b_1(x_2)b_3(x_2)b_5(x_2)} \quad (11.7.5)$$

For high values of Q_L, the constant K, as computed from the purely reactive network, has approximately the same value as for the dissipative case. Hence from Example 11.4.1, $K = 0.014376 \times 10^{-6}$, which except for Q_L determines the bridge network of Fig. 11.4.2b at x_2, since R_1 is given in Example 11.4.1.

The minimum loss, i.e., the loss at the zeros of $Z(x)$, here assumed the same at all zeros, and that of the pad, may be computed as the loss at x_2 by the formula

$$A_{Imin} = A_I(x_2) = 20 \log\left|1 + \frac{R_1 Z(x_2)}{R_1 + Z(x_2)}\right|$$

$$= 20 \log (1 + R_p) \quad (11.7.6)$$

The pad resistance is, then,

$$R_p = \frac{R_1 Z(x_2)}{R_1 + Z(x_2)} \tag{11.7.7}$$

and is a function of Q_L, see Eq. (11.7.5).

The determination of a value for the pad resistance and so the minimum transfer loss can be effected from the last three formulas by choosing a value for Q_L. Such a choice is more or less a blind one but can be much facilitated by plotting curves of R_p vs Q_L, A_{Imin} vs Q_L, and Q vs Q_L. From such a set of curves the upper limit of Q, for example, can be used at once to determine R_p and A_{Imin}, i.e., plotting the curves makes working blindly through choosing values of Q_L unnecessary. From such a set of curves or from direct trial and error computation the following numerical values result:

$$Q_L = 120, \quad Q = 200, \quad A_{Imin} = 2.55 \text{ db}, \quad R_p = 0.34 \text{ ohm}$$

The equalizer design at this point specifies that:

1. The minimum transfer loss ($\Delta_2 A_I$ of Fig. 11.6.1e) at the zeros of the purely reactive bridge network is the pad loss of 2.55 db, in this case less than $\Delta_1 A_I = 3$ db.
2. The maximum transfer loss of the dissipative equalizer (at the poles of the purely reactive bridge network, Fig. 11.4.2b) is the loss associated with R_1 of Fig. 11.4.2 (Example 11.4.1) plus the pad loss, i.e., $11.2 + 2.55 = 13.75$ db.
3. The coils have a $Q = 200$.
4. The factor ρ which determines the element values for the dissipative network from those of the nondissipative network is

$$\rho = \frac{(1 + R_p + R_p/R_1)^2}{1 + R_p} = \frac{(1 + 0.34 + 0.34/2.63)^2}{1.34} = 1.611$$

from which, according to Fig. 11.6.1c,

$$R_b = R_1 \sqrt{\rho(1 + R_p)} = 3.86 \text{ ohms}$$

5. The transfer loss is that of the nondissipative network added to a flat loss of 2.55 db.

Whether the equalizer thus established has the transfer loss characteristic for which it is designed can be determined at this point only by computation and finally construction and testing. Computation must be used to indicate whether the design deviates appreciably from the requirement.

Certain approximations may be made in the formulas used to check-compute the transfer loss with the assurance that the computed results are not far wrong. The transfer loss may be computed from

$$A_I(x) = 20 \log \left| 1 + \frac{1}{Y_b(x)} \right|$$

$$= 20 \log \left| 1 + \frac{1}{G_b + Y'_b(x)} \right| \qquad (11.7.8)$$

where
$$Y_b(x) = G_b + Y'_b(x) \qquad (11.7.9)$$

The components of this admittance are

$$G_b = \frac{1}{R_b} = \frac{1}{3.86} = 0.2588 \quad \text{mho}$$

as given in (4) immediately preceding, and

$$Y'_b(x) = \frac{1}{\rho Z(x)} = \frac{1}{Z_b(x)}$$

$$= \frac{-j\omega_m x}{K_b} \frac{[b_1(x) + jd][b_3(x) + jd][b_5(x) + jd]}{(1 - jd)[b_2(x) + jd][b_4(x) + jd]} \qquad (11.7.10)$$

which is the reciprocal of Eq. (11.7.4) except that K must be replaced by $K_b = \rho K$, since use of ρL and C/ρ to replace L and C multiplies $Z(x)$ by ρ. Therefore

$$\frac{1}{K_b} = \frac{1}{\rho K} = 0.8924 \times 10^{-8}$$

Certain approximations may be made in Eq. (11.7.10), depending on the frequency range over which the formula is used. Thus:

$$Y_b(x) = G_b - j\omega_m \frac{x}{K_b} \frac{[b_1(x) + jd]b_3(x)b_5(x)}{(b_2(x) + jd)b_4(x)}$$

$$\text{(300 kc} < f < 311 \text{ kc)} \quad (11.7.11)$$

$$Y_b(x) = G_b - j\omega_m \frac{x}{K_b} \frac{b_1(x)b_3(x)b_5(x)}{b_2(x)b_4(x)}$$

$$\text{(311 kc} < f < 550 \text{ kc)} \quad (11.7.12)$$

$$Y_b(x) = G_b - j\omega_m \frac{x}{K_b} \frac{b_1(x)b_3(x)[b_5(x) + jd]}{b_2(x)[b_4(x) + jd]}$$

$$\text{(550 kc} < f < 563 \text{ kc)} \quad (11.7.13)$$

The control frequencies to be used are given at the end of Example 11.4.1. The result of calculating the transfer loss from these last three formulas is shown by the curve so marked on Fig. 11.7.1. The required transfer loss of Fig. 11.4.1 plus the 2.55 db pad loss is also shown. Comparison of the two curves in this graph shows a correspondence

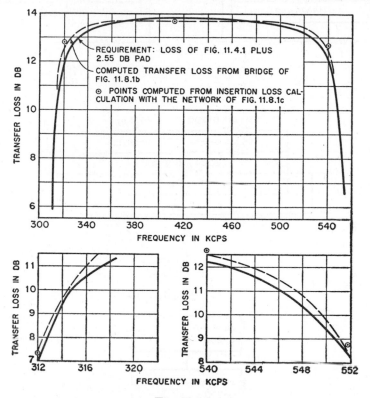

Fig. 11.7.1

which is good enough for some purposes, although for very precise equalization requirements a retrial may be required.

11.8 Element value determination

Once the element values of the $Z(x)$ of the dissipationless equalizer bridge (Fig. 11.4.2) are determined, the dissipative equalizer element values follow as indicated by Figs. 11.6.1a and 11.6.1c. The first problem, therefore, is to determine the L's and C's for the nondissipative bridge network. Such a problem is discussed in detail in Chapter 1 and needs no further consideration here. The values of the elements

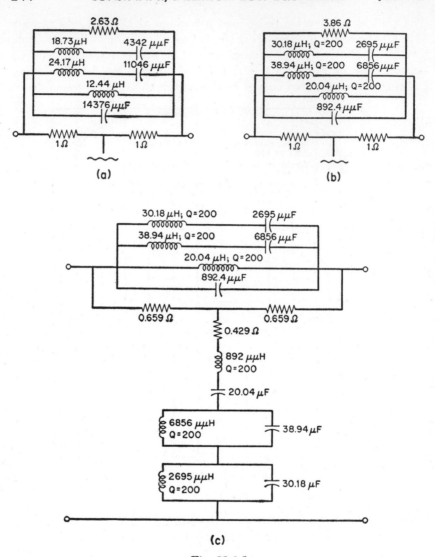

Fig. 11.8.1

of the nondissipative bridge are shown by Fig. 11.8.1a. The dissipative bridge is shown by Fig. 11.8.1b and is evaluated in accordance with Fig. 11.5.2d. Finally, the complete bridged-T equalizer is specified by Fig. 11.8.1c. A π to T transformation is used to eliminate the bridge resistance. The shunt network is not strictly the inverse of the bridge with respect to one ohm. Strictly the inductor should be paralleled by a resistor rather than have series resistance such that $Q = 200$. However, as discussed in Chapter 8, locating the uniform dissipation in the L's rather than in the C's has essentially the same effect.

As a final check on the design, the points indicated on Fig. 11.7.1 by the circle-dot are points determined by actual computation of insertion loss.

The results given are on a one-ohm basis, i.e., the element values are on a one-ohm basis. To change to any other R value multiply all resistance and all inductance values by R and divide all capacitance values by R.

Problems

11.1 Show that the insertion loss of the series impedance and the shunt impedance equalizers of Fig. p.11.1 are as shown on the figure.

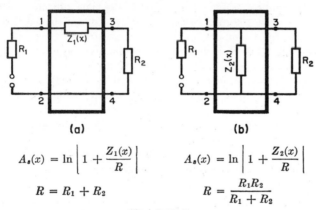

$$A_s(x) = \ln \left| 1 + \frac{Z_1(x)}{R} \right| \qquad A_s(x) = \ln \left| 1 + \frac{Z_2(x)}{R} \right|$$

$$R = R_1 + R_2 \qquad\qquad R = \frac{R_1 R_2}{R_1 + R_2}$$

Fig. P.11.1

11.2 Curves of transfer loss in decibels plotted on a logarithmic abscissa are useful for equalizer design purposes. Plot two sets of families (fixed R_1 and different $Z(\omega)$ and vice versa) of such curves for the following Z's (one-ohm basis):

(a) $Z_b(\omega) = j\omega L$.

(b) $Z_b(\omega) = \dfrac{1}{j\omega C}$.

(c) $Z_b(\omega) = j\omega L + \dfrac{1}{j\omega C}$.

(d) $Y_b(\omega) = \dfrac{1}{Z_b(\omega)} = j\omega C + \dfrac{1}{j\omega L}$.

11.3 Work out the details for establishing the formulas given by Eq. (11.1.8).

11.4 Establish the result given by Eq. (11.4.4).

11.5 The transfer loss of the upper curve of Fig. 11.4.1 may be expected to be approximated by connecting three simple equalizers in tandem. The Z of these equalizers should be: (a) capacitor in parallel with a series resonator, (b) inductor in parallel with a series resonator, (c) parallel resonator. Determine the location of the control frequencies and the purely reactive $Z(x)$ of each of the equalizers for as good a match of transfer loss as can be worked out.

11.6 Work out the details of Eq. (11.5.4).

11.7 (a) Show that the 2TN equivalents shown on Fig. 11.5.2 are valid.

(b) Determine the alternate form Fig. 11.5.2a for the shunt 2TN of Fig. 11.5.1f.

11.8 Show directly by algebraic manipulation that the minimum loss of the equalizer with the bridge network of Fig. 11.6.1c is that of the pad with a bridge of R_p only.

11.9 Determine a bridged-T equalizer of the type indicated by the bridge of Fig. 11.6.1c on a 100-ohm basis. Coil Q's must not exceed 200. Use the following schedule of computations:

(a) The resistance R_1 is determined by the maximum loss of the nondissipative equalizer. Suppose that this loss is 10 db.

(b) The resonant frequency is specified by $\omega_r = 3000$, and the equalizer transfer loss at $\omega' = 2500$ is $A_I(2500) = 5$ db. Determine from this information values for L and C.

(c) Determine the pad resistance R_p and the minimum loss from the known value of R_1 and estimated Q_L.

(d) Determine $Q \leq 200$, ρ, and so the final equalizer.

(e) By direct computation from the final design plot the curve of transfer loss for $0 \leq \omega \leq 3000$.

11.10 Repeat the preceding problem with the series LC combination replaced by a parallel LC combination. Locate the pole at $\omega_p = 3000$. Use the same match point.

11.11 Plot three curves R_p vs Q_L, A_{Imin} vs Q_L, and Q vs Q_L as suggested following Eq. (11.7.7). Use these curves to find R_p, A_{Imin} for a maximum allowable Q of 150. Determine the element values of the bridged-T equalizer of example 11.4.1.

11.12 The element values, particularly the inductances of the shunt network, of the equalizer of Fig. 11.8.1c are much too small for practical realization. Improvement of this situation may be expected from constructing the equalizer in the form of two identical equalizers in tandem. Design such an equalizer combination.

11.13 The equalizer transfer loss curve of Fig. 11.4.1 can be approached, at least, by an equalizer with a bridge consisting of two series resonators, i.e., an inductor and capacitor can be omitted from the bridge of Fig. 11.8.1. Design such an equalizer.

11.14 Design a bridged-T equalizer to match the following transfer loss curve:

db	f(kc)	db	f(kc)	db	f(kc)
0.4	312	5.7	318	7.4	339
2.6	313	6.3	321	7.6	350
3.7	314	6.6	323	7.8	371
4.4	315	6.9	326	8.0	411
4.9	316	7.2	332	8.2	511

11.15 Determine the simplest possible bridged-T equalizer which will equalize the pass-band insertion loss, given in the following tabulation, to a flat ±0.1 db from 4.2 kc to 52 kc. Specify the block region loss also.

kc	loss, db	kc	loss, db	kc	loss, db
4.2	4.15	12	0.85	45	1.20
5.0	3.20	20	0.50	50	2.50
6.0	2.35	30	0.50	52	3.50
8.0	1.56	40	0.70		

Index